The Mathematics of Games and Puzzles: From Cards to Sudoku

Arthur T. Benjamin, Ph.D.

THE
GREAT
COURSES®

PUBLISHED BY:

THE GREAT COURSES
Corporate Headquarters
4840 Westfields Boulevard, Suite 500
Chantilly, Virginia 20151-2299
Phone: 1-800-832-2412
Fax: 703-378-3819
www.thegreatcourses.com

Arthur T. Benjamin, Ph.D.

Professor of Mathematics
Harvey Mudd College

Professor Arthur T. Benjamin is a Professor of Mathematics at Harvey Mudd College. In 1983, he graduated from Carnegie Mellon University, earning his B.S. in Applied Mathematics with university honors. In 1989, he received his Ph.D. in Mathematical Sciences from Johns Hopkins University, where he was supported by a National Science Foundation graduate fellowship and a Rufus P. Isaacs fellowship. Since 1989, Professor Benjamin has been a faculty member of the Department of Mathematics at Harvey Mudd College, where he has served as Department Chair. He has spent sabbatical visits at the California Institute of Technology; Brandeis University; the University of New South Wales in Sydney, Australia; and the University of Oxford.

In 1999, Professor Benjamin received the Southern California-Nevada Section Award for Distinguished College or University Teaching of Mathematics from the Mathematical Association of America (MAA), and in 2000, he received the MAA's national Deborah and Franklin Tepper Haimo Award for Distinguished College or University Teaching of Mathematics. He was also named the 2006–2008 George Pólya Lecturer by the MAA. Professor Benjamin was chosen by The Princeton Review as one of its Best 300 Professors. In 2012, he was selected as an inaugural Fellow of the American Mathematical Society. Professor Benjamin has given wide-reaching TED talks, one of which has been viewed more than five million times. In 2005, *Reader's Digest* named him "America's Best Math Whiz." An avid game player, Professor Benjamin is a previous winner of the American Backgammon Tour.

Professor Benjamin's research interests include combinatorics, game theory, and number theory, with a special fondness for Fibonacci numbers. Many of these ideas appear in his book (coauthored with Jennifer Quinn) *Proofs*

That Really Count: The Art of Combinatorial Proof, published by the MAA. In 2006, *Proofs That Really Count* received the MAA's Beckenbach Book Prize. From 2004 to 2008, Professors Benjamin and Quinn served as the coeditors of *Math Horizons* magazine, which is published by the MAA and enjoyed by more than 20,000 readers, mostly undergraduate math students and their teachers. In 2009, the MAA published Professor Benjamin's latest book, *Biscuits of Number Theory*, coedited with Ezra Brown.

Professor Benjamin is also a professional magician. He has given thousands of "mathemagics" shows in venues around the world, from primary schools to scientific conferences, in which he demonstrates and explains his calculating talents. His techniques are explained in his book *Secrets of Mental Math: The Mathemagician's Guide to Lightning Calculation and Amazing Math Tricks*. Prolific math and science writer Martin Gardner called the book "the clearest, simplest, most entertaining, and best book yet on the art of calculating in your head."

Professor Benjamin has appeared on dozens of television and radio programs, including the *TODAY* show and *The Colbert Report* as well as CNN and National Public Radio. He has been featured in *Scientific American*, *Omni*, *Discover*, *People*, *Esquire*, *The New York Times*, the *Los Angeles Times*, and *Reader's Digest*.

Professor Benjamin has taught three other Great Courses: *The Joy of Mathematics*, *Discrete Mathematics*, and *The Secrets of Mental Math*. ∎

Table of Contents

Table of Contents

Acknowledgments

This course would not have been possible without the generous assistance of so many people, especially many of my former students. The idea for this course began with a class I taught at Harvey Mudd College called The Mathematics of Games and Gambling. My teaching assistant for that course was Louis Ryan (a master of many games and puzzles, and now a graduate student in Applied Mathematics at Harvard), and we met weekly to discuss course material. My friend Jay Cordes (who, among other accomplishments, has written a prize-winning poker-playing program) provided useful feedback on all of the lectures, especially in regard to poker. Joe Kisenwether (of Craftsman Gaming) and Fritz Juhnke (mathematics graduate student and past Arimaa World Champion) also looked at drafts of every lecture and provided me with extremely helpful advice. Finally, Elizabeth (Lizard) Reiland (soon to be a graduate student in mathematics) watched all of the video lectures with her ever-careful eye for detail.

I was given the opportunity to deliver many of these lectures to test audiences, who provided me with invaluable experience and useful feedback. For these opportunities, I am tremendously grateful to Lisa Loop (Director of Operations in the Teacher Education Program at the Claremont Graduate University), Dan Uhlman (head of the mathematics department at the Taipei American School) and George Gilbert (chair of the Department of Mathematics at Texas Christian University).

Although I have always been a lover of games and puzzles, I was fortunate to have the assistance of several game experts along the way. I learned the Rubik's Cube algorithm from John George and Tyson Mao and benefited from practice sessions with Sam Ettinger and Louis Ryan. Many thanks to "cube wranglers" David Chao, Theo Faust, and Peter Gunnarson for invaluable assistance in the studio. For my sudoku education, I am grateful to Linda Barrett, Jared Levine, Jason Linhart, and especially Palmer Mebane, Thomas Snyder (grandmasterpuzzles.com), and Laura Taalman (brainfreezepuzzles.com). My poker days would have been numbered (or at least not as numberful) without the assistance of Jon Jacobsen, Richard

Lederer, and especially Jay Cordes. Thanks to David Levy, Dana Mackenzie, and Scott Nollet for looking over my chess material. Frank Frigo and Perry Gartner are players that I "counted on" for backgammon advice. Special thanks to Harvey Gillis and the U.S. Backgammon Federation (USBGF. org) for permission to quote from Harvey's insightful article "Backgammon: Decision Analysis for Success," which appeared in the March 2011 issue of *PrimeTime Backgammon.*

I am also grateful to those people and organizations that let me use their products on camera. Specifically, I want to thank Jason Linhart for his sudoku app (Enjoy Sudoku), Xavier Dufaure de Citres for his backgammon app (XG Mobile), AppAnnex for their 15 Puzzle Challenge, Seven Towns for permission to use the Rubik's Cube, Robert Fuhrer and Nextoy for KenKen®, Ed Rosenblum (EssentialBG.com) for his magnificent massive magnetic backgammon board, Michael Gray for permission to display Hasbro products, and Jim Pressman for permission to display the products of Pressman Toy Corporation.

Most of the work for this course took place during my sabbatical, and I am ever grateful to Harvey Mudd College for supporting me during this time. My deepest thanks to Dr. Richard Hartzell of Taipei American School and Steven Biller of the University of Oxford Department of Physics for their hospitality during my sabbatical.

I couldn't have created this course without the patience and support of my family. My wonderful wife Deena offered suggestions about every aspect of the course and helped me rehearse every lecture. My brilliant daughters, Laurel and Ariel, were also great assistants.

Finally, it's always a pleasure to work with the very professional staff at The Great Courses, who helped me every step of the way. Special thanks to Jay Tate, Susan Dyer, and Zachary H. Rhoades for working so tirelessly behind the scenes to make this course the best it can be. ■

The Mathematics of Games and Puzzles:
From Cards to Sudoku

Scope:

This course takes a mathematical approach to playing games and solving puzzles. In this course, you will be introduced to all kinds of games—from games of pure strategy (like chess) to games of pure luck (like many casino games) to games that mix strategy and luck (like blackjack, backgammon, and poker). You will analyze puzzles that have stumped people for centuries to modern favorites like sudoku and Rubik's Cube. The advice that you will receive ranges from the fundamentally practical to the mathematically interesting. You will improve your ability to play these games and solve these puzzles, but you will also learn some interesting mathematics along the way.

Lecture 1: Let the Games Begin!

How does a mathematician look at games and puzzles? Games and puzzles can be classified in a number of ways. Is there randomness involved or not? Do you have an intelligent adversary or not? Using examples from games and puzzles such as tic-tac-toe, ghost, 20 questions, the Tower of Hanoi, Mastermind, and bridge, you will learn some effective strategies, such as the art of working backward, exploiting symmetry, and careful counting.

Lecture 2: Games of Chance and Winning Wagers

What are the best games of chance to play (and avoid)? How can you quantify your advantage or disadvantage? Using popular games of chance that are encountered at casinos and carnivals—like roulette, chuck-a-luck, and craps—you will learn which games give you the most bang for your buck. Also, once you know the size of your advantage or disadvantage, how much should you bet?

Lecture 3: Optimal Blackjack and Simple Card Counting

When should you stand, hit, double down, or split? You will learn the optimal basic strategy and the underlying reasoning behind it. If you play this game properly, it can be the fairest game in the casino. Play it wrong, and you're throwing your money away.

Lecture 4: Mixed Strategies and the Art of Bluffing
How should you play against an intelligent adversary whose interests are diametrically opposed to yours? In such games, you don't want your actions to be predictable. Whether you are playing rock-paper-scissors or poker, it definitely pays to vary your strategy.

Lecture 5: Practical Poker Probabilities
This lecture discusses the mathematics that is essential for successful poker playing. The lecture focuses on the game Texas Hold'em, but the mathematical ideas, like the counting of outs and pot odds, can be applied to all poker games. The lecture also presents optimal strategies for playing video poker.

Lecture 6: Expert Backgammon
The exciting dice game known as backgammon is loaded with mathematics. You will learn about the rules of the game, how to count shots, opening strategy, and the all-important doubling cube.

Lecture 7: Games You Can't Lose and Sneaky Puzzles
There are many games that seem very innocent and fair but actually offer you a big advantage. You will also explore challenging-sounding puzzles that have deviously simple solutions.

Lecture 8: Solving "Impossible" Puzzles
This lecture presents some puzzles that have been driving people crazy for decades, even centuries. These puzzles involve jumping pegs, sliding blocks, or blinking lights. Most of these puzzles have easy solutions, once you know the secret, but sometimes tweaking the problem a tiny bit can make it mathematically impossible.

Lecture 9: Mastering Rubik's Cube
You will learn a fast and easy strategy to solve the world's most popular puzzle, along with some of the mathematics behind it.

Lecture 10: Solving Sudoku

This lecture presents some simple strategies, and their underlying logic, that will enable you to solve more sudoku puzzles quickly and easily. The strategy given is the one recommended by a world sudoku champion.

Lecture 11: Mathematics and Chess

Mathematics and chess are both activities that train your brain to look for patterns and think logically. You will see where mathematical ideas appear in the opening, middle game, and endgame of chess and learn an easy solution to the world's most famous chess puzzle.

Lecture 12: Winning Ways—It's Your Move!

The course concludes with more games of strategy in which a player who is armed with the proper mathematical insights will have a decisive advantage.

Of course, the main reason we play games and solve puzzles is to have fun and to experience the intellectual satisfaction of rising to a challenge. Games train you to be a better decision maker in general. We take calculated risks every day of our lives. In this course, you will learn how to do some of these calculations while having fun at the same time.

Games are a great family activity that can be appreciated on multiple levels by children and adults. They are also a fun way to learn some really beautiful mathematics. And, of course, games and puzzles are a great way to keep your mind active and sharp at any age.

By the end of this course, you will have a fun and mentally stimulating set of skills that you can apply to countless games and puzzles. ■

Let the Games Begin!
Lecture 1

I n this course, you will learn that with the simplest of mathematical tools, you can vastly improve your ability to play and understand a tremendous number of games and puzzles. In fact, mathematicians have been among the world's best games players, and games have also motivated some very interesting mathematics. Games and puzzles can be classified in a number of ways: Is there randomness involved? Do you have an intelligent adversary? If so, do both players have the same information? In this lecture, you will learn about the games of 21 and 15, tic-tac-toe, and the Tower of Hanoi.

The Game of 21

- To play the game of 21 (not the card game), the first person chooses a number between 1 and 3. Then, the second person adds a number from 1 to 3 to the first person's number to create a new total. This continues until the total reaches 21. Whichever person gets to 21 is the winner.

- After playing a few games, you'll notice that if you ever reach a total of 17, then you are guaranteed to win because you are 4 away from 21, so for any number that your opponent adds to 17—a 1, 2, or 3—you will be able to add the opposite number—3, 2, or 1—to reach 21. By working backward, the goal of this game is really to get to 17.

- If you continue that logic, then if you can get to 13, which is 4 below 17, then you can be assured of reaching 17 because if you can get to 17, then you can get to 21. Therefore, 13 is your new goal. Subtracting 4 from 13, you can force a win if you can get to 9—or, continuing to subtract 4, if you can get to 5 or 1.

- If you want to guarantee that you can win no matter how your opponent plays, you should start with a total of 1. Thereafter, you should jump to the totals of 5, 9, 13, 17, and finally 21. When playing this game against a new player, wait a few turns before jumping to one of your winning numbers because you don't want your opponent to see any pattern too soon.

- This game illustrates one of the strategies for successful game and puzzle solving: Work backward from your goal. This strategy is a useful tool for games of pure strategy, but it can also be applied to other games of chance.

The Game of 15

- In the game of 15, another game that is similar to 21, if you know the secret, you can never lose—although it is possible for the game to be a draw. In this game, two players take turns choosing numbers from 1 to 9, and they are not allowed to repeat numbers. The numbers 1 through 9 can be represented by cards from a deck of playing cards.

- Players take turns choosing numbers, and the first player to obtain 3 numbers that add to 15 is the winner. If nobody scores 15, then the game is a draw. Because the first player has the advantage, you should alternate who goes first each game.

- For example, suppose that you start with the number 2, and your opponent picks the number 9. Then, you pick the number 6. With 2 and 6, you are threatening to get 15, so your opponent is going to have to counter that by taking 7 so that you can't get to 15. Then, your opponent adds up to 16. You're not worried about your opponent scoring a 15 this time. You take the number 8. Now, you're in a guaranteed winning position because next turn, you are either going to make 15 by having 8, 6, and 1 or by having 8, 2, and 5. Your opponent won't be able to stop you.

- There are eight ways to create 15 numbers using 3 different numbers from 1 through 9. You can arrange these combinations in a tic-tac-toe board. All eight combinations appear as lines on a tic-tac-toe board—horizontally, vertically, and diagonally. Mathematicians call this a magic square.

- Playing the game of 15 is really the same as playing tic-tac-toe, and if your opponent doesn't notice this, then you'll win most of the time and never lose.

- The game of 15 illustrates another useful tip: Find a mathematical structure to represent your game or puzzle. You won't always be able to do this, but when you can, it will often provide you with insights that would not otherwise be apparent.

Tic-Tac-Toe
- In the game of tic-tac-toe, the first player, X, has the advantage because if X plays properly, he or she can never lose—and can even sometimes force a win. As a practical matter, X should start in one of the four corners because then O has only one safe response, which is to play in the middle. If O doesn't play in the middle, then X can force a win.

© iStockphoto/Thinkstock.

Tic-Tac-Toe game.

- Suppose we change the rules so that if someone gets three in a row, instead of becoming the winner, he or she loses. The game changes, becoming much more interesting. This time, because X goes first and has to make five of the nine moves, X is at a disadvantage. You would think that the worst place for X to start would be in the center because it's involved in the most three-in-a-row combinations, but if X plays anywhere other than the center, then O can actually force a win.

- This idea of exploiting symmetry is very useful in many games and puzzles. As for the strategy of mimicking your opponent, not only does it sometimes lead to a draw, but it can also sometimes lead to a win. For example, with Cram, a game that is a cross between checkers and dominoes, the strategy of copying your opponent's moves is sometimes known as strategy stealing, and it can be used to prove some interesting results about games.

The Tower of Hanoi

- Some of the world's best game players have been mathematicians. Mathematicians have been national and world champions at many games, including chess and checkers, as well as other games like Scrabble, backgammon, bridge, blackjack and poker. Mathematicians are leading authorities on famous puzzles like Rubik's Cube and sudoku.

- Mathematician Édouard Lucas was an expert on the Fibonacci numbers, and he invented a famous puzzle called the Tower of Hanoi, sometimes called the Lucas Tower in his honor.

- The challenge of this puzzle is to move the pieces one at a time from the first peg to one of the other pegs with the restriction that you're never allowed to put a bigger piece on top of a smaller piece. How do you begin to solve this puzzle, and can you do it in the fewest number of moves?

- For each piece, the number of moves doubles plus 1. In general, the problem with n pieces can be solved in $2^n - 1$ moves. The original puzzle, which comes with $n = 9$ pieces, can be solved in $2^9 - 1 = 511$ moves. There is a quick way to solve this puzzle in 31 moves.

- Another way to understand the Tower of Hanoi is by using an object that mathematicians call a graph. The graph shows you that the Tower of Hanoi puzzle is connected in that it's always possible to get from any position to any other position in a legal sequence of moves.

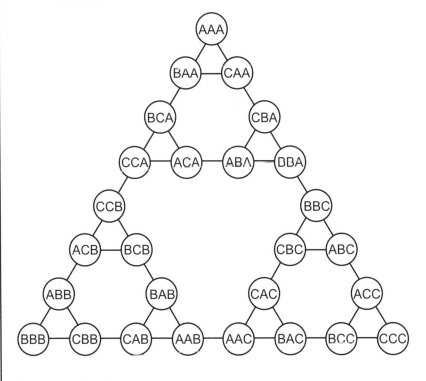

Games and Puzzles

- Mathematicians have been very good for improving our understanding of games. On the other hand, the reverse is also true: Games and puzzles have inspired many people to study mathematics and have even led to the creation of entirely new branches of mathematics.

- Games come in all different shapes and sizes, and mathematicians classify them in many different ways. For example, random games use objects like cards and dice. If a game has no randomness and is just pure strategy, like with chess or checkers, then it's called deterministic.

- In addition, games can be classified by the type of strategy your opponent uses. Is it predetermined, like in most casino games, or can your opponent use an intelligent strategy to maximize his chances of defeating you, like in poker or chess? Depending on the presence of randomness and how your opponent plays, we can put most games into one of four categories.

- Most games of pure strategy—like chess and checkers—are in the first category: deterministic versus an intelligent opponent. Deterministic games against neutral opponents are less common, but it's probably true of most video games where you're playing against a computer. Most puzzles could be classified as deterministic one-player games; typically, all of your information is present, and there's no randomness. Examples include the Tower of Hanoi, Rubik's Cube, and sudoku.

- Random games against intelligent opponents include games like poker, bridge, Scrabble, and backgammon. Random games against opponents with predetermined strategies include games like roulette, craps, blackjack, and slot machines. In fact, we could even classify random games according to where the randomness occurs. In bridge, it happens at the beginning of the game, when the cards are dealt. In backgammon, there's no hidden information. In games like Scrabble, blackjack, and poker, there is randomness on both ends.

Suggested Reading

Ball and Coxeter, *Mathematical Recreations and Essays.*

Beasley, *The Mathematics of Games.*

Bewersdorff, *Luck, Logic, and White Lies.*

Browne, *Connection Games.*

Browne, *Hex Strategy.*

Epstein, *The Theory of Gambling and Statistical Logic.*

Hess, *Mental Gymnastics.*

MacKinnon, *Bridge, Probability, and Information.*

Niederman, *The Puzzler's Dilemma.*

Packel, *The Mathematics of Games and Gambling.*

Rubens, *Expert Bridge Simplified.*

Wells, *Book of Curious and Interesting Puzzles.*

Problems

1. Suppose you and your friend play the game of 51, where you take turns adding numbers from 1 to 6. Whoever reaches 51 is the winner. Would you rather go first or second, and what is the winning strategy?

2. You play tic-tac-toe and start in the upper right corner. Your opponent plays in the square below you. What is the winning response?

3. Explain why the Tower of Hanoi with n pieces will have 3^n positions.

Let the Games Begin!
Lecture 1—Transcript

Let the games begin! For as long as I can remember, I've always loved games and puzzles. In fact, it was probably my love of numbers, games, and puzzles that led to me becoming a mathematician. And as I learned more math, I found myself winning more games and solving more puzzles, which made them even more enjoyable. In this course I will show you that with the simplest of mathematical tools, you can vastly improve your ability to play and understand a tremendous number of games and puzzles. Conversely, we'll see how studying games and puzzles can be a wonderful way to learn some very interesting mathematics. I like the expression "Let the games begin" because in most games and puzzles it's of the utmost importance that you make the right decisions right from the beginning.

Let's begin with a game that's fun to play and requires no equipment. You can even play it in the car. I call it the Game of 21, not the card game, we'll talk about that one later. Here's how this one goes. I pick a number between one and three. You, then, add a number from one to three to create a new total. I add another number from one to three to that total, and we continue like this until the total reaches 21. Whoever gets to 21 is the winner, okay? So for example, suppose I start with three, and you add two to that to get five. Then I add three to that to get eight. You add one to that to get nine and so on. I go to 10. You go to 12. I say 13. You say 16. I say 17. You say 18, and then I win by adding three to that to get 21. To make the game fair, you should take turns going first, but if you know the secret, then you'll almost always be able to beat an opponent who does not know the secret. Before I give you the solution, play the game a few times to get a feel for it. Okay? Alright?

So what's the secret? After playing a few games, you'll notice that if I ever reach a total of 17, then I'm guaranteed to win, since I am four away from 21. So any number that you add to 17, whether you add one, two, or three, I'll be able to add the opposite number, three, two or one, to reach 21. So by working backwards, the goal of this game is really to get to 17. Now if we continue that logic, if I can get to 13, which is four below 17, I can be assured of reaching 17. And if I can get to 17, I can get to 21. So 13 is my new goal. Well, subtracting four from that, if I can get to nine, or five, or one, then I can force a win. Got it? So if you get to go first in this game, how should you begin? If you want to guarantee that you—if you want to guarantee—that you can win no matter how your opponent plays, you should start with a total of one. Thereafter you should jump to the totals of 5, which you'll always be able to do, then 9, then 13, then 17, and finally 21. Now, when playing this game against a new player, I usually wait a few turns before jumping to one of my winning numbers. It's not that I'm being nice; I just don't want my opponent to see any pattern too soon. So interestingly, to determine the best way for the game to begin, we had to go all the way to the end. This game illustrates one of our first strategies for successful game and puzzle solving: Work backwards from your goal. This strategy is a useful tool for games of pure strategy, but we'll also see in this course how it can be applied to other games of chance.

Now here's another game, similar to 21, that if you know the secret you can literally never lose, although it is possible for the game to be a draw. This one is called the Game of 15. Now here, two players take turns choosing numbers from one to nine, and you're not allowed to repeat numbers. Here, I'll have the numbers one through nine represented by these cards, you know, so we each, we continuously take cards. Alright? Players take turns choosing numbers, and the first player to obtain three numbers that add to 15 is the winner. That's why we call it the Game of 15. If nobody scores 15, then the game is a draw. Okay? Since the first player has the advantage, you should alternate who goes first each game. Again, you might want to play this game a few times with your friends just to get the hang of it.

For example, suppose that I start with the number two, and you pick the number nine. Okay? Then I will pick the number six. Now notice with two and six I'm threatening to get 15 so you're going to have to counter that by taking seven so I can't do that. You add up to 16. I'm not worried about you scoring a 15 this time. I'm going to take the number eight. Alright? Now I, now I'm in a guaranteed win position because next turn I'm either going to make 15 by going eight, six, one, or, eight, two, five. You won't be able to stop me getting 15 with two, eight, five or six, eight, one, OK?

So I won't say that this game is as easy as A B C or as one, two, three, but it is easy as tic-tac-toe. Let's look at all possible ways to create number 15 using three different numbers from one through nine. Here they are. There are eight ways to do it, and we can arrange these combinations in a tic-tac-toe board. Look, all eight combinations appear as lines on a tic-tac-toe board—horizontally, vertically and diagonally. Mathematicians call this a magic square. So playing the 15 game is really the same as playing tic-tac-toe, and if your opponent doesn't see this, you'll win most of the time and never lose.

Thus, in our last game of 15, when I started by choosing the number two, and you chose the number nine, that was like starting a game of tic-tac-toe where I played an X here and you played an O there. I could then easily win by picking a six in this corner forcing you to play a seven here, thus if I pick five or eight next, I'm guaranteed to win on my next move. The game of 15 illustrates another useful tip, namely, find a mathematical structure to represent your game or puzzle. You won't always be able to do this, but when you can, it will often provide you with insights that would not otherwise be apparent.

Let me say a few more words about tic-tac-toe. Now most people—here let's bring up a tic-tac-toe board. Most people know that the first player, X, has the advantage, since, if X plays properly, he can never lose, and he can sometimes force a win. As a practical matter, X should start in one of the four corners, let's say over here, since O has only one safe response, which is to play in the middle? If O doesn't play in the middle, X can force a win. For example, if O chooses one of these corners, like, let's say, here, then X can force a win like so. X plays here. O has to play there. X then plays here. Now what can O do? Let's see. O will block by going here. X now wins by playing there. Okay?

But now, suppose we change the rules so that if someone gets three in a row, instead of becoming the winner, they lose instead. Now how does that change the game? It becomes much more interesting, right? This time since X goes first and has to make five of the nine moves, X is at a disadvantage, but there's a surprise answer. Where would be the worst place for X to start? You would think the worst place would be in the center, right? Because it's involved in the most three in a row combinations, and yet, I'll show you that if X plays anywhere other than the center, O can actually force a win. For example, let's say X starts here in the corner, then O should play a knight's move away from him, like say, here. Now if X's next move is in any one of these six squares, alright, like one of these six squares, then notice that O can just patiently wait until X is forced to create three in a row, right? If X was here, then O can just avoid that square, and eventually X is going to have to make three in a row. So to avoid that situation, X really has to play here. Right? That's the only sensible move. But then O responds here, and now Xs only safe move that avoids one of those lines is here. Right? But then O can play here, and X doesn't have any safe places to go. For instance, if X plays over here, then O will play here, forcing X to go there, and X now loses with three in a row. I'll let you have the fun of figuring out O's other winning strategies, but check this out.

If X starts in the middle, he can avoid three in a row by always responding to O's move by making the symmetrically opposite play. Like let's say X starts here in the middle, and if O plays here, then X plays here, right? X will never make three in a row unless O makes three in a row first, right? If O continues, let's say, by playing over here, then what does X do? X plays there, the symmetrically opposite play, and so on. If O goes here then X goes here. If O goes here, then X plays here, right? And in this way, X did not lose even though X had five of the nine symbols.

We will find this idea of exploiting symmetry to be very useful in many games and puzzles in this course. As for the strategy of mimicking your opponent, not only does it sometimes lead to a draw, but it can sometimes lead to a win. For example, here's a game that you might say is a cross between checkers and dominoes. It's called Cram. It's played on an eight-by-eight checkerboard. Here I'll bring out a checkerboard here and a bunch of dominoes. The players take turns placing dominoes on the board, and each domino has to occupy two adjacent squares, and no square is allowed to have two or more dominoes on it. So the game might start this way. You know, you might go here. Then I might go there. Then you might go here. Then I might go there. And we keep playing until somebody has no legal moves. Whoever makes the last move is the winner. So my question to you is, who has the advantage in the game? Would you rather be first or second in this game of Cram?

As it turns out, the second player has the advantage, and by that I mean, the second player can force a win by playing properly. Specifically, the second player can exploit symmetry by always making the symmetrically opposite play of the first player. So for instance, if your first move, say, is here, then I'll make the symmetrically opposite play here. If you, then, play here, I will play here, and so on. As any time you make a legal move, I'll be able to match it with a symmetrically opposite legal move of my own, thus I am guaranteed to make the last legal move of the game.

The strategy of copying your opponent's moves is sometimes known as strategy stealing, and it can even be used to prove some interesting results about games. Let's consider the game of Hex, invented by the Danish mathematician and poet Piet Hein. It's played with hexagonally-shaped pieces on a board that looks like this. There are two players, who I will call Red and Blue, who take turns placing pieces of their own color on the board. Red is trying to build a bridge of red hexagons between the red sides of the board and Blue is trying to build a blue bridge between her sides. So for example, in this position, we see that Red has won the game because he was able to build a red bridge between the red sides. Now what makes this game interesting is that it can actually never end in a draw. It's impossible. This fact was originally noticed by mathematician and Nobel Laureate John Nash. No matter how the pieces are placed, by the time the board is completely covered, there will always be a successful red bridge or a successful blue bridge.

Here's an intuitive explanation for this. Think of the two blue boundaries as representing a body of water and the blue pieces as more water. If a blue bridge is created, then that water will flow from one blue side to the other. If the water doesn't flow, then there had to be a red bridge between them, between the red sides, which prevented the blue water from flowing. Either way, we must either have a blue or a red bridge. I'll leave it up to you to decide if that argument holds water. Anyway, because the game cannot end in a draw and because having a piece of your color on an occupied space can only be a good thing—it can't get you in trouble to have more territory—

then it must be the case that the first player has an advantage. Thus, if the first player uses an optimal strategy, then he's guaranteed to be the winner. What's interesting here is that we can prove that no matter how large that board is, we know that the game is a theoretical win for the first player, even though nobody knows what the perfect strategy is yet. So how should you begin this game?

As you might expect on this 11-by-11 board, the strongest first move would be in the dead center of the board, but this move is so strong that in most Hex matches online and in tournaments, they give the second player a way to make things more even. I'll give the details and say more about fairness in the final lecture.

Games and puzzles have an interesting relationship. Sometimes a good puzzle can turn into an interesting game, but sometimes a bad puzzle can lead to an even more interesting game. For instance, consider this four-by-four grid of pegs and beads. Suppose I gave you 32 white beads and 32 black beads to place on the poles in such a way that there's no four in a row on any row, column, or diagonal. This is a bad puzzle since it has no solution. On the other hand, that leads to an interesting tic-tac-toe-like game played in three dimensions where you try to get four of your colors in a row, column, or diagonal. Since ties are impossible, there's guaranteed to be a winner every time.

Another approach to playing games and solving puzzles is through some kind of exhaustive analysis where you somehow examine every possible position. This works for a small game, like tic-tac-toe, but most interesting games have too many possible positions to be handled by this brute force kind of strategy. For instance, the games of Go, Chess, and Hex have yet to be completely solved, even by a computer. There are more legal positions in these games than there are atoms in the universe. In fact, games like Connect Four and Checkers can now be played perfectly by some computers, but they're still enjoyable for most people.

Sometimes a solution can be found by applying a smart-searching strategy, even without a computer. For example, consider the game of 20 Questions, another great game that needs no equipment. Suppose I gave you a dictionary and I asked you to pick any word from it. I can determine that word by just asking you 20 questions. Many are initially surprised by this. Right? I mean suppose–but here's all I'd have to do. If I have a dictionary in front of me, then for my first question I find the word that's exactly in the middle of the dictionary. Let's say it's the word mathematics. I then ask you if your word is mathematics or earlier in the dictionary. Regardless of your answer, I have cut the number of possible words in half. So if this dictionary has 100,000 words, there are now just 50,000 words remaining. Suppose you say, yes, it's below mathematics. Now I'll ask for the word that's in the middle of that list, some word between A and mathematics. Let's say it's the word game and ask if the word is between A and game, inclusive. Your answer will reduce the search space to 25,000 words, so if you say no, then I'll find a word between game and mathematics, let's say jeopardy and continue from there. As our table here illustrates, after 17 guesses we'll have narrowed the possibilities to just one word, and we'd be guaranteeing to get it in our 18th guess.

Now how does this apply to the real game of 20 Questions? You should typically try to take guesses that have about a 50-percent chance of getting a yes answer so the number of possibilities gets cut in half either way. Good questions to start with, say, you know if a person is male or female, alive or dead, someone you know or don't. The process of constantly cutting your search in half is known as binary search, and if you're allowed n guesses, then you can have as many as 2^n possible items and narrow it down to one possibility after your last question.

In 1977, Donald Knuth, one of the world's leading mathematical computer scientists, used a smart search strategy to analyze the game of Mastermind. Now, in the standard game of Mastermind, your opponent, the code maker, picks a four-digit number using only the digits from one through six. So for example, the code could be 3 1 4 1 or 6 3 2 1. Now in some commercial versions of this game, like here, the code uses six colors, but I'll use numbers since they're easier to list and allows you to play the game with just pencil and paper.

Your goal is to break the code using just a small number of guesses. For instance, your first guess might be the number 1 2 3 4. After you guess, the code maker tells you how many of your numbers match the code and how many of those are in the right position. He doesn't tell you which numbers match or which positions are right, just how many. Alright? Now in the commercial version, the code maker answers with black and white pegs or maybe red and white pegs. The black pegs indicate how many matching digits are in the right position. The white pegs indicate how many matching digits are in the wrong position. So for example–let's do an example here, if the code maker's number was 6 2 4 1 and your guess was 1 2 3 4, you would have three matching digits, 1, 2, and 4, one of which is in the right position, 2. So you'd score one black peg and two white pegs. On the other hand if you guessed 1 1 2 2, then you'd have two matching digits, but none of them are in the right position, so you'd score two white pegs.

Now here's a math question for you: How many code words are possible? So for our four-digit number there are six choices for the first number, six choices for the second, six choices for the third, and six choices for the fourth. So the number of possible code words is 6^4 power, 1,296. Your goal is to try to determine the code in a small number of turns based on the responses of the code maker. So what should your strategy be?

Now the answer will depend on your objective. Are you trying to minimize the maximum number of guesses, you know, the worst case scenario? Or are you trying to minimize the average number of guesses? Or maybe you're just trying to find a simple strategy that does well most of the time. If your goal is to minimize the maximum number of guesses, then what Knuth proved was that if you choose your clues properly, you can always get the answer by the fifth guess. Amazing—1,296 possibilities—you can always figure out the answer by the fifth guess. That is, you would know the answer with certainty after just four of your guesses. We call a method for solving a problem an algorithm, and Knuth's algorithm takes five guesses in the worse case and about 4.5 guesses on average. If your objective is to minimize the average number of guesses required, then the best algorithm breaks the code in about 4.3 guesses on average, but it occasionally requires six guesses.

So what's the best opening guess? I always started by picking four different numbers like 1 2 3 4, but that turns out not to be the best opening. What is the best opening depends on your objective. To minimize the worse-case scenario, the worse-case number of guesses, you should start with 1 1 2 2 or any two numbers repeated twice, right? But if you wanted to minimize the average number of guesses, then it's best to begin with three different numbers, not four different numbers, three different numbers, like guess 1 1 2 3, or if you were using colors, red, red, blue, green. Now I've always used a pretty simple algorithm for playing Mastermind. I would start with a random guess, and on each subsequent guess I would only make guesses that could be a possible solution to the code. I wouldn't try to figure out the best guess, just any guess that would potentially be right. As it happens, this naïve strategy performs very well. Although it sometimes takes six guesses, it's been shown that this simple strategy takes, on average, about 4.6 guesses, which is almost as good as Knuth's algorithm.

Here's another curious property of Knuth's algorithm, is that it's not always the case that the best guess is a potential code word, although that's usually the case. And here's another interesting mathematical result. In 1983, mathematician Vašek Chvátal showed that you could start with these six guesses, and no matter what peg, no matter what responses the code-maker gives, you will always be able to determine the code on the next guess. So this guarantees a solution within seven guesses.

Some games and puzzles are approached using a greedy strategy. For example, when I played the game Monopoly as a kid, I thought the best strategy was to simply buy any property that you landed on. I doubt I was playing the game perfectly, but that seemed like the right way to play. Now for most interesting games, when you're just getting started, using a greedy strategy is probably not likely to be optimal, but a greedy strategy is better than no strategy at all. As you gain more experience, which is a nice way of saying, as you lose to better players, you'll probably switch from using a greedy strategy to something better. In most games, it pays to delay your gratification. For example, we'll see in Lecture 11 on Chess that if you focus too early on trying to checkmate your opponent, it can lead to bad results. It's better to try to win slowly and gradually. Try to capture an extra piece or a few pawns first, then simplify the position before going after your opponent's king.

Another example comes from that great procrastinating card game known as Solitaire, sometimes referred to as Klondike or Patience. Solitaire is sort of a mix between a game and a puzzle. You have no opponent, and once the cards are dealt, you can think of it as a puzzle of how to eventually bring all of your cards up to the top level, but if you act too impatiently, then you can lose flexibility. It often pays to delay your immediate gratification. For example, in this position, even though we're ready to move the three of hearts to the top, that would be premature, since, without a three of diamonds on the board, we might not have any place to put our black twos if they show up later among the down cards.

There are even mathematical considerations in word games, like, say, Scrabble or Words with Friends. Many computer programs play these games using a greedy algorithm—play the word that scores the most points. These programs do tend to play very well against humans, but sometimes, playing greedy can be penny wise, but pound foolish. For example, if you have the letter S in your rack, you should not pluralize your word just to earn you an extra point or two. Instead, you should save that S for a much higher scoring opportunity later. My first tip for a beginning Scrabble player is to only use your blanks and S tiles for very high-scoring opportunities.

Here's another enjoyable word game that doesn't require any equipment, so it can be played anywhere. And there's enough variety in this game to keep it interesting for a while. In the game of Ghost, two players take turns saying letters where the goal is to not create a word that's three letters or more. So, for example, suppose you start with the letter L and then I continue with the letter I, you could respond with the letter O and then only word, at least the only word that I know of, that starts L-I-O is lion so I'm going to lose that game. If I try to weasel out of it by saying another letter like Q, then you could challenge me to give a legal word that starts L-I-O-Q, and since I can't do it, I would lose the round.

Now, if you start with L, then a much better response from me would be the letter L, since the only continuing words have the next letter as A. So if I reply with—so, so it's you say L, I say L, you have to say A, or otherwise I'll challenge you, then I'll reply with M, and you're going to forced to lose with llama. So if this game is about words, where does the math come in? Notice that the first player wants to create an even-length word, while the second player wants to create an odd-length word. To use a mathematical term, we're interested in the parity of the lengths. The first player wants lengths of even parity, the second player wants lengths of odd parity. In this course, we'll see many games and puzzles where parity plays a major role. Now if you play Ghost and allow any legal word in the Scrabble player's dictionary, then I'm told that the second player can always force a win. But if you only use common words, let's say those that would be recognized by most computer spellcheckers, then there's a nice strategy for winning devised by Randall Munroe, who creates the web cartoon xkcd.

Depending on your word list, the strategy might change, but all of these words are definitely worth learning. The first player can win by starting with H, J, M or Z. For example, starting with J, the first player can always force the second player to lose with one of these four-letter words: jazz, jest, jilt, jowl, or just. For example, if I say J and you say A, then I'll continue with Z, and you'll be forced to spell jazz. Here are the only words that the first player needs to know to win with the first letters of H, J, M and Z. Notice all of these words have even length. The way the game is usually played, is that when you lose a round, you acquire a letter. First G, then H, then O, then S, then T. Once you've spelled Ghost, you're gone. For the cut-throat Ghost player, here are some good words that the second player can usually win with from the other 22 letters. Notice all the words have an odd number of letters. Curiously, the word ghost is one of the winning words for the second player. Maybe that's where the game got its name.

Some of the world's best game players have been mathematicians, and we'll meet many of them in this course. Mathematicians have been national and world champions at many games, including Chess and Checkers, as well as other games like Scrabble, Backgammon, Bridge, blackjack, and Poker. Mathematicians are leading authorities on famous puzzles like Rubik's cube and Sudoku. One of my favorite mathematicians was Édouard Lucas. He was an expert on the Fibonacci numbers, and he wrote an important book on the mathematics of games and puzzles called *Récréations Mathématiques*. Lucas invented a famous puzzle called the Tower of Hanoi, sometimes called the Lucas Tower in his honor. The challenge of this puzzle is to move the pieces one at a time from the first peg to one of the other pegs with the restriction that you're never allowed to put a bigger piece on top of a smaller piece. For example, if your first move is here, then your next move could not be here because that would place a larger piece on top of a smaller one. So how do you begin to solve this puzzle, and can you do it in the fewest number of moves? Now the great mathematician George Pólya wrote a book called *How to Solve It* where he outlined general strategies for solving problems, mathematical and otherwise. My favorite piece of advice was "If there's a problem you can't solve, then there's an easier problem that you can solve. Find it."

So instead of n equals nine pieces, let's solve the two-piece puzzle. Let's let n equal two, and that's an easy one to solve, right? We can just go one piece here, and then two, and then three. So in three steps we've solved this problem. Let's now do a three-piece puzzle. Okay? Now the three-piece puzzle, we can do this in seven moves, and it goes like this. We can go one, two, three, like in the two-piece puzzle, then transfer the big piece over here. That's move number four, and then, in three moves, I can solve a two-piece puzzle—five, six, and seven.

Let's solve the four-piece puzzle using—without going through every little step. Here's the big idea. I know that if I want to get these pieces from here to there, I know that in seven moves I can solve the three-piece puzzle and bring them to here. Then in one move, I can move the biggest piece over—that's move number eight, and then I can do another seven moves to get these back to here. So I've solved the problem in 15 moves.

For each piece, the number of moves doubles plus one, right? We went to one move, three moves, seven, fifteen moves, and so on. In general, the problem with n pieces can be solved in $2^n - 1$ moves. So the original puzzle, which comes with n equals nine pieces, can be solved in $2^9 - 1$, 511 moves. According to legend, there exists a giant 64-piece puzzle that's being solved day and night by a priest, and when he solves it, the world will end. If the priest can make one move per second, then his solution will take at least $2^{64} - 1$ seconds, which is over 500 billion years, so we're safe for now.

By the way, if you want to learn how to solve this puzzle quickly, then here's a method that's as easy as one, two, three. Let's call the three smallest pieces one, two, and three, and the smallest piece, one, is going to move every other turn, always in the same direction. So I want you to repeat after me the following mantra: one, two, one, three, one, two, one, big. Say it. One, two, one, three, one, two, one, big. Whenever you say a one, just move the smallest piece to your right. I always use my right hand when I do this. So when you say two, three or big, move that piece with your left hand to whichever space is legal. That sounds confusing, but here, let me do it with five pieces really fast. It's going to take 31 moves, so we're going to have to repeat our mantra four times. Alright? Here we go. One, two, one, three, one, two, one, big. One, two, one, three, one, two, one, big. One, two, one, three, one, two, one, big. One, two, one, three, one, two, one, big finish.

At this point, I should say, as with all of my courses, I'm told that I sometimes go through things pretty quickly. I do that because there's so much good material that I want to share with you. Also, you have control of the remote, so feel free to pause and rewind me as often as you'd like. I don't mind, really.

Another way to understand the Tower of Hanoi is by using an object that mathematicians call a graph. Every point on the graph represents a legal position, and those points have a line between them if you can get from one position to another in just one move. For example, with one piece, let's look at the one-piece puzzle, and there are three positions—there are three pegs. Let's call them A, B, and C. So in one move you can go from A to B. You can go from A to C. You could go from B to C. And that's what's represented by that graph. It's graphed as just a triangle. With two pieces then there are nine positions. For example, the point A-C, so the little one is on A, and the big one's on C. From here there are three legal moves you can make. You can either go from A-C to B-C. You could go from A-C to A-B. Or, you could go from A-C to C-C. So there are nine positions in this graph.

With three pieces, there are 27 positions, and the graph looks like this. When you add more and more pieces, the shape of the graph looks like the fractal image known as Sierpinski's triangle. Here's the graph for the seven-piece puzzle. Isn't that awesome?

One thing that the graph shows us is that the Tower of Hanoi puzzle is connected in that it's always possible to get from any position to any other position in a legal sequence of moves. As we'll see later in this course, there are many puzzles, like the Rubik's cube and the sliding-block puzzle, where just because a position is theoretically possible, doesn't mean that it's actually achievable from the starting position. But the real reason I show it to you is to give you the idea that there's some beautiful mathematics lurking beneath even the simplest of games and puzzles.

As we'll see in this course, mathematicians have been very good for improving our understanding of games. On the other hand, the reverse is also true. Games and puzzles have inspired many a person to study mathematics and have even led to the creation of entirely new branches of mathematics. For example, a puzzle about whether it was possible to walk across every bridge in the town of Konigsberg led the great mathematician Leonard Euler to discover the important mathematical subjects of graph theory and topology. For another example, the subject of probability was essentially born by chance, games of chance, that is. Even though probability and statistics are essential topics for understanding psychology, economics, medicine, and more, they were initially invented to improve people's ability to understand and profit from games.

Here's a typical probability problem with a somewhat surprising answer. Suppose you flip a coin four times and you keep track of heads and tails. Now let me ask you what is the most probable outcome: that all four flips are the same? That three are the same and one is different? Or you get two heads and two tails? What do you think? Most people expect two heads and two tails to be the most probable, and yet that's not the case. To see this, notice that there are 16 different possible sequences, all with the same probability. Notice that there are two ways to get a four-zero split, either all heads or all tails. There are eight ways to get a three-one split, four of them have three heads and four of them have three tails. And there are just six ways to get a two-two split. Hence, there are more ways to get a three-one split than a two-two split, which comes as a surprise to many. By the way, Bridge players use similar reasoning when planning their play of the hand. If you and your partner, say, have nine spades between you, it's more probable that the other four spades have split three-one than split two-two.

Games come in all different shapes and sizes, and mathematicians classify them in many different ways. For example, we've seen random games using objects like cards and dice. If a game has no randomness and is just pure strategy, like with Chess or Checkers, then it's called deterministic. We can also ask, what kind of strategy does your opponent use? Is it predetermined, like in most casino games? Or can your opponent use an intelligent strategy to maximize his chances of defeating you, like in Poker or Chess? Depending on the presence of randomness and how your opponent plays, we can put most games into one of four categories. Most games of pure strategy, like Chess, Checkers and Go, are in the first category: deterministic versus an intelligent opponent. Deterministic games against neutral opponents are less common, but we've seen it with the game of Mastermind, and it's probably true of most video games where you're playing against a computer. Most puzzles could be classified as deterministic one-player games. Typically, all of your information is present, and there's no randomness. Examples here include the Tower of Hanoi, Rubik's Cube and Sudoku.

Random games against intelligent opponents include games like Poker, Bridge, Scrabble, and Backgammon. Random games against opponents with predetermined strategies include games like roulette, craps, blackjack and slot machines including video Poker. In fact, we could even classify random games according to where the randomness occurs. In Bridge, it happens right at the beginning of the game when the cards are dealt. After that, it's all about using strategy to infer the missing information. In Backgammon, there's no hidden information. Players must cope with the randomness of future events, which are dictated by the dice. And in games like Scrabble, blackjack and Poker, you have randomness on both ends.

And while we're on the topic of random games, let me say right now that this course does not in any way advocate gambling. On those games where bets are placed, I really just want you to understand the mathematics of the games involved and how to play them. In fact, I'd bet that—alright, bad choice of words. I'm confident that the more you know about the odds and probability, the less likely you are to pursue games of chance, most of which are pretty bad for your bank account. But if you're going to gamble, you may as well at least be smart about it. And besides, many games have real-life applications. We all take calculated risks nearly every day of our lives. In this course, I'll teach you how to do some of those calculations better.

Here's a quick preview of what's coming up. The first few lectures will look at specific games of chance from casino games like roulette, craps, and blackjack to more complicated games like Poker and Backgammon. We'll also learn about optimal wagering strategies and the theory of bluffing. After that, we'll look at everything from puzzles you can't solve to games you can't lose, all the way to modern favorites like Rubik's Cube and Sudoku. We'll end with more games of strategy, including an entire lecture on the game of Chess. So as we turn our attention to games of chance like the ones you may find at carnivals or casinos, you may wonder which games are the best and which games are the worst. There's just one way to find out. Do the math and join me for Lecture 2.

Games of Chance and Winning Wagers
Lecture 2

T here's only one way to find out which games of chance—such as those found at carnivals or casinos—are the best and which are the worst: Do the math. Once you know the odds of winning a game, how much should you bet? The answer depends on whether you are playing a game where the odds are in your favor or against you and what your financial objectives are. In this lecture, you will be introduced to roulette, sic bo, and craps.

Roulette
- An American roulette wheel has 38 numbers, 18 of which are red and 18 of which are black. Two of the numbers, 0 and 00, are green. The simplest bet in roulette is to bet on one of the main colors—for example, red. Let's say that you bet $1 on red. It's an even money bet, which means that if you bet $1, then you'll either win or lose $1, depending on whether or not a red number appears.

- Now what are your chances of winning? Because there are 38 numbers, each of which has the same chance of occurring, and 18 of these numbers are red, then the probability that you win is 18/38, which is a little less than 50%. Clearly, you have a disadvantage at this game. We can quantify this disadvantage using the very important concept of expected value.

- The expected value of a bet is a weighted average of how much you can win or lose. When you bet on red in roulette, you'll either win $1 with probability 18/38, or you'll lose $1, which could also be interpreted as winning –$1 with probability 20/38 because there are 18 red numbers and 20 numbers that aren't red. Hence, your expected value is 1(18/38) + (–1)(20/38), which equals –2/38, or –0.0526. Therefore, on average, you'll lose about 5.3¢ for every dollar that you bet.

- In roulette, you can bet on other things besides color. For instance, you can bet that a number between 1 and 12 shows up. Let's say that you bet $1 that one of the first 12 numbers shows up. The casino pays two-to-one odds for this bet, which means that if you bet $1 and you win, then the casino pays you $2.

- When you bet $1, you're going to win $2 with a probability of 12 numbers out of 38, and you're going to lose $1 with probability 26/38 because if you win 12 times out of 38, you lose 26 times out of 38. Hence, the expected value of this bet is $2(12/38) + (-1)(26/38) = -2/38 = -0.0526$, which is the same number as before.

- Suppose you bet on a single number, such as 17. In this case, the casino pays 35-to-1 odds. Thus, when you make this bet, then you either win $35 with probability 1/38, just one winning number out of all 38, or you lose $1 with probability 37/38. When you calculate the expected value, $35(1/38) + (-1)(37/38)$, once again you get $-2/38$, or $-5.3¢$.

- Interestingly, when you play roulette, practically every bet has the exact same expected value of $-5.3¢$ per $1 bet. When your expected value is negative like in roulette, then that bet is called unfavorable. If the expected value is positive, which is very rare in a casino, then the bet is called favorable. If a bet has an expected value of 0, then the bet is called fair.

- When you make a $1 bet on the number 17, the casino is paying you 35-to-1 odds, which is unfavorable. The true odds of this bet are 37 to 1 because there are 37 unfavorable numbers, or 37 numbers that make you lose, and just 1 good number. If the casino paid 37-to-1 odds, then the game would be fair because $37(1/38) + (-1)(37/38)$ equals 0.

- If you decide to bet on red twice in a row, then you either win twice with a probability of about 22%, win once with a probability of about 50%, or lose twice with a probability of about 28%. Notice that the sum of these probabilities is exactly 100%, or 1. This is not a coincidence. Whenever you sum all distinct possibilities, the probabilities have to sum to 1.

Sic Bo

- A carnival game known as chuck-a-luck has been around for years, but more recently, a variation of the game has been brought to the casinos with the name "sic bo," which is Chinese for "dice pair." The game is played with 3 dice. You place a wager on one number from 1 to 6. Let's say you bet $1 on the number 4. Then, the dice are rolled, and if a 4 appears, you win $1.

- It almost sounds like a fair game, because each die has a 1-in-6 chance of being a 4. Furthermore, if your number shows up twice, then you'd win $2, and if it shows up three times, then you'd win $3.

- Your chance of winning $3 is extremely low. To win $3, each die must be 4, and the probability that the red die is 4 is 1 out of 6. The probability that the yellow die is 4 is 1 out of 6. The probability that the blue die is 4 is 1 out of 6, and because the dice rolls are very independent, the probability that all of them are 4s is $(1/6)(1/6)(1/6)$ $= 1/6^3 = 1/216$, which is less than 1%.

- On the other hand, the chance of losing $1 is actually pretty high. For that to happen, none of the dice can be 4s. What's the chance of that? Well, the chance that the red die is not a 4 is 5 out of 6. Likewise, the probability that the yellow die is not a 4 is 5 out of 6, and the probability that the blue die is not a 4 is 5 out of 6. Therefore, the probability that they are all not equal to 4 is $(5/6)^3$, which is 125/216, which is about 58%. So, you actually lose money in this game more than half the time.

- What are your chances of winning $1? To do this, you need exactly one of these 3 dice to be a 4. There are three ways that this can happen. You can either have a red 4 and yellow and blue not be 4, or you could have a yellow 4 only, or you could have a blue 4 only. The chance of having a red 4 and no yellow and blue 4 would be $(1/6)(5/6)(5/6) = 25/216$. Likewise, there's a 25/216 chance of seeing just a yellow 4 and a 25/216 chance of seeing just a blue 4. Therefore, the total chance of seeing exactly one 4 is 75/216, which is about 35%. Similarly, the probability of winning $2 is 15/216, about 7%.

- The probabilities sum to 1, or 216/216. If they don't, then you've made a mistake in at least one of your earlier calculations. Your expected profit is $75/216 (1) + 15/216(2) + 1/216 (3) + 125/216(-1) = -17/216 = -0.08$. In other words, you can expect to lose about 8¢ for every dollar that you bet in this game. This game is very unfavorable and should be avoided.

Number of 4s	Probability
0 (Lose $1)	125/216
1 (Win $1)	75/216
2 (Win $2)	15/216
3 (Win $3)	1/216
Total	216/216 = 1

Craps

- The most popular dice game in the casino is the game of craps. The rules of the game are pretty simple. You place your bet and roll two dice. If the total is 7 or 11, you win. If the total is 2, 3, or 12, you lose. If the total is something else, then that number becomes your point, and you keep rolling the dice until your point appears or 7 appears. If your point appears first, you win. If 7 appears first, you lose.

- If you rolled a 4, for example, on your first roll, what are the chances that you win? There are a few ways to calculate this probability, all of which lead to the same answer: 1/3. If you look at all the possible totals when you roll two dice—for example, a red and a green die—you have 36 possible outcomes: 6 for the red and 6 for the green, each of which is equally likely. Of these, 3 have a total of 4, and 6 have a total of 7.

- Once you rolled that first 4, you just keep rolling the dice until a 4 appears or a 7 appears. So, there are nine outcomes that end the game: Three are winners; six are losers. Therefore, your chance of winning is 3 out of 9, or 1/3. Thus, your chance of losing is 2/3. This makes sense because you have twice as many ways to roll a 7 than to roll a 4.

- We can use these numbers to figure out your overall chance of winning using what's called the law of total probability, which says that your overall winning chance is a weighted average of your chances of winning from each opening roll. In other words, we weight each opening roll based on how likely it is to occur on the first roll. The sum of these weights is necessarily 1.

Opening Roll	Weight	Winning chances	Product
2	1/36	0	0
3	2/36	0	0
4	3/36	3/9	9/324 = .0278
5	4/36	4/10	16/360 = .0444
6	5/36	5/11	25/396 = .0631
7	6/36	1	6/36 = .1667
8	5/36	5/11	25/396 = .0631
9	4/36	4/10	16/360 = .0444
10	3/36	3/9	9/324 = .0278
11	2/36	1	2/36 = .0556
12	1/36	0	0
Total	1		244/495 = .493

- When we multiply each winning chance by its weight and take the sum, and then reduce the fraction, it turns out to be 244/495, which is 0.493. This equates to there being a 49.3% chance of winning the game of craps. When you bet $1, you're either going to win $1 with probability 0.493, or you're going to lose $1 with probability 0.507.

- Your expected value for craps is $1(0.493) + (-1)(0.507) = -0.014$, which equals 1.4¢ for every dollar that you bet. This makes the game of craps much fairer than roulette and chuck-a-luck, but it's still an unfavorable game.

Suggested Reading

Beasley, *The Mathematics of Games.*

Bewersdorff, *Luck, Logic, and White Lies.*

Epstein, *The Theory of Gambling and Statistical Logic.*

Gillis, *Backgammon.*

Haigh, *Taking Chances.*

Packel, *The Mathematics of Games and Gambling.*

Poundstone, *Fortune's Formula.*

Rosenhouse, *The Monty Hall Problem.*

Problems

1. The casino game of sic bo allows other bets as well. For instance, you can bet that when you roll three dice, the total will be "small." If your total is 10 or smaller, but not three of a kind (all 1s, 2s, or 3s), then you win. Answer the following questions, keeping in mind that you are rolling three six-sided dice.

    a. What is the probability of rolling three of the same number?

    b. Use symmetry to explain why the probability that the total is 10 or less is the same as the probability that the total is 11 or greater.

    c. Use a.) and b.) to determine the probability of winning the sic bo bet described above.

    d. What is your expected value when placing a $1 bet?

2. In the game of craps, a "field bet" pays even money if your opening roll has a total of 3, 4, 9, 10, or 11, and it pays two to one if the opening roll is 2 or 12. What is the probability of winning, and what is the expected value of this bet?

3. Suppose you play a fair game where you win or lose $5 on each bet.

    a.   Starting with $15, what are the chances of reaching $60 before going broke?

    b.   Suppose you boldly try to reach $60 by betting everything twice in a row. What are your chances of success?

    c.   Answer questions a.) and b.) when your probability of winning each bet is 0.6.

Games of Chance and Winning Wagers
Lecture 2—Transcript

Suppose that you find yourself in a city with a casino, and you have $60 in your pocket. There's a concert in town that you really want to see, but the tickets cost $100. You decide that you'll place $1 bets until you either reach $100 or you go broke. The question is, which game should you play, and how likely are you to reach your goal? Also, does it make sense to make $1 bets, or should you make one big $40 bet instead? To answer these questions we need to be able to quantitatively compare games by determining your probability of winning, as well as your average profit per $1 bet. By far, the easiest game to analyze is the game of roulette.

A roulette wheel has 38 numbers. Eighteen of these numbers are red. Eighteen of these numbers are black. And two of the numbers, 0 and 00, are green. By the way, I'm describing American roulette; the European version has just one green number. The simplest bet in roulette is to bet on one of the main colors. Let's say red. Okay? So I'm going to bet $1 on red. It's an even-money bet, which means that if you bet $1, then you'll either win or lose $1, depending on whether or not a red number appears. Here, let's give it a try here—red, 27, I win.

Now what are your chances of winning? Since there are 38 numbers, each of which has the same chance of occurring, and 18 of these numbers are red, then the probability that you win is $^{18}/_{38}$, which is a little less than 50%. Clearly, you have a disadvantage at this game. We can quantify this disadvantage using the very important concept of expected value. If you only remember one concept from this lecture, this is what I want you to remember. The expected value of a bet is a weighted average of how much you can win or lose. When you bet on red in roulette, you'll either win $1 with probability $^{18}/_{38}$, or you'll lose $1, or you could say, win $-1 with probability $^{20}/_{38}$. Right? Because there are 18 red numbers and 20 numbers that aren't red. Hence, your expected value is $(1 \times {}^{18}/_{38}) + (-1 \times {}^{20}/_{38})$. That's $^{-2}/_{38}$; -0.0526. What this means is that, on average, you'll lose about 5.3 cents for every dollar that you bet.

Now, in roulette you can bet on other things besides color. For instance, you can bet that a number between 1 and 12 shows up. Here, let me show you here. So let's say we bet $1 that one of the first 12 numbers shows up. The casino pays two-to-one odds for this bet, which means that if you bet $1 and you win, then the casino pays you $2. Okay? So, let's calculate our expected value here. So when you bet $1 you're going to win $2 with probability what? Twelve numbers out of 38. And you're going to lose $1 with probability $^{26}/_{38}$, because if you win 12 times out of 38, you lose 26 times out of 38. Hence, the expected value of this bet is two. That's what you win, $^{12}/_{38}$ times, plus -1, that's for losing one, 26 out of 38 times. When you do the math, that's $^{-2}/_{38}$, -0.0526, which is the same number as before.

Or, suppose you bet on a single number. Let's say I like lucky number 17. Here the casino pays 35-to-1 odds. Thus, when you make this bet, then you either win $35 with probability 1/38—just one winning number out of all 38—or, you lose $1 with probability $^{37}/_{38}$. So when you calculate the expected value, $35 \times {}^{1}/_{38} + (-1) \times {}^{37}/_{38}$, once again, you get $^{-2}/_{38}$. We still get -5.3 cents. Interestingly, when you play roulette, practically every bet has the exact same expected value of -5.3 cents per dollar bet. When your expected value is negative, like in roulette, then that bet is called unfavorable. If the expected value is positive, which is very rare in a casino, then the bet is called favorable. If a bet has an expected value of zero, then the bet is called fair. When we make a $1 bet on the number 17, the casino is paying us 35-to-1 odds, which we've shown to be unfavorable. The true odds of this bet is 37 to 1. Why is it 37 to 1? Because there are 37 unfavorable numbers—37 numbers that make us lose and just 1 good number. If the casino paid you 37-to-1 odds, then the game would be fair since $(37 \times {}^{1}/_{38}) + (-1 \times {}^{37}/_{38})$ is 0.

Here, let's do one more probability calculation with roulette. Suppose you decide to bet on red twice in a row, okay? You're going to bet on red, and then, no matter what happens, win or lose, you're going to bet on red again. So, what are your chances of winning both bets—that you win the first bet and the second one? The key notion here is that each spin of the wheel is independent. That is one spin of the wheel has no influence on the other. When events are independent, to determine the probability that both events happen, we multiply their probabilities. So, if you bet on red twice, then the probability that you win on the first spin is $^{18}/_{38}$, and the probability that you win on the second spin is $^{18}/_{38}$. So the probability that you win both times is $(^{18}/_{38})^2$, which is about 22%. Similarly, the probability that you lose both times would be $(^{20}/_{38})^2$, which is about 28%. So, what about the probability of winning exactly once? Notice that there are two ways that this can happen. We can either win, then lose, right? That has probability $^{18}/_{38} \times {}^{20}/_{38}$. Or we can lose, then win. That has probability $^{20}/_{38} \times {}^{18}/_{38}$. Adding these probabilities together, the probability of winning once is $^{720}/_{1444}$. That's about 49.9%.

So, to summarize, we've shown that when you bet on red twice, you either win twice with probability about 22%. You win once with probability about 50%. And you lose twice with probability 28%. Notice that the sum of these probabilities is exactly 1, 100%. This is not a coincidence. Whenever you sum over all distinct possibilities, the probabilities have to sum to 1.

Now I can't resist showing you what the expected value is when you bet red twice in a row. After two bets of $1 each, how much are you going to have? You'll either be up $2, or you'll be down $2, or you'll be even, depending on whether you won twice, lost twice, or won one apiece. Thus from our previous table, you're expected profit is exactly $-^{4}/_{38}$, between -10.5 and -10.6¢, and that's exactly what you'd expect from making two bets that each had an expected value of $^{-2}/_{38}$. To take it further, if you made 100 bets, each with an expected value of about -5.3¢, then on average, you'd be down about $5.30. With 1000 bets, you could expect to be down about $53, and so on. In fact, the more bets you make, the more certain it is that you'll end up a loser. However, as Stephen Colbert once said to me, "But then they comp your room."

Here's another example that you see all the time, raffles. Suppose that a charity sells raffle tickets for $1 apiece. The winner gets half the money. Now suppose n tickets are sold, and you buy one ticket. What is your expected profit? Now, here your chance of winning is 1 out of n, and when you win, your profit is $^{n}/_{\$2}$. Half the prize pool minus the $1 that you paid. Now, when you lose, and the probability that you lose is $1 - ^{1}/_{n}$, then you lose $1. When we do the expected-value calculation, the ns disappear, and the answer simplifies to exactly -0.5. So you expect to lose 50¢ on average no matter how many tickets are sold. At first that sounds funny. Right? But it actually makes sense, or cents, right, since half of your dollar goes to the charity and half goes to the winner.

Here's another example that's very easy to analyze. It's been around for years as a carnival game known as chuck-a-luck, and more recently a variation of that game has been brought to the casinos with the name sic bo, which is Chinese for precious dice. The game is played with three dice. You place a wager on one number from one to six. Let's say you bet $1 on the number four. Then the dice are rolled, and if a four appears, you win $1. Let's see what we have here, a four, six, and a one. I'd win $1. That almost sounds like a fair game since each die has a one in six chance of being a four. Furthermore, if your number shows up twice, let's say I had two fours over here, right, then you'd win $2, and if it shows up three times, then you'd win $3. What could be fairer than that? As we'll see, plenty.

First, let me show you that your chance of winning $3 is extremely low. To win $3, each die must be four, and the probability that the red die is four, is one out of six. The probability that the yellow die is four, is one out of six. The probability that the blue die is four, is one out of six, and since the dice rolls are very independent, the probability that all of them are fours is $\frac{1}{6} \times \frac{1}{6} \times \frac{1}{6}$. That's $(\frac{1}{6})^3$, which is 1 out of 216. That's less than 1%. On the other hand, the chance of losing $1 is actually pretty high. For that to happen, none of the dice can be fours. And what's the chance of that? Well the chance that the red die is not a four is five out of six. Likewise, the probability that the yellow die is not a four is five out of six, and the probability that the blue die is not a four is five out of six. So the probability that they are all not equal to four is $(\frac{5}{6})^3$. That's $\frac{125}{216}$, which is about 58%. So you actually lose money in this game more than half the time.

Now, what are your chances of winning $1? To do this, you need exactly one of these three dice to be four. You need exactly one of them, wow, I got two of them there, to be fours. Alright? So, there are three ways that this can happen. You can either have a red four and yellow and blue not be four, or you could have a yellow four only, or you could have a blue four only. Those are the three ways of getting one four. The chance of having a red four and no yellow and blue four would be $\frac{1}{6} \times \frac{5}{6} \times \frac{5}{6}$, which is $\frac{25}{216}$. Likewise, there's a $\frac{25}{216}$ chance of seeing just a yellow four and a 25 out of 216 chance of seeing just a blue four. Therefore, our total chance of seeing exactly one four is 75 out of 216. That's about 35%. Similarly, the probability of winning $2, for that we have three situations. We can either have a red and a yellow four and not a blue four, or we could have red-blue being four, or we could have yellow-blue being four. So those are the three situations. The chance of having a red-yellow four is $\frac{1}{6} \times \frac{1}{6} \times \frac{5}{6}$. That's 5 out of 216. The other two situations also have probability 5 out of 216, and when we add all these together we get that your probability of winning exactly $2 is $\frac{15}{216}$. That's about 7%. Summarizing our information in a table, notice that our probabilities sum to 1 exactly—$\frac{216}{216}$. If they don't, then you've made a mistake in at least one of your earlier calculations. When we calculate our expected profit, we get an expected value of about -0.08. In other words, you can expect to lose about 8¢ for every dollar that you bet in this game. As you can see, this game is very fair for the casino.

Now let's consider the most popular dice game in the casino, the game of Craps. The rules of the game are pretty simple. You place your bet and roll two dice. If the total is 7 or 11, you win. If the total is 2, 3, or 12, you lose. If the total is something else, then that number becomes your point. Then you keep rolling the dice until your point appears or seven appears. If your point appears first, you win. If seven appears first, you lose. Let's try a game here. I roll a dice. It's a nine, so I keep rolling until a 7…a 9 appeared! Hey! I win. So, if you rolled, let's say, a four on your first roll, what are the chances that you win? There are a few ways to calculate this probability, all of which lead to the same answer: one-third. Here is the most intuitive way to obtain this answer. Let's look at all the possible totals when you roll two dice. We see that there are, if you roll two dice, let's say a red and a green die, you have 36 possible outcomes—six for the red, six for the green–each of which is equally likely. How many of these have a total of four? Well, we see from our table that three of them do. How many of these have a total of seven? Six of them do, and once we rolled that first four we just keep rolling the dice until a four appears or a seven appears. So there are nine outcomes that end the game. Three are winners; six are losers. So your chance of winning is three out of nine, or one-third. And, thus, your chance of losing is two-thirds. This makes sense since you have twice as many ways to roll a seven than to roll a four.

Okay. What if your opening roll is a five? Then this time you have four winning numbers and six losing numbers, right? We can see that from our table. So here there are 10 outcomes that end the game; four are winners, six are losers. So your chance of winning when you start with a five, when your point is a five, is four out of 10. Similarly, if you open with a six, now you have five winners and six losers so your chance of winning is five out of 11. Using this logic we can figure out the chance of winning from every opening roll, right? And here it is. For instance, notice that if your opening roll is a two, your chance of winning the game is zero. If your opening roll is a seven, your chance of winning is one, 100%, And if your opening roll is a four, then your chance of winning is three out of nine, or one-third.

We can use these numbers to figure out your overall chance of winning using what's called the law of total probability. The law of total probability says that your overall winning chance is a weighted average of your chances of winning from each opening roll. We weigh each opening roll based on how likely it is to occur on the first roll. Now that's a mouthful; let me explain that. So here there's a 1-in-36 chance of an initial roll of two, and there's a 2-out-of-36 chance of an initial roll of three, and a 3-out-of-36 chance of an initial roll of four, and so on. Notice that the sum of these weights is necessarily 1.

Now when we multiply each winning chance by its weight, and we take the sum, then the reduced fraction, when you do the arithmetic, turns out to be $244/_{495}$. That's 0.493, 49.3% chance of winning the game of Craps. So, when you bet \$1, you're either going to win \$1 with probability 0.493, or you're going to lose \$1 with probability with 0.507. So your expected value for this game is $(1 \times 0.493) + (-1 \times 0.507)$. That's -0.014; -1.4¢ for every dollar that you bet. This makes the game of Craps much fairer than roulette and chuck-a-luck, but it's still an unfavorable game. Now I don't have a number yet for blackjack or Video Poker. We'll talk about those games later. By the way, I don't list Slot Machines on this list either since they come in so many different varieties, but with the possible exception of Video Poker, Slot Machines are best avoided. And don't take my word for it. If you rearrange the letters of Slot Machines, you actually get Cash Lost in 'em, so be careful.

Okay. Getting back to Craps. A 49.3% chance of winnings seems almost fair, you might say. Right? It's very close to 50%. How much of a disadvantage is that, really? Well, let's recall the question at the beginning of this lecture. You enter a casino with $60 and you want to turn it into $100 so that you can see a concert. Remember that. You decide to play at a Craps table, making $1 bets until you either reach $100 or you go broke with $0, okay? You have $60 to start with. You're going to reach $100 or die trying. What are your chances of success?

This is known as the Gambler's Ruin Problem, and it has a very beautiful answer. The general question goes like this. Suppose you make $1 bets on a game where you win $1 with probability p, and you lose $1 with probability 1−p and let's say you start with I dollars, I, as in initial investment, and your goal is to reach n dollars before going broke. What is your chance of reaching your goal? Let's call this answer A(I). Let's first consider the answer when the game is fair. That is when p, your probability of winning, is exactly one half. When p is a half, your chance of success, starting with I dollar, A(I), is exactly I divided by n. So, for example, if you're playing a fair game, and you start with I equals $60, and you want to reach n equals $100, then A(60), your chance of winning, is $^{60}/_{100}$, 60%. Now this answer feels right. Right? Because if we start with $60 we are 60% of the way to our goal, and each bet is just as likely to gain as to lose. This is sometimes called the Symmetric Random Walk. Symmetric Random Walks, by the way, are used outside of gambling problems. They're also used for modeling stock prices and describing the movement of molecules. So this I over n formula, which is very simple, also satisfies other nice properties. Notice, for example, that A(0) is 0/n. That's 0. This makes sense because if you start with nothing, you can't possibly reach your goal. Likewise, A(n) is n/n. That's 1, 100%. That makes sense because if you have n dollars, then you don't need to bet at all since you're already at your goal.

It can be shown, by the way, that the I/n formula is the only internally consistent formula that gets the right answer when I is 0 or n. Now here's what I mean by internally consistent. Let's say we started with $60, and our goal is $100. Then after $1 bet we either have $59 if we lose or $61 if we win. So the formula tells us that half the time—remember, we win or lose half the time—half the time we have a 59% chance and half the time we'll have a 61% chance, taking the average we get a 60% chance. So the formula is internally consistent. So now we perfectly understand the symmetric game, the fair game, when p is a half.

What if the game is not fair so that p is not a half? Then if we take—let's use the letter Q to represent the probability of losing, so Q is $1 - p$. Here we get that the probability of turning I dollars into n dollars, our A(I) formula, is $(1 - Q/_p)^I / (1 - Q/_p)^n$, Now I'll leave it as an exercise for you to show, plug into this formula, that A(0) is 0, that A(n) is 1, and with a little bit more work, that's it's internally consistent.

Now for the fun part. Let's plug some numbers into this beautiful formula. Again, if we start with I equals $60, and we want to reach n equals $100, then if we bet $1 at a time, let's look at our chances. So for the game of Craps here, we know that p, your probability of winning, is 49.3%, 0.493. When we plug that into the A(60) formula, betting on, let's say, you know, just rolling the dice each time, you have a 49.3% chance of winning each bet. Your chance of turning $60 into $100, when we plug into the formula, is about 28%. Now what if we round 49.3% down to an even 49%? Now our chance of success even though we just went tiny bit down from 0.493 to 0.49, our chance of winning—of successfully turning $60 into $100—is only 18%. And if we reduce that 49% to 48%, our chance of success plummets down to 4%. And if we try betting on red each time in roulette, then lots of luck since your chance of succeeding—of turning that $60 into $100—is only 1.4%. Now I don't have chuck-a-luck on this chart because it doesn't exactly fit the Gambler's Ruin format since it's possible to win more than $1 on a $1 bet. But you can be sure that the probability of making it to $100 would be even worse than roulette. Computer simulations put that number around 0.07%.

Now suppose we play a fair game. Let's say where you actually have a 50% chance of winning each time. Then our chance of success—of turning 60 into $100—we use our I/n formula, and that tells us that our chance of success is exactly 60%. And suppose that we are skillful enough to be playing a favorable game where you actually have a 51% chance of winning each time, then your chance of success is a whopping 92.6%. So as you can see, a little advantage can go a long way. Now our calculations show that if you bring $60 to a Craps table and you bet $1 at a time, then you have a 28% chance of reaching $100, but, a better strategy is to, instead of betting $1 at a time, boldly bet $40 right away giving you a 49.3% chance of getting to $100 in a single bet. Right? Because if I have $60, I bet 40, I only have to win once, and we know that that has a 49.3% chance of working. Right? In fact, if you lose that $40 bet, you still have $20 left in your pocket, and you could still reach $100 if you win your next three bets in a row. So there's at least two ways of getting to $100. You can either win right away, or, you could lose, but then win the next three bets. Right? Because you'll go from 20 to 40 to 80 and then to $100. In fact, if you always bet what you need to reach $100, okay, or everything, if you have under $50, then you actually have about a 59% chance of reaching your goal.

Now wait a second. Look what we have here. We've just shown that there's a better than 50% chance of turning $60 into $100. Why aren't the casinos afraid of this? Why doesn't everyone just use this strategy? The answer, if you think about it, it's not obvious, the answer is that when you win, you've only gained $40. Right? You've turned 60 into 100, but when you lose you've lost all $60. So if you're risking $60 to gain $40, you need at least a 60% chance to make the bet profitable. As it happens, our bet-it-all strategy has a 59% chance of success, but that's below 60% so the casinos are safe.

By the way, here's another well-known betting strategy that's doomed to failure. It's called the Martingale strategy, or Double your Bet strategy. Suppose you're playing a game, any game, let's say roulette, and you bet $5 on red. If you win your bet, you go home with a $5 profit. If you lose your bet, you place another $5 on red, but this time you bet $10. If you win, then your overall profit, you last $5, but you just won $10 is a profit of $5. If you lose, well now you're down $15, right? $5 and $10 so you bet $20, and if you win you go home with a $5 profit. Otherwise, you're down $35, and you bet $40 next time. Each time you lose, you double your previous bet. Since red has to show up eventually, when that happens, you'll have made your $5 profit. So what's wrong with this strategy?

In every casino game they impose a maximum bet that you are not allowed to exceed. For instance, the roulette table might not let you bet more than $500. Thus if you lose 7 bets in a row, $5, $10, $20, $40, $80, $160, $320, you are now down $635. You will not be allowed to place a $640 bet, and the odds are good that you will never recover that loss. Now what are the chances that you lose seven bets in a row? I know, pretty unlikely, right? In roulette, if you bet on red, then with each bet your chance of losing, if you recall, is $^{20}/_{38}$, 52.6%. So the chance of losing seven bets in a row is about 0.526^7. That's about 1.1%. So if 100 people played this strategy, you could expect 99 of those people to win their $5, and that will cost the casino 99 × 5 dollars, $495, but one of those people will be down $635, which makes up for the $495. So as usual, the casino makes a profit.

Let me reemphasize, when you are playing an unfavorable game and the casino imposes a maximum bet, there is no system of money management that can make the game profitable in the long run. You cannot combine games with a negative expected value and turn it into a game with a positive expected value. When you're playing an unfavorable game, the best long-term strategy is simply, don't bet.

But now let's turn our attention to favorable games, where you have a positive expected value. You don't see these often in a casino, but you might see these in some investment situations. The question is, if you're playing a game with a positive expected value, how much should you bet? Let's say you're playing a game, where on each wager you have a 51% chance of winning, okay? If you safely bet $1, then your expected value, when you bet $1, is $(1 × 0.51) – (1 × 0.49)$ is 2 cents. If you start with exactly $1000, and you bet $1 each time, you'll almost certainly not go broke, but you will only make about 2 cents per bet, which is not very much. On the other hand, if you bet all your money each time, you're likely to be completely broke in a very short amount of time. Even if you bet half your money each time or a third of your money each time, your money would not last very long. So the question is, what is the happy medium where your money grows quickly, but where your chance of going broke is small?

One popular strategy is to bet your edge as a fraction of your bankroll. What do I mean by that? If your chance of winning is 51%, and your chance of losing is 49%, then you have a 2% edge. The Kelly Criterion says you should bet 2% of your bankroll. So if you start with $1,000, then you should begin by betting $20 per bet—that's 2% of 1,000. As you win, you should gradually increase your bet. For instance, when you reach $1,500 you should be betting $30 per bet and when you reach $2,000, you should be betting $40 per bet, and if you hit a losing streak, and you find yourself down to $500, you should reduce your wager to $10 per bet. It can be shown that when you bet your edge, your bankroll is expected, but not guaranteed, to grow exponentially with the highest growth rate with only a small risk of going bust. Although, many investors will bet half their edge to further reduce the chance of going broke because nobody likes going bust.

Here's the result that I find most surprising. It can be shown that if you bet more than twice your edge, then in the long run you will go broke. For instance, in a game, where you have a 51 to 49 advantage, a 2% edge, if you bet more than 4% of your bankroll each time, then in the long run your bankroll will eventually be less than $1. That's pretty scary, and surprising, since you're playing a favorable game. The moral here is that even when you have an advantage, you can still lose your shirt, so be careful.

The last problem I want to share with you is known as the Monty Hall problem. Imagine you're on a game show and—Let's Make a Deal and the host of the show, Monty Hall, shows you three doors, and makes the following proposition. Behind one of these doors is a brand new car, and behind each of the other doors is a goat. He asks you to choose one of the doors, and let's say you pick door number one. He then says, before I show you what's behind door number one, let me show you that behind door number three, there's a goat. Now, do you want to stick with door number one or do you want to switch to door number two? Assuming you'd prefer to win the car instead of the goat, what should you do? Should you stick with your instincts, stick with door number one? Or should you make the switch? Or does it not matter? Maybe you're 50/50 either way. What do you think?

Most people are surprised to learn that you should definitely make the switch. Why is that? I'm going to give you two explanations. Here's one way to look at the problem. Let's suppose that you and I both get to play on this game show for 300 straight days, and on each of these days, you and I start by picking door number one. Then Monty shows us one of the doors with a goat. We'll assume that if the car really is behind door number one that he shows us either two or three with equal probability. He doesn't have favorites with these doors. When he asks if we'd like to keep or switch doors, you stubbornly stick with door number one, while I eagerly make the switch. Now we get to play this game 300 times. On each of these days, one of us is going to go away with the car. Right? Of those 300 days, when do you win? You win precisely on those days where the car is behind door number one. That's roughly one-third of the time. Right? About 100 of those 300 days you're the winner. I win the other 200 days. Hence, the switching strategy has a two-thirds chance of success. Some people will not be convinced by this argument, and I can sympathize with them since there's a very subtle change to this problem that would make it in such a way that there'd be no advantage to switching.

Suppose that you and I appear on this game show, and, we pick door number one. And just as before, before Monty had a chance to say anything, a big gust of wind comes along and knocks down door number three, revealing a goat to the entire audience. Now this is not the same problem as before because it's possible that the car was behind door number three, and then everyone's embarrassed. Everyone sees where the car was, and the game would be over. But in the original problem, Monty will never actually show you where the car was, right? Monty would never say, oh, look what's behind door number three, the car. That would be kind of silly. So in this game, you know, when the gust of wind knocks down and reveals a goat, then there would actually be no advantage to switching. You would be just as likely to win with door number one as door number two. To use my earlier argument, if we both chose door number one and then I switched, then you would win 100 times when the car is behind door number one. I would win 100 times when the car is behind door number two, and we would both lose in the 100 times when the car was accidentally revealed behind door number three.

Now if you're still unconvinced, let's extend the Monty Hall problem to use 52 doors instead of three, and I have 52 doors right here, as represented by this deck of cards Let's say that in this game you choose one of the 52 cards, and you win the big prize only if it's the ace of spades, okay? So after you choose your card, okay, let's say, you pick this card, I, then, look through the rest of the cards, and I pick one of them, and then I show you all the other cards. Ok I'm going to show you all the other cards, and you see that none of them are the ace of spades. So, now I ask you, do you want to keep your card or switch for the card that I have. That's like you picking door number one, Monty showing you 50 doors with goats and leaving one door concealed, one door closed. Now which card do you want? You want your card or mine? Everyone instinctively says yeah, this card is more likely to be the ace of spades than that one. So, okay, on the other hand, let's suppose, instead, suppose that you chose a card. Okay, let's say you picked that one, and then all of a sudden a big gust of wind came along, and a bunch of cards fell on the floor. We looked at the cards, and we saw that none of them was the ace of spades, but there's one card left in my hand. Now, which card is more likely to be the ace of spades? Yours or mine? Now it really is 50/50 whether your card was the ace of spades or mine was.

We've now looked at some popular games, like roulette, Craps, and more, but we've not yet tackled the game of blackjack, which, depending how you play it, is either the best or the worst game in the casino. In our next lecture, we'll see how you can get the best of blackjack before it gets the best of you.

Optimal Blackjack and Simple Card Counting
Lecture 3

Blackjack is the fairest game in the casino—if you play your cards right. In blackjack, there are many decisions for the player: Should you hit, stand, split, double down, or buy insurance? The answer will depend on your cards and the card that the dealer is showing. In this lecture, you will learn the optimal basic strategy for playing blackjack without counting cards. You will also learn techniques for counting cards, which can sometimes give you an advantage over the house.

Blackjack

- In blackjack, you and the dealer are initially dealt two cards, and you can see one of the dealer's cards, called the up card. Next, you add up your card values: Cards 2 through 9 have values 2 through 9; ten, jack, queen, and king have value 10; and aces are worth either 1 or 11.

- A hand with an ace in it can be 1 or 11. If it can be used as either a 1 or 11, it's called a soft hand. For example, a hand that consists of an ace and a 6 is a soft 17 because the hand can also be counted as a 7—in other words, it's a 17 that can be softened to a 7. However, a hand that consists of an ace, a 6, and a queen is a hard 17 because for these hands, 17 is the only legal total.

- You may continue to take cards—which is called hitting—as long as your total is under 21. If your total goes over 21, then you are busted, and you automatically lose your bet. If you stop taking cards—which is called standing—without going bust, then the dealer takes cards until his or her total is 17 or higher.

- If neither you nor the dealer busts, then whoever has a total that is closer to 21 wins the bet. If you and the dealer have the same total, then you neither win nor lose; it's a tie, known in blackjack as a push.

- If two cards that you are originally dealt add up to 21—for example, if you get an ace and a king as your first two cards—then your hand is called a blackjack, and the casino pays three to two. Thus, if you initially bet $2 and you get dealt a blackjack, then the casino pays you $3—unless the dealer also has a blackjack, in which case it is a push.

- Sometimes, the player has additional options. After you get your initial two cards, you can double your bet and get exactly one more card. This is called doubling down. For example, let's say your total is 11, which is excellent, and the dealer has a 9 showing. Then, if you were betting $2, you can double your bet to get $4. You tell the dealer that you want one more card. If your card ends up being a 3, for example, even though you'd like to take another card, you cannot because you doubled down. You just have to hope that the dealer busts, because if the dealer gets 17 to 21, the dealer wins.

When to Double Down

Your first two cards	Double if dealer has
Total 11	10 or below
Total 10	9 or below
Total 9	4, 5, or 6
A2 thru A7	4, 5, or 6

- If your first two cards have the same value, then you're allowed to split the cards and play the two hands for an additional bet. For example, let's say you bet $2 and you're dealt a pair of 8s, and the dealer has an up card of 5. Instead of playing one hand with a rather poor total of 16, you'd rather play two hands that start with a total of 8. You tell the dealer that you're splitting, and you can take your original bet and essentially double it, so now you're playing two hands each worth $2 against the dealer's 5.

When to Split

When do you split...	If dealer has...
A, 8	Any card
4, 5, 10	Never!
2, 3, 6, 7	2,3,4,5, or 6
9	2,3,4,5,6,8,9

- If you split aces, then the dealer will give you just one more card. If you get a blackjack, it only pays even money. Some casinos will even let you re-split any cards except for aces, and most casinos will not let you double down after splitting.

- The final option is called insurance. If the dealer's face-up card is an ace, then you are allowed to bet up to half of your initial bet that the dealer has a 10, jack, queen, or king underneath. If so, that bet pays two-to-one odds.

- Taking insurance is generally a bad bet. When you make an insurance bet, there are four cards that win for you. If the down card is a 10, jack, queen, or king, then you win your insurance bet on those four card values. The other nine card values—ace through 9—would lose for you. For the insurance bet to be fair with four winning cards and nine losing cards, the casino should pay you nine-to-four odds, but the casino is only offering you two-to-one odds.

- Who has the advantage in blackjack? On the one hand, the player has many more options than the dealer. After all, the player can stand before reaching 17, double down, split, and take insurance. The player also gets paid three to two for blackjacks. However, the dealer has one advantage that offsets all of the player's options: If the player and the dealer both bust, then the dealer still wins.

The Optimal Basic Strategy
- Most casinos play with more than one deck, meaning that they shuffle several decks together and you play with those cards. The

optimal basic strategy can vary slightly, depending on the number of decks in use, but your overall advantage won't change much. Consider the following to be an extremely good strategy that's easy to remember and works for any number of decks.

- If your cards have a hard total of 17 or higher, then you should always stand. If your cards have a hard total of 11 or lower, then you should never stand—because there's nothing to lose by taking another card.

- The situation is more interesting when you have a hard total between 12 and 16. If the dealer shows a good card — a 7, 8, 9, 10, or ace—then you should hit. In your head, think of the dealer as having a total of at least 17. If the dealer has a bad card—a 4, 5, or 6—then take no chances and stand. These are bad cards because they have a tendency to become 14s, 15s, or 16s, which have a tendency to bust. If the dealer shows a 2 or a 3—a so-so card—then you should hit with a hard total of 12 but stand on 13, 14, 15, or 16.

- When you have a soft hand, the strategy changes. If you have a soft 16 or lower, such as an ace and a 5, then you should always hit because you have nothing to lose. Also, according to basic strategy, you should always hit if you have a soft 17. Some people are surprised by this rule, but it is supported by math.

- You should always stand on a soft 19 or higher. If you have a soft 18, such as an ace and a 7, then you should hit if the dealer shows a 9, 10, or ace. Otherwise, you should stand.

- The rules for doubling down are very simple: If you have a total of 11, then you should double down if the dealer's card is 10 or below. If you have a total of 10, you should double down if the dealer's card is 9 or below. In other words, if your total is 10 or 11, you should double down if your total is better than the dealer's up card. The only other times when you might double down is when your total is 9 or if your hand is soft. In these situations, you should only double down if the dealer shows a bad card—a 4, 5, or 6.

- The rules for splitting are easy to remember. Always split aces and 8s. Never split 4s, 5s, or 10s because you're going from a good total (8, 10, or 20) to a bad total (4 or 5) or, at least in the case of 10, to a worse total. For almost everything else, you should split your cards when the dealer has a low card showing—a 2, 3, 4, 5, or 6. There's only one exotic exception: You split your 9s when the dealer has 2 through 9, except 7.

Card Counting

- In 1966, mathematician Edward Thorp wrote a book called *Beat the Dealer* that changed the way people played blackjack, also known as the game of 21. Thorp observed that blackjack is different from most other casino games because your winning chances can actually change as you go from one deal to the next.

- Many people think that card counting involves memorizing all the cards that have been played, but in fact, card counting usually just consists of keeping track of a single number, and it's pretty easy to do. It's also not as profitable as people think.

- Specifically, if the deck contains a much higher proportion of 10s and aces, then that will benefit the player. The extra 10s and aces lead to more blackjacks, and that pays three to two to the player, but only even money to the dealer, so the player benefits more than the dealer the more blackjacks there are.

- The additional 10s help the player in a few other ways. Most of the time that you double down, you have a total of 10 or 11, and you're hoping to get a 10 card. Therefore, the more 10s that are left in the deck, the better it is for you. The 10s are bad for the dealer because they cause the dealer to bust more often. It is also true that the 10s cause the player to bust more often, but the player won't bust as often because the player is allowed to stop before reaching 17. On the other hand, the dealer has to keep taking cards until he or she gets to 17, so the dealer busts more often.

- When the count gets high—which is going to happen when there have been a lot of low cards that have been played and a lot of 10s and aces left in the deck—you can make some adjustments to basic strategy. For example, if there are enough 10s left in the deck, it can even be worthwhile to take insurance when it favors the player, but most of all, when there are enough 10s and aces, you typically want to bet more because you now have an advantage in the game.

- The essence of card counting is as follows: When the deck is against you, which is most of the time, bet low. When it's for you, bet high—but not too high.

- The simplest and most frequently used card-counting system is called the high-low system. You start with zero, and every time you see a low card—a 2, 3, 4, 5, or 6—you add one to your count. Every time you see a high card—a 10, jack, queen, king, or ace—you subtract one from your count. If you have a middle card—a 7, 8, or 9—you don't change your count at all (you add zero). There are five low cards (2, 3, 4, 5, 6) and five high cards (10, jack, queen, king, ace), so the count should usually be around zero.

Suggested Reading

Griffin, *The Theory of Blackjack.*

Schlesinger, *Blackjack Attack.*

Snyder, *Blackbelt in Blackjack.*

Thorp, *Beat the Dealer.*

Vancura and Fuchs, *Knock-Out Blackjack*

Problems

21 questions! For the following blackjack scenarios, what does basic strategy tell you to do: stand, hit, double down, or split?

1. 10 5 vs. 7 (that is, you have 10 and 5; the dealer's face-up card is 7).

2. 9 3 vs. 5.

3. 8 8 vs. 10.

4. 5 5 vs. 5.

5. 7 6 vs. 2.

6. A 7 vs. Q.

7. 8 3 vs. J.

8. A 6 vs. 7.

9. A 2 3 4 vs. 9.

10. Q 2 vs. 3.

11. J 7 vs. A.

12. 9 5 vs. 10.

13. A 6 vs. 4.

14. 9 9 vs. 7.

15. A 4 2 vs. 6.

16. A 7 vs. 5.

17. 7 2 vs. 4.

18. 4 4 vs. 6.

19. 7 7 vs. 3.

20. 7 4 vs. 8.

21. Basic strategy says to never take insurance, but if there are 26 unseen cards remaining, at least how many of them have to be 10, J, Q, or K for insurance to be the correct action?

Optimal Blackjack and Simple Card Counting
Lecture 3—Transcript

Among all games that you play against the casino, blackjack is the game that gives you the best chance of winning if you play it properly. On the other hand, if you don't use the proper strategy, blackjack can be a very expensive game. Blackjack is also one of the most interesting games in the casino since you have some real decisions to make, and the right answer may be far from obvious. For instance, suppose you are dealt two cards that add up to 12, and the dealer has a four showing. What should you do? Should you take another card in hopes of getting closer to 21, or, do not take any chances and hope the dealer loses by reaching a total that exceeds 21? We'll learn the answer to this question and many more like it during this lecture.

Since most people are already familiar with the basic rules of blackjack, I'll just give a quick review. You and the dealer are initially dealt two cards, and you can see one of the dealer's cards. That's called the up card. So here, this four would be the dealer's up card. The dealer is allowed to see your cards, but that doesn't actually matter. He's not allowed to take advantage of that. Next, you add up your card values, so cards two through nine have values two through nine Ten, jack, queen, and king have value 10, and aces are worth one or 11.

Now, first, some terminology, a hand with an ace in it can be one or 11. If it can be used as a one or 11, it's called a soft hand. For example, ace-six is a soft 17 since the hand can also be counted as a seven. It's a 17 that can be softened to a seven but a hand like ace-six-queen or nine-eight, that's a hard 17 since for these hands 17 is the only legal total. You may continue to take cards—that's called hitting—as long as your total is under 21. If your total goes over 21, then you are busted and you automatically lose your bet.

For example, in this situation, if you take a card, and it's a 10, then your total would be 22, and you would be busted. If you stop taking cards, that's called standing without going bust, then the dealer takes cards until his total is 17 or higher. If neither you nor the dealer busts, then whoever has a total that's closer to 21 wins the bet. Suppose you decide to hit this hand, and instead of being dealt a 10 you're dealt a seven, giving you a total of 19. Since that's a good total, you correctly stand. Now the dealer has a down card of three for a total of seven, and then the dealer has to take a card, it's a queen, for a total of 17. Since the dealer has to stop when he's at 17 or higher, you win the hand. Even though the dealer sees that you have 19, he can't take advantage of that. If you and the dealer have the same total, then you neither win nor lose. It's a tie known in blackjack as a push.

If two cards that you are originally dealt add up to 21, let's say you get an ace and a king as your first two cards, then your hand is called a blackjack, and the casino pays three to two. Thus, if you initially bet $2, and you get dealt a blackjack, then the casino pays you $3. Unless the dealer also has a blackjack, in which case it's a push. Sometimes the player has additional options. After you get your initial two cards, you can double your bet and get exactly one more card. This is called doubling down. So, for example, let's say your total is 11. That's excellent, and the dealer has a nine showing, then if you were betting $2, you can double your bet to get $4, so you double down. You just say, okay, I want one more card. Let's see, so your card here is a three, not a very good card. Even though you'd like to take another card, you cannot because you doubled down. You just have to hope that the dealer busts because if the dealer gets 17 to 21 the dealer wins.

Here's another option. If your first two cards have the same value, then you're allowed to split the cards and play the two hands for an additional bet. For example, let's say you bet $2, and you're dealt a pair of eights, and the dealer has an up card of five. Now, instead of playing one hand with a rather poor total of 16, you'd rather play two hands that start with a total of eight. So you say, I'm splitting, and now you can take your original bet and double that, essentially, so now you're playing two hands each worth $2 against the five.

Let's see what happens. So gets the— hits the eight for a 10. That's an 18. Definitely going to stand there. Here a three is an 11. Another card is four, 15. We'll stop there. And, what happens to the dealer? The dealer had a seven showing, has a total of seven with an ace. That makes 18, so this is a push, okay, that you neither win nor lose this hand. But this, the 18, beats the 15, so you would lose that bet to the dealer. Note, by the way, that if you split aces, then the dealer will give you just one more card. And if you get a blackjack, it only pays even money. Some casinos will even let you re-split any cards, except for aces, and most of them will not let you double down after splitting. So after that eight-three with an 11, you might have wanted to double down. Most casinos won't let you do that.

The final option is called insurance. If the dealer's face-up card is an ace, then you are allowed to bet up to half your initial bet that the dealer has a 10, jack, queen or king underneath. If so, that bet pays two-to-one odds. So here, the dealer has an ace showing. You have a 20, and now, if you want— and let's say you bet $2 initially—so an insurance bet is you can bet up to half of your initial bet, $1, one chip, we'll put that here on the side, as an insurance bet. So if this card is a 10, jack, queen, or king then that $1 will win $2. So let's see what happens in this hand. You say, okay, I'm going to take insurance. The dealer looks at the cards, sees it's not a 10, jack, queen or king. Sorry. You lose that $1 bet. Now what do you want to do with your hand? You're going to stand. The dealer has a three or 13, takes another card. It's a nine or 19. Since it's 19, the dealer stands, and now you win. Your 20 would win the $2 against the 19. Let's see why taking insurance is generally a bad bet.

When you make an insurance bet there are four cards that win for you. Right? You look at this down card; you don't know what it is, but if it's a 10, jack, queen, or king, then you win your insurance bet on those four card values. And the other nine card values, ace through 9, those would lose for you. So for the insurance bet to be fair with four winning cards and nine losing cards, the casino should pay you nine-to-four odds for insurance to be a fair bet, but the casino is only offering you two-to-one odds. That's the same as eight to four, and since that is worse than getting the fair odds of nine to four, you should usually not make the insurance bet. Now I said usually because if you keep track of the cards, then it could be a correct bet if there are enough 10s, jacks, queens, and kings left in the deck. More on that later when we talk about card counting.

So the big question is, without doing any card counting, when should you stand, when should you hit, when should you double, when should you split? The answer will depend on your cards and the card that the dealer is showing. For example, if your total is 16, and, let's say, the dealer shows a seven, should you hit? Now, before we talk about this, let's discuss who has the advantage in blackjack. On the one hand, the player has way more options than the dealer. After all, the player can stand before reaching 17, the player can double down, the player can split, the player gets paid three to two for blackjacks, and the player can take insurance. The dealer can't do any of this. The dealer has just one advantage, but it's a big one, and it offsets all of the other player's options. If the player and the dealer both bust, then the dealer still wins. Once you are busted, you lose your bet, no matter what happens to the dealer. This gives the dealer an overall advantage. But if you play your cards right, blackjack is the fairest game in the casino.

So how do you play your cards right? I will now present to you what is known as the optimal basic strategy. Most casinos play with more than one deck, meaning they shuffle several decks together, and you play with these cards. The optimal basic strategy can vary slightly—very slightly— depending on the number of decks in use, but your overall advantage won't change much. So consider what I'm about to give you to be an extremely good strategy that's easy to remember that works for any number of decks. I'll explain how these rules are derived later, but let's first learn what the rules are. Let's start with when should you hit versus when you should stand, when you have a hard hand; we'll start with hard hands.

We'll address soft hands, doubling and splitting after that. If your cards have a hard total of 17 or higher, then you should always stand. If your cards have a hard total of 11 or lower, then you should never stand since there's nothing to lose by taking another card. The situation is more interesting when you have a hard total between 12 and 16. If the dealer shows a good card, a 7, 8, 9, 10, or ace, then you should hit. In your head, think of the dealer as having a total of at least 17. If the dealer has one of his bad cards a four, five, or six, then take no chances and stand. Now why are the four, five, and six bad for the dealer? Well four, five, and sixes have a tendency to become 14s, 15s or 16s, which have a tendency to bust. So these are the dealer's worst cards. Finally, if the dealer shows a two or a three, a so-so card, then you should hit with a hard total of 12, but stand on 13, 14, 15, or 16. So you only take a chance if you have a 12. And that's everything you need to know about hitting and standing when you have a hard hand.

I've summarized these decisions in this table. If the dealer's up card is 7, 8, 9, 10, or ace, then you hit until you reach 17. If the dealer's up card is a four, five, or six, then you hit until you reach 12, and don't take any chances. If the dealer's up card is a two or a three, then you hit until you reach 13. So let's look at some situations. What should we do in this situation of a 16 versus a seven? What's the right decision here? You have a total of 16. The dealer has a seven. This is a good card for the dealer, so you have to assume that the dealer has 17 or higher, so the correct decision is to hit. It's an eight, so we are busted. Now as it turned out, notice the dealer's down card was a jack, so you would have lost the hand either way.

When you have a soft hand, the strategy changes. Naturally, if you have a soft 16 or lower, like an ace-five, then you should always hit. You literally have nothing to lose by hitting. Also, according to basic strategy, you should—and this is important to remember—basic strategy says, always hit soft 17. Some people are surprised by this rule, but later we'll learn the math that bears it out. So let's look at an example here. So you have an ace-six. That's a soft 17. The dealer has a nine showing. What do you do? Always hit soft 17. So we do that. We hit it. Now our total is 12. It's now a hard 12, right? Because ace-six-five can only give you 12. Against a nine, what do you do? You have to hit it. Alright, now your total's 20. Great. What does the dealer have? You stand with the 20. The dealer has a 10 underneath—19. Congratulations. You win. So that is what you get for, for hitting soft 17.

Not surprisingly, you should always stand on a soft 19 or higher. What if you have a soft 18? Let's say you had an ace and a seven. Then you should hit if the dealer shows a 9, 10, or ace. Otherwise, you should stand. So summarizing this information another way, remember if the dealer has a 9, 10, or ace, if you have a soft hand, you should hit until you reach soft 19. If the dealer's up card is eight or below, then you should aim for soft 18, but remember the important corollary: always hit soft 17.

The rules for doubling down are very simple. If you have a total of 11, then you should double down if the dealer's card is 10 or below. If you have a total of 10, you should double down if the dealer's card is nine or below. In other words, if your total is 10 or 11, you should double down if your total is better than the dealer's up card. The only other times when you might double down is when your total is nine or if your hand is soft. In these situations you should only double if the dealer shows a bad card, a four, five, or six.

I'm deviating slightly from perfect strategy here, but not by much. The rules I'm giving here are easy to remember. Likewise for my splitting rules. Here are the splitting decisions. So when do you split? Always split aces and eights. Never split 4s, 5s, or 10s because you're going from a good total, 8, 10, or 20, to a bad total, 4 or 5, or, at least in the case of 10, you have a worse total. And for almost everything else, you should split your cards when the dealer has a low card showing, a two, three, four, five, or six. There's only one exotic exception. It's my favorite rule. You split your nines when the dealer has two through nine, except seven. And that's it for basic strategy.

As I said, my splitting and doubling rules deviate slightly from optimal strategy, but my rules are much easier to remember, so you'll make fewer mistakes. I strongly encourage you to pause and deal through several practice hands until basic strategy becomes second nature. Most casinos will not let you bring a cheat sheet to the table. Once you've mastered this basic strategy, what is your approximate advantage? Suppose you're playing against a casino that's playing with four or more decks using the standard rules. The basic strategy gives you an expected value of -0.5¢ for every dollar bet. Now let's compare that with other games that we've looked at so far. If you're betting $2 per hand, then you expect to lose about 1¢ per hand, so if an average $1 bet loses 0.5¢, that makes blackjack the fairest game in the casino. Remember that for every $1 bet, craps had an expected value of -1.4¢, which is about three times worse than blackjack, right? Blackjack loses 0.5¢ per dollar bet. And roulette has an expected value that's -5.3¢. That's about 10 times worse than blackjack. But what happens when the casinos change the rules? This can affect your overall expected value, usually for the worse.

First, let's look at a good change. If you're lucky enough to be playing against a dealer that only uses two decks, then your expected loss is only about $1/3$ of a cent instead of 0.5¢, and if they only use one deck, then you are virtually dead even with the house. But unfortunately, most casinos use four or more decks these days.

There are two more common rule variations that are becoming increasingly common among casinos that drop your advantage a little bit more. If the casino is required to hit on soft-17—remember how you like to hit on soft 17? The casinos would like to do that too. If the casinos are required to hit on soft-17, that will drop your expected value by another 0.2¢, and if the casino only allows you to double down on 10 or 11, in other words, it won't let you double down if you have a nine or a soft hand, then that also drops your expected value by another 0.2¢. Thus, if the casino is using six decks, and the dealer hits soft-17, and you could only double down on 10s and 11s, then instead of losing 0.5¢ per dollar bet, you'd expect to lose about 0.9¢ per dollar bet, but that is still better than craps and way better than roulette.

On the other hand, there are some rules that make the game extremely unfavorable. Luckily, you don't see these that often, but you should be aware of them just in case. If being dealt a blackjack pays even money to you instead of three-to-two odds, then your expected value drops by another 2.3¢. So if you were losing 0.9¢ per dollar under the previous rules, you're now losing 3.2¢ per dollar with this rule. Increasingly common these days are casinos that pay seven to five or worse, six to five on blackjacks instead of three-to-two odds. Those changes cost the player 0.45¢ and 1.4¢ per dollar bet. And if the dealer wins all ties, as sometimes happens in charity casino nights, then that costs you an extra 9.3¢ per dollar, but at least your money's going to charity.

Okay. So how is optimal basic strategy derived? How does the math come up with these results? Mostly using computer simulations, but we can get pretty much the same results on the back of an envelope using a technique called dynamic programming, sometimes called the art of working backwards. To simplify our analysis, I'll make what is sometimes called the infinite-deck assumption, that every card has a 1 in 13 chance of appearing as the next card, independent of what's already appeared. In other words, the chance that the next card is an ace is 1 in 13. The chance that the next card is a deuce is 1 in 13. The chance that the next card is a 3 is 1 in 13. Every card value has a 1-in-13 chance of happening. But the probability that your next card is a 10, jack, queen, or king—it has a value of 10—that has probability 4 out of 13. Because there are four cards that have a value of 10.

With this assumption, let's tackle a problem that I always argued about with my father. Suppose your cards total 16, and the dealer shows a seven. We saw that hand earlier. Basic strategy says that you should hit. Now I remember explaining this to my father, and he refused to believe it. He'd say, if you take a card, then you're a favorite to bust, right? You've got a 16. I'd say, but if you don't take a card, you can only win if the dealer busts, and that's much less likely. So, let me try to convince you, and my father, of this argument by teaching you a little bit about dynamic programming.

First we need to ask the question, if the dealer shows a seven, what is the chance that he busts? Let's call the answer $B(7)$. $B(7)$ is the chance that the dealer busts when the dealer starts with a seven. But before we determine $B(7)$, because it's not obvious, let's compute $D(16)$. That's an easier problem, the chance that the dealer busts with a hard total of 16. If the dealer has 16, the chance that he busts is the chance that the next card has a value of 6, 7, 8, 9, or 10. Any of those cards will cause the dealer to bust, and the probability of that is 1 in 13, plus 1 in 13, plus 1 in 13, plus 1 in 13, plus 4 in 13. That's eight out of 13. So B of 16, $B(16)$, the chance that the dealer busts, is $^8/_{13}$, about 0.615.

Now let's take a step back and compute $B(15)$, the probability that the dealer busts from a total of 15. Here, if the dealer's next card is 7, 8, 9, or 10, which has probability $^1/_{13}$, $^1/_{13}$, $^1/_{13}$, $^4/_{13}$, that's seven out of 13, then the dealer busts immediately. So if the dealer's next card is 7, 8, 9, or 10, the dealer busts. So $B(15)$ is at least $^7/_{13}$. But there's another way that the dealer can bust. How else can the dealer bust? He could get an ace next turn and bust after that. The chance of getting an ace next turn is 1 in 13, and the chance of busting after that? Well, the dealer now has a total of 16, and the chance of busting after that is $B(16)$. And since we've already calculated $B(16)$, we know it's 0.615, we can now compute $B(15)$. It's $^7/_{13}$ that he busts immediately, plus, $^1/_{13}$ of $B(16)$, and when you substitute 0.615 for $B(16)$, you get an answer of 0.586.

So we now know $B(16)$ and $B(15)$. What do we do next? We take a step back, and we compute $B(14)$. What's $B(14)$? By the same sort of argument, $^6/_{13}$ of the time you bust immediately from a 14 if your card is an 8, 9, or 10—four ways to get a 10. Or $^1/_{13}$ of the time you get an ace, and you bust from that B(15) of the time. And $^1/_{13}$ of the time, the dealer gets a deuce and busts from there B(16) of the time. We plug in those numbers, and we get B(14) is 55.4%.

I'll spare you the rest of the calculations. Working backwards like this, we can successively determine B(13), B(12), and so on, all the way down to B(7), using this chart. This is sort of what the back of my envelope would look like. It would kind of look like this chart here. Notice at the very bottom of that chart, there's B(7), the quantity I was interested in, the chance of busting with a seven is 0.262, 26%. Using this same process we can determine the probability, not only that the dealer busts, we can compute the probability that the dealer reaches any total, 17, 18, 19, 20, 21, or bust, given the dealer's up card. So here's what the final results look like on my table. It's the probability that the dealer reaches any given total from a specific up card. Notice on this table how unlikely it is for the dealer to bust when the up card is 7, 8, 9, 10, and especially ace. With an ace there's only an 11.5% chance that the dealer will bust when the ace is the dealer's up card. Let's use this information to answer some questions.

Suppose you have a total of 17, and the dealer shows a seven. Let's do this hand here. Let's say you have a total of 17, and the dealer has a seven. So, should you hit? Well, the basic strategy says no. You have 17; that's a good hand to stand on, and let's see why. If you stand on 17, your chance of winning is what? If you stand on 17, your chance of winning is B(7). That is, if the dealer busts from the seven, then your 17 is going to win—that's about 26%. But there's another way, another outcome, that could happen. You could also tie if the dealer reaches a total of 17. From our table, the dealer, starting from a seven, will reach a total of 17 with probability 0.369.

We treat ties by saying that you will win half of them. Thus, if you stand with your 17, you have an effective win probability of 26.2% for winning when the dealer busts, plus half of the 0.369 when the dealer gets a 17 himself. That gives you about a 45% effective win probability, but if you hit 17, you only have four safe cards, ace, 2, 3 and 4, and your chances of getting an ace, 2, 3, or 4 is 4 out of 13. That's about 31%. That's way less than the effective-win probability of 45% chance. So it can't possibly be worth taking another card because your chance of winning would be, at most, 31% if you did. So you should definitely stand on 17 versus a 7.

But let's get back to my father's question. What about 16? What about 16 versus 7? If you stand on 16, your only chance of winning is if the dealer busts with a seven, which we've already computed to be about 26%. If you hit, then your total will be 17 or 18 or 19 or 20 or 21 or busting. Using our table and doing calculations similar to what we did with 17 versus 7, you get an effective-win probability of about 29%, and that's larger than the 26% chance that we get when we stand. Thus, we should hit 16 versus 7 as the basic strategy suggests. The difference in these probabilities is about 3%. You are favored to lose in both situations, but your chances are worse if you stand. Consequently, if you insist on standing on that 16 versus 7 instead of hitting, this will cost you in the long run about 6¢ per dollar bet every time you face this situation.

Let me switch gears now and say a few words about card counting. In 1966, mathematician Ed Thorp wrote a book called *Beat the Dealer,* which changed the way people played blackjack, known as the game of 21. Thorp observed that blackjack is different from most other casino games because your winning chances can actually change as you go from one deal to the next. Many people think that card counting involves memorizing all the cards that have been played and requires some sort of *Rain Man* type of ability, but in fact, card counting usually just consists of keeping track of a single number, and it's pretty easy to do. It's also not as profitable as people think, but I'll discuss that later.

Specifically, if the deck contains a much higher proportion of 10s and aces, then that will benefit the player. That benefits you. Why? Well, the extra 10s and aces leads to more blackjacks, and that pays three to two to you, the player, but only even money to the dealer, so the more blackjacks there are, that's going to benefit the player more than the dealer. The additional 10s, those help the player in a few other ways. Most of the time that you double down, right, if you have a total of 10 or 11, you're hoping to get a 10 card. So the more 10s that are left in the deck, that's good for you. Also, the 10s are bad for the dealer since they cause the dealer to bust more often. Now I know you're thinking, well, it'll cause the player to bust more often, that's true, but the player won't bust as much because the player is allowed to stop before reaching 17. The dealer has to keep playing cards until they get to 17, so the dealer will bust more often.

When the count gets high, that's going to happen when there have been a lot of low cards that have been played and a lot of 10s and aces left in the deck, you can even make some adjustments to basic strategy. For example, if there are enough 10s left in the deck, it can even be worthwhile to take insurance when it favors the player. But most of all, when there are enough 10s and aces, you typically want to bet more, since you now have an advantage in the game. That is the essence of card counting. When the deck is against you, which is most of the time, bet low. When it's for you, bet high, but, caution, not too high.

The simplest and most frequently used card-counting system is called Hi-Lo. Here you start with the number zero, and every time you see a low card, a two three, four, five, or six, you add one to your count. Every time you see a high card, a 10, jack, queen, king, or ace, you subtract one from your count, and if you have a middle card, a seven, eight, or nine, then you don't change your count at all. You add zero. Notice there are five low cards, two, three, four, five, six, and five high cards, 10, jack, queen, king, ace. So the count should usually be around zero.

Let's practice here. I'll take out a new deck for this. I'll deal some cards in pairs because that's the way they come out in the casino, right? You see two cards at a time among the other players, and let's keep a running count here.

We start with a six and a two. That's two low cards, so if we're card counting we have a one and a one because those are low cards, so your running count is two. Now you see a jack and a two come out. That's a high and a low card. They cancel each other out. We add zero for that. Right? They just cancel each other out. Your running count is still two. Now you see two big cards, king and ace—ten, jack, queen, king, ace, so you subtract two from…your running count was two; you subtract two. You get zero. Here's two more cards. Alright, nine and four, what are those? That's a low card. You add one for that, and the nine, that's neutral. These two cards add up to one. Where were we? We were at zero before. Now we're at one. Now let's do another pair of cards, okay, two court cards; we subtract two. That gives us a running count of negative one. Here, I'll do two more. See what we have here. Here's a negative and a neutral. So now our running count is negative two.

So, since a deck has an equal number of high cards as low cards, then if you count through an entire deck, and if you've done everything correctly, then your final count should be zero. Let's suppose I counted 50 cards from this deck, and let's say after going through the whole deck, oh, after going through 50 cards in the deck, I had a count of positive one. Then what can I say about the two last cards. If all of this added up to positive one, then these two cards must add up to negative one. So one of these cards must be a 10, jack, queen, king or ace, and the other card must be a 7, 8 or 9. That's the only way you could get two cards to add up to -1, is to have a negative and a neutral.

Naturally, in a game of blackjack the cards will never be dealt this low. Usually, the dealer only deals about two-thirds of the way through the deck, so in a six-deck game, you might only see about four decks worth of cards before they get reshuffled. By the way, one of the myths about card counting is that when the dealer uses many decks, that card counting becomes harder. That's a myth. That's not the reason. The reason that using multiple decks helps the casino is not because card counting gets harder. It's just as easy to add and subtract ones, but that it becomes less likely that the deck will reach a point where the proportion of 10s and aces is high enough to give the player an advantage. Remember on the first deal of the deck you have a disadvantage. You expect to lose 0.5¢ per dollar bet, so if the number of decks is huge, or if the cards are continuously shuffled, then you will remain at a slight disadvantage. If during the deal the count gets sufficiently positive—because lots of low cards have come out, and there's still a lot of 10s and aces left in the deck—then you have a small advantage, and in those situations, you should bet more.

How high does the count have to be for you to have an advantage? In general, your count needs to be better than twice the number of decks remaining. If you were playing a game with six decks, and if about 50 cards have been dealt, then there are five decks remaining. If your count is 10 or above, then you should bet more, but you can't bet too much more. One reason has to do with the optimal bet sizing, which we discussed in the previous lecture. As a rule of thumb, your largest bet should not exceed more than 1% of your gambling bankroll. So if you only have $1,000 to play with, then you should keep all of your bets under $10, or else you run a serious risk of going broke, even if you have a slight advantage. The other reason you don't want to spread your bet too much is that the dealer will get suspicious and either shuffle the cards on you or ask you to stop playing altogether.

Some players have found a way to make large bets when the deck is very positive by the use of team play, and here's how it goes. Let's say I have a team of five other card counters, and they're each sitting at a different table, and they're making the minimum bet; they're not doing anything suspicious; they're just playing basic strategy, but, they are counting the cards, and I walk in, and I got a big Texas hat on, and I got a young lady on my arm, and we're walking around and, you know, looking like we're ready to spend some big money. And we walk around and, we wait for one of our card counters to give us a signal, you know, that the deck is positive, is very positive, ready for a big bet. So we just walk on down and say, okay, I'm going to bet, you know, like an enormous bet here. Much bigger than the small bets that the card counters were making. They were making $5 bets. I walk in and place down a $100 bet. So that has the effect of the card counters making small bets all the time, and the big player making big bets and continues to make big bets while the deck is positive, very positive. Once it becomes not profitable, then the card counter gives us another signal, and the young lady on my arm says, oh, I'm bored with this table. I don't like the way the dealer's looking at me. Let's go somewhere else. In doing so these teams of players have sometimes been able to create an advantage. They've even written books and done movies about situations like this.

By the way, some casinos guard against team play by adopting what you might call countermeasures against this strategy by only allowing bets from people who were playing when the cards were initially shuffled. You might see a sign that says No Mid-Shoe Entry allowed. You can't start playing until the whole deck, the whole thing, gets reshuffled. Nonetheless, players continue to think up new strategies to try and beat this fascinating game.

As I've said before, when played correctly, blackjack is the fairest game in the casino. On the other hand, if you ignore the basic strategy and play with your gut, like my father did, then blackjack can be the worst game in the house, and you'd be better off playing craps, where you won't have any real decisions to make.

I hope that I've shown you that card counting is also not a hard thing to do. Yes, you need to be able to add and subtract ones and twos pretty quickly, since the dealer turns the cards over pretty fast. But the main thing it requires is mental stamina. When my students ask me what it's like to count cards, I say that, honestly, it's pretty boring. And anyone who has the mental agility and toughness to be able to add and subtract ones for a few hours while playing a memorized basic strategy, probably has the ability to make even more money using their brain for a more profitable and interesting activity. Take, for example, Edward O. Thorp, the father of card counting. He applied the same kind of thinking that he used in blackjack to find favorable situations that arise in the stock market and options pricing, and he made a fortune through investing without ever having to worry about whether the dealer was cheating or what the pit boss was thinking.

In blackjack, your opponent is the dealer who must always follow a fixed strategy, but there are other games where your opponent can alter their strategy to actively try to defeat you. Then the situation becomes much more complicated, and you need more skills. To succeed at these games, you'll need to randomize your strategy by bluffing and playing unpredictably. We'll learn about these skills and their underlying mathematics in the next lecture, which I predict you'll enjoy. I'll see you then.

Mixed Strategies and the Art of Bluffing
Lecture 4

In blackjack, your opponent is the dealer, who must always follow a fixed strategy, but there are other games in which your opponent can alter his or her strategy to actively try to defeat you. In this lecture, you will learn how to play against an intelligent adversary whose interests are diametrically opposed to yours. You will learn this fundamental skill, along with the underlying mathematics, with simple games like rock-paper-scissors, the penny-matching game, and Le Her—all of which show you how it pays to vary your strategy.

Rock-Paper-Scissors
- In many games like roulette, craps, and blackjack, your chance of winning can be calculated. In these games, your fate is determined by the spin of a wheel, the roll of the dice, or the dealer's cards. But what happens when you're faced with an intelligent adversary whose goals are diametrically opposed to yours?

- When both players are allowed to pick their own strategy, and when one person's gain is the other person's loss, these are called zero-sum games, and their analysis can be very interesting.

- Rock-paper-scissors is a typical zero-sum game because when one player wins, the other player loses, and the players are allowed to vary their strategy. When you're playing against an intelligent opponent, it can be dangerous to be predictable. This game is a fair game, because no player has a built-in strategic advantage over the other.

- In general, zero-sum games have the following features. They're played by two players, Rose and Colin, for example. The players each choose a strategy, and they reveal it simultaneously. In a zero-sum game, every dollar that Rose wins, Colin loses—and vice versa. A zero-sum game can be represented by a payoff matrix.

- For example, in the game rock-paper-scissors, Rose chooses one of the rows and Colin chooses one of the columns in the payoff matrix. A matrix is just a collection of numbers arranged in a rectangular box. In the matrix, if Rose plays rock and Colin plays scissors, then Rose wins $1. On the other hand, if Rose plays rock and Colin plays paper, then Rose loses $1. Colin's payoff matrix is just the opposite (the negatives) of Rose's.

Rock-Paper-Scissors: Rose's Payoff Matrix

	Rock	Paper	Scissors
Rock	0	-1	1
Paper	1	0	-1
Scissors	-1	1	0

The Penny-Matching Game

- In a game called the penny-matching game, Rose and Colin have just two strategies, but the payoffs are not symmetrical. In this game, Rose and Colin simultaneously show one side of a coin to each other. They don't actually flip the coins; rather, they just show each other one side of their coin.

- For example, maybe Rose announces that she is choosing heads and Colin announces that he is choosing tails. If both players show heads, then Colin wins $3. If both players show tails, then Colin wins $1. If one shows heads and the other shows tails, then Rose wins $2.

The Penny-Matching Game: Rose's Payoff Matrix

	H	T
H	-3	2
T	2	-1

- Suppose that Rose had to tell Colin her strategy in advance. Should she play heads or tails? Obviously, if Colin knows what she's going to do, she's going to pick tails because she's only going to lose $1—whereas if she played heads, then Colin would play heads, and she'd lose $3.

- Instead of simply choosing tails, Rose can actually do better by employing a randomized, or mixed, strategy. Suppose that she tells Colin that she's going to flip her coin and use whatever lands. If Colin knows that she's going to flip her coin, what should he do?

- Assuming that Rose is flipping a fair and balanced coin, then Colin knows that Rose will choose heads or tails with probability 0.5. Knowing that, what should Colin do? If Colin decides to play heads, then half the time Rose is going to lose $3, and half the time she's going to win $2, which turns out to be –1/2. So, on average, she'll lose 50¢ with that strategy.

- On the other hand, if Colin plays tails, then half the time Rose wins $2, and half the time Rose loses $1, which gives Rose an expected payoff of 1/2. Colin wants Rose to do poorly, so if he knew that Rose was flipping a fair coin, he would choose the heads strategy, giving Rose an expected value of –1/2.

- This coin-flipping strategy is better than Rose always picking tails because the worst Rose can lose on average is 50¢, whereas if she uses the strategy of always picking tails, then she's going to lose on average $1, if Colin could exploit that.

- Suppose that instead of playing heads and tails with equal probability, she chooses heads with probability 3/8 and tails with probability 5/8. Knowing that, what should Colin do? Notice that when Colin plays heads, then Rose's expected value is $3/8(–3) + 5/8(2)$, which equals 1/8. Rose has a positive expected value.

- On the other hand, when Colin plays tails, then 3/8 of the time Rose wins $2, and 5/8 of the time she loses $1: $3/8(2) + 5/8(–1)$, which equals 1/8. No matter what Colin plays, Rose has an expected value of 1/8.

- In fact, even if Colin decides to get into the act and randomly mix between heads and tails, Rose will still get an expected value of 1/8, or 12.5¢. This game is good for Rose. In fact, there is nothing Rose can do to force this number any higher than 1/8.

- In this example, 1/8 is the value of the game ($V = 1/8$). Rose's (3/8, 5/8) strategy is called her optimal strategy, or equilibrium strategy. It guarantees the highest expected payoff, and it has the nice feature that Rose can reveal this strategy to Colin, and he won't be able to exploit this information. Another feature of the equilibrium strategy is that if your opponent is using his or her equilibrium strategy against you, then you can do no better than to use your equilibrium strategy against your opponent.

- Rose can execute the (3/8, 5/8) strategy by flipping her coin three times. When you flip a coin three times, there are eight equally likely outcomes, and three of those outcomes have exactly one head. In other words, when you flip your coin three times, the probability of getting one head is 3/8. Rose flips her coin three times: tails, tails, tails. If heads appears once, she can show heads. Otherwise, she shows tails.

- When a player has only two strategies, like showing heads or tails, then there's a simple algebraic solution. Suppose Rose chose heads with probability x and, therefore, tails with probability $1 - x$, then when Colin chooses heads, Rose gets an expected value of $-3x + 2(1 - x) = 2 - 5x$.

- On the other hand, when Colin chooses tails, then Rose gets an expected value of $2x + (-1)(1 - x) = 3x - 1$. When she plays heads with probability x, her expected value is guaranteed to be at least $2 - 5x$ or $3x - 1$, whichever is smaller. These lines intersect when $2 - 5x = 3x - 1$, which occurs when $x = 3/8$.

- For two-person games in which both players have more than two strategies, can we be sure that an equilibrium solution even exists? This question was proved by one of the 20th century's greatest thinkers, John Von Neumann. He proved that every two-person zero-sum game has a value and that both players have mixed strategies that achieve that value. This theorem was later extended by John Nash to games that were not required to be zero-sum games.

Le Her

- A poker variation called Le Her is a classic game that dates back to the 18th century and may have been the first game ever analyzed where the optimal solution employed a mixed strategy.

- The game begins with several players, but it eventually reduces to a two-person game: the dealer and the receiver. The game is played from a deck of 13 cards, ace through king, where ace is the lowest card and king is the highest card. Both players are dealt one card facedown.

- The players look at their own cards, and then the receiver must decide whether to keep the card he or she was dealt or switch it for the dealer's card, which is unknown to him or her. Once the receiver has switched the card or not, the dealer then decides whether to keep the card that is now in front of him or her or switch it for the top card of the deck. Whoever has the higher card wins.

- Most people expect that the dealer has the advantage in this game, but the receiver actually has the edge. The payoff matrix for the receiver is a 13-by-13 matrix. For example, when the receiver (Rose) plays strategy 8, that means that she will keep any card that is 8 or higher. When the dealer (Colin) plays strategy 9, that means that if Rose swaps her card, then he makes the obvious decision—because he knows what his card and what her card is—so he's going to keep his card if it's higher and swap it if it's lower. But when Rose keeps her card, then playing strategy 9 means that Colin will keep his card if it's 9 or above.

Le Her: Receiver's Payoff Matrix

	A	2	3	4	5	6	7	8	9	10	J	Q	K
A	.50	.46	.43	.40	.39	.37	.36	.36	.37	.39	.40	.43	.46
2	.54	.50	.47	.44	.42	.41	.40	.40	.41	.42	.44	.47	.50
3	.57	.54	.51	.48	.46	.45	.44	.44	.45	.46	.48	.50	.53
4	.60	.57	.54	.52	.50	.48	.47	.47	.48	.49	.51	.53	.56
5	.61	.59	.57	.55	.53	.51	.50	.50	.50	.51	.53	.55	.58
6	.62	.61	.59	.57	.56	.54	.53	.52	.52	.53	.54	.56	.59
7	.62	.61	.60	.59	.57	.56	.55	.54	.54	.54	.55	.57	.59
8	.61	.60	.60	.59	.58	.57	.56	.55	.55	.55	.55	.56	.57
9	.60	.59	.58	.58	.57	.57	.56	.56	.55	.55	.55	.56	.57
10	.57	.56	.56	56.	.55	.55	.55	.54	.54	.54	.53	.54	.55
J	.53	.52	.52	.52	.52	.52	.52	.51	.51	.51	.51	.51	.51
Q	.47	.47	.47	.47	.47	.47	.47	.47	.47	.47	.47	.47	.47
K	.41	.41	.41	.41	.41	.41	.41	41	.41	41	.41	.41	.41

- Even though the matrix has 13 rows and 13 columns, we can actually reduce this problem to a two-by-two game through something called dominated strategies. First, Rose should never use strategies 1 through 6 because no matter what column is played, all of those numbers are dominated by row 7. Because of that, we can remove rows 1 through 6 from the matrix.

- By similar logic, Colin prefers small numbers because they represent Rose's probabilities. If we examine the remaining rows, then we realize that column 9 dominates all of the columns to its left, so we can remove columns 1 through 8. Row 9 dominates rows 10 through king, so those can be removed as well. Then, column 10 dominates jack, queen, and king, so we can eliminate those columns. Finally, row 8 dominates row 7, so row 7 can be eliminated. We're left with just a two-by-two game.

The Reduced Two-by-Two Game

	9	10
8	.547	.548
9	.549	.545

- The receiver should play strategy 8 80% of the time and strategy 9 20% of the time. This means that the receiver should always swap 7s and below and should always keep 9s and above. The only questionable card is 8, and according to our mixed strategy, the receiver should keep 8s 80% of the time and swap 8s 20% of the time. Similarly, the dealer should always swap 8s and below, always keep 10s and above, and keep 9s 56% of the time.

- The value of this game is 0.547, so using this strategy, the receiver has a 54.7% chance to win. Most people are surprised by this result, because they expect the dealer to have the advantage. However, it is true that the dealer sometimes has more information than the receiver and can exploit this.

Suggested Reading

Beasley, *The Mathematics of Games.*

Binmore, *Fun and Games.*

Bewersdorff, *Luck, Logic, and White Lies.*

Epstein, *The Theory of Gambling and Statistical Logic.*

Packel, *The Mathematics of Games and Gambling.*

Von Neumann and Morgenstern, *Theory of Games and Economic Behavior.*

Problems

1. Determine the equilibrium strategies for the row and column players when the payoff matrix is given below, and determine the value of the game.

2	−3
−5	8

2. Consider a general two-by-two game, as follows.

A	B
C	D

Assuming that there are not dominated strategies and that $A + D \neq B + C$, define $E = A + D - B - C$.

    a.   Prove that the value of this game is $V = (AD - BC)/E$ by showing that the row player can assure a payout of V by playing row 1 with probability $(D - C)/E$ (and, therefore, row 2 with probability $(A - B)/E$) and that the column player can assure that same payout by playing column 1 with probability $(D - B)/E$ (and, therefore, column 2 with probability $(A - C)/E$).

    b.   Verify your answer in problem 1) using this formula.

3. In the game of weighted rock-paper-scissors, the game is played in the usual way, but if you win with rock, you get $10; if you win with paper, you get $3; and if you win with scissors, you get $1.

    a.   Construct the payoff matrix for this game.

    b.   Verify that the equilibrium strategy for both players is to play rock-paper-scissors with respective probabilities 1/14, 10/14, 3/14.

    c.   What would the equilibrium strategy be if the weights were positive numbers a, b, and c?

Mixed Strategies and the Art of Bluffing
Lecture 4—Transcript

In many games like roulette, craps, and blackjack, your chance of winning can be calculated using the techniques we've learned in the previous lectures. In these games, your fate was determined by a spin of a wheel, the roll of the dice, or the dealer's cards. But what happens when you're faced with an intelligent adversary whose goals are diametrically opposed to yours? When both players are allowed to pick their own strategy, and when one person's gain is the other person's loss, these are called zero-sum games, and their analysis can be very interesting.

When we looked at the game of blackjack, we saw that when you were faced with the problem of deciding whether to hit a total of 16 when the dealer shows a seven, we saw that it always makes sense to hit. Or if you're playing roulette and you wish to always bet on 17, you don't have to worry about the wheel exploiting that fact. But when you're playing against an intelligent opponent, it can be dangerous to be so predictable. For instance, let's look at the game rock-paper-scissors. You and your opponent simultaneously choose rock, paper, or scissors. The winner is determined by the usual rules, right? Scissors cuts paper. Paper covers rock, and rock smashes the scissors. In this game it would be foolish to always use the same strategy, say rock, since your opponent could exploit that strategy by playing paper most of the time. Intuitively, you'd want to vary your objects in an unpredictable way. Rock-paper-scissors is a typical zero-sum game, since when one player wins, the other player loses, and the players are allowed to vary their strategy.

In general, a zero-sum game has the following features. They're played by two players, whom I'll call Rose and Colin, for reasons you'll see in a minute. The players each choose a strategy, and they reveal it simultaneously. Zero sum means that every dollar that Rose wins, Colin loses, and vice versa. Now a zero-sum game can be represented by a payoff matrix for Rose. For example, in the game rock-paper-scissors, the payoff matrix looks like this. Right here Rose chooses one of the rows, Colin chooses one of the columns. That's why I named them Rose and Colin. By the way, a matrix is just a collection of numbers arranged in a rectangular box. This box has three rows. Row one is when Rose plays rock. Row two represents paper, and row three represents scissors.

Likewise, the matrix has three columns representing Colin's strategies. So for example, if Rose plays rock and Colin plays scissors, then Rose wins $1. On the other hand, if Rose plays rock and Colin plays paper, then Rose loses $1, and that's reflected by the negative one. We don't need a payoff matrix for Colin since his payoff is just the opposite of Rose's—just the negatives of Rose's. We'll say more about this game later, but it's intuitively clear that this game is a fair game, since no player has a built-in, strategic advantage over the other.

Let's look at a more interesting game. This time Rose and Colin have just two strategies, but the payoffs are not symmetrical. It's called the Penny Matching Game. Here, Rose and Colin simultaneously show one side of a coin to each other. They don't actually flip the coins; rather, they just show each other one side of their coin. Here maybe Rose says heads and Colin says tails. If both players show heads, then Colin wins $3. If both players show tails, Colin wins $1, and if they don't match, if one shows heads and the other shows tails, then Rose wins $2. So Rose's payoff matrix would look like this. If both play heads, Rose loses three—that's the negative three. If both play tails, then Rose loses one, and if the coins don't match, then Rose wins two. So who has the advantage in this game? Is the advantage for Rose? Is it Colin? Or maybe the game is fair. What do you think? Just take a guess.

It's not entirely clear. Let's do the math and find out. We begin by finding a good strategy for Rose. So let's suppose that Rose had to tell Colin her strategy in advance, or maybe she's afraid that Colin is telepathic, or maybe she's afraid that there's a spy, you know, a spy in her midst who's going to tell Colin what she's going to do. Now if that's the case, what is she going to do? Is she going to play heads or tails? Obviously, if Colin knows that she's going to do, she's going to pick tails because she's only going to lose one, whereas if she played heads, then Colin would play heads and she'd lose three. So by announcing tails, by playing the tails strategy, she's only going to lose one if she's worried about a spy. But, Rose can actually do better by employing a randomized, or mixed, strategy. Suppose that she tells Colin, and any spies that are listening, that she's going to flip her coin and use whatever lands. If Colin knows this, that she's going to flip her coin, what should he do? Now assuming she's flipping a fair and balanced coin, then he knows that Rose will choose heads or tails with probability of half. She has a 50% chance of playing heads and a 50% chance of playing tails. Knowing that, what should Colin do? Well notice that if Colin chooses column one, that is if Colin decides to play heads, then Rose has an expected payoff of, let's see, half the time she's going to lose three, half the time she's going to win two, and that turns out to be negative a half, that on average she'll, she'll lose 50¢ with that strategy. On the other hand, if Colin plays tails, then half the time Rose wins two and half the time Rose loses one, and that gives Rose an expected payoff of positive a half. So what does Colin like, the heads or the tails? Well, Colin wants Rose to do poorly, so if he knew that Rose was flipping a fair coin, he would choose column one; he would use the heads strategy giving Rose an expected value of negative a half.

Notice that this coin-flipping strategy is better than Rose always picking tails since the worst Rose can lose on average is 50¢, whereas if she uses the strategy of always picking tails, then she's going to lose on average $1 if Colin could exploit that. And yet, Rose can do even better. In fact, she can do so much better that she can actually have an advantage in this game. How does she do it? Essentially by flipping her coin three times, and I'll explain what I mean by that later. Suppose that instead of playing heads and tails with equal probability, she chooses heads with probability $3/8$ and tails with probability $5/8$. Knowing that, what should Colin do? Notice that when Colin plays heads, then Rose's expected value is $(3/8 \times -3) + (5/8 \times 2)$, and that's exactly $1/8$, so Rose has a positive expected value there.

On the other hand, when Colin plays tails, then Rose has an expected value of, well, $3/8$ of the time she wins two, $5/8$ of the time she loses one, $6/8 - 5/8$, that's $1/8$. So no matter what Colin plays, Rose has an expected value of $1/8$. In fact, even if Colin decides to get into the act and randomly mix between heads and tails, Rose will still get an expected value of $1/8$, so even if Colin knows that Rose is using this mixed strategy, $3/8$ heads and $5/8$ tails, he can't avoid giving Rose an expected payoff of $1/8$ of a dollar or 12.5¢. So this game is good for Rose. Can Rose bring this number any higher? Maybe she can be more clever and get more than a 12.5¢ per bet. No, because if Colin randomly chooses heads and tails with, as it turns out, the same probabilities, $^3/_8$ and $^5/_8$, then Rose is forced to have an expected value of $^1/_8$ as well. So there's nothing Rose can do to force this number any higher than $^1/_8$.

So in this example, we call $^1/_8$ the value of the game. We say V is equal to $^1/_8$. Rose's $^3/_8$, $^5/_8$ strategy is called her optimal strategy, or equilibrium strategy. It guarantees the highest expected payoff, and it has the nice feature that Rose can reveal this strategy to Colin and he won't be able to exploit this information. Another feature of the equilibrium strategy is that if your opponent is using their equilibrium strategy against you, then you can do no better than to use your equilibrium strategy against them.

Now you may ask, how does Rose implement the $^3/_8$, $^5/_8$ strategy? And how did we discover that strategy in the first place? And how would we discover it for other games? First of all, suppose you wish to choose heads with probability $^3/_8$. How would you go about doing that? Now there are a few ways. If you have, let's say, eight cards, say, numbered one through eight and you chose one of them at random. You pick one and if it's a one, two, or three, then you go with heads, and if it's a four, five, six, seven, or eight, then you go with tails. That'll work. You'll pick heads $^3/_8$ of the time. Or if you have a calculator that has some kind of random button on it, okay, so this phone here has a rand button on it. I press a number. It's going to give some number between zero and one. When I press this rand button, it gives me 0.258. Since that number is between zero and $^3/_8$, 0.375, then we're going to choose heads. Otherwise, we're going to choose tails. Here, I'll do it again. This number is 0.79. Since that's bigger than $^3/_8$, then I'm going to choose tails.

Since we're dealing with coins, here's another way of doing it, Rose can flip her coin three times. And notice that when you flip a coin three times there are eight equally likely outcomes, and three of those outcomes have exactly one head. That is to say the probability when you flip your coin three times of getting one head is $^3/_8$. So what does she do? She flips her coin three times—tails, tails, tails. If head appears once, she can show heads. Otherwise, she shows tails.

But now you're wondering how did we determine that choosing heads with probability $^3/_8$ would be the best mixed strategy? When a player has only two strategies, like showing heads or tails, then there's a simple algebraic solution. Suppose Rose chose, that sounds poetic, suppose Rose chose heads with probability x and, therefore, tails with probability $1 - x$ then when Colin chooses heads, Rose gets an expected value of, let's see, $(-3 \times x) + (2 \times 1 - x)$. That's $2 - 5x$. On the other hand, when Colin chooses tails, then Rose gets an expected value of $(2 \times x) + (-1) \times (1 - x)$. That's $3x - 1$. When she plays heads with probability x, her expected value is guaranteed to be at least $2 - 5x$, or $3x - 1$, whichever is smaller. If we graph the lines $y = 2 - 5x$ and $y = 3x - 1$, we get the following interesting picture. For each value of x between zero and one we're going to look at the smaller of the two lines. This is the worst case scenario. This gives Rose's minimum expected value, which she's trying to maximize.

Now these lines intersect when $3x - 1 = 2 - 5x$. Algebraically that's $8x = 3$ or $x = ^3/_8$. So that's where we got the number $^3/_8$ from. This graphical strategy can be used whenever one or both of the players have exactly two possible strategies. For larger two-person games when both players have more than two strategies, can we be sure that an equilibrium solution even exists? This is a nontrivial question, and it was proved by one of the 20th century's greatest thinkers, John Von Neumann. He proved that every two-person, zero-sum game has a value and that both players have mixed strategies that achieve that value. This theorem was later extended by John Nash to games that were not required to be zero sum. For that he won the Nobel Prize in economics.

This graphical strategy can be used whenever one or both of the players have exactly two possible strategies. Now for larger games, the solution can be found using techniques of linear programming, but sometimes they can be solved by trial and error or just educated guessing. For example, it's no surprise that the game of rock-paper-scissors has a value of zero, it's a perfectly symmetrical game, and that the equilibrium strategy for Rose and also for Colin is to play each strategy with probability $^1/_3$. Although personally I'm partial to a variation of rock-paper-scissors called rock-paper-scissors, Lizard, Spock. In addition to the standard symbols for rock, paper, and scissors, you also have Lizard and Spock. So it's a perfectly symmetrical game, and the equilibrium strategy is for both players to play each strategy one-fifth of the time, but the rules are fun to say. So here's my almost-rhyming version.

In addition to the usual rock-paper-scissors rule, we have Spock smashes scissors, which decapitates the lizard. The lizard eats the paper, and the paper puzzles Spock. Spock blasts the rock, and the rock pounds the lizard. The lizard poisons Spock, which then sends him into shock. Thank you.

And speaking of lizards, I recently learned that when male lizards are competing for females, there's actually a rock-paper-scissors type of dominance. Apparently, among the common side-blotched lizards, *Uta stansburiana*, orange beats blue, blue beats yellow, and yet yellow beats orange.

Here's another game that can be solved by educated guessing that could be called Hide and Seek. Suppose I tell you that I've put under this cup a bill, and it's either a $2, $5 or $10, a $2 bill, $5 bill, or $10 bill. You guess which one it is, and if it's correct then you keep the money. So, how much should you be willing to pay to play this game, and what is the optimal strategy for both players? Would you be willing to pay $1 to play this game? The payoff matrix for this game looks like this: 2, 5, and 10 on the diagonal, zeros everywhere else. In other words, if you guess $2 and there was $2 there, then you'd win it. If you guess $5 and there was a $5 bill underneath, then you'd win $5, and so on. So if you as the guesser choose each number with probability $1/_3$, then your expected reward would either be $2/_3$, $5/_3$ or $10/_3$ depending on what the hider did. I mean, if the hider put it under two then $1/_3$ of the time you'd win two and $2/_3$ of the time you'd win zero. That's where the $2/_3$ comes from.

This strategy would only ensure that you would win at least 67¢, $2/_3$ of $1. How could you do better? Let's say you guessed 2, 5 or 10 with respective probabilities x, y, and z. When the hider hides $2, this strategy has an expected value of 2x. When the hider hides $5 this strategy has an expected value of 5y. And when the hider hides $10, this strategy has an expected value of 10z. So this game has a value of V and all those numbers have to be equal—2x, 5y, 10z—they all have to equal the same thing; they all have to equal V. So x is $V/_2$, y is $V/_5$, and z is $V/_{10}$, but there's one other piece of information that'll help us. Since our probabilities x, y, and z must sum to 1, we know that x + y + z has to equal 1. That says $V/_2 + V/_5 + V/_{10} = 1$. In other words, $^8/_{10}$ of V is 1. So V must be $^{10}/_8$ or 1.25. And moreover, x is $V/_2$ is going to be $^5/_8$, y is going to be $^2/_8$, and z is going to be $^1/_8$, so those are the probabilities.

By the way, Colin uses the same mixed strategy. The take-home message in this kind of Hide-and-Seek game is that your probability of guessing or hiding an object should be inversely proportional to its value. The more valuable it is, the less likely it is to be hidden, and therefore the less likely it is that you should guess it. More generally, if the objects have positive values, a, b, and c, then the value of the game has this intriguing reciprocal formula. V is $^1/_{(1/a + 1/b + 1/c)}$. And by the way, this same sort of formula works even when we have more than three objects.

As you can imagine, game theory has many uses, from military and security applications, to the modeling of sports and games, from penalty kicks in soccer, to bluffing in poker. Let's illustrate this with a very, very simplified version of poker called One Card Poker. So let me get out some chips, and we have Rose over here and Colin over here, and One Card Poker is played with six cards. Three kings and three queens. So here we go. Rose and Colin begin by each betting $1, one chip. Rose is dealt one of these six cards, which Colin doesn't get to see. Let's say Rose gets this card here. Colin does not get a card either. This is just One Card Poker. The kings are winning cards and the queens are losing cards. So we have three kings and three queens so there's a 50/50 chance whether Rose gets a winning card or a losing card. But, after Rose looks at her card—here let's have Rose look at her card; here you can see it too—she can either bet $1, or she can fold. And if she folds she loses her original $1. If she bets, then Colin has to either call or fold. If he calls, and that card is a queen, then he wins all the money. If he folds, then it doesn't matter what this card was, he loses his original $1.

So the question is, what are their optimal strategies? First of all, clearly Rose should always bet kings. There's no reason in the world, if she has a king, that she should bluff by folding, right, because she's guaranteed to win something if she has a king, but maybe she should sometimes bluff when she has a queen. So Rose has two strategies, either bet her queens, play aggressively, or fold her queens, play conservatively. If Rose bets, then Colin can either call or fold. He doesn't know what that card is, so Rose bets, and he's either going to call the bet or fold the bet. Let's create the 2 x 2 payoff matrix when each player chooses their strategy.

This is going to be Rose's payoff matrix. First of all, let's look at the situation where Rose always bets and Colin always folds. In this case, Rose always wins $1. Or, if Rose always bets and Colin always calls, then in that case Rose either wins $2 or loses $2, so that averages out to zero. Or suppose Rose only bets kings, but Colin always folds. Then half the time Rose wins $1, and half the time, when she gets a queen, she loses $1, so in that situation her expected payoff is zero. And finally, the most interesting situation is what would happen here if Rose only bets when she has a king and Colin always calls? Then this time when she gets a king, that's half the time, she's going to win $2, and when she gets a queen, she just folds, and she's going to lose $1. Here the expected value turns out to be $^1/_2$, 50¢.

Clearly, this is a favorable game for Rose, especially if she bluffs occasionally. So, what is her optimal strategy? Notice that this game has the same diagonal structure as the Hide and Seek game that we looked at a moment ago. And the same logic and formula we came up with reveals that Rose should use the bluffing strategy $^1/_3$ of the time—the aggressive strategy $^1/_3$ of the time—and the non-bluffing strategy $^2/_3$ of the time. When she does this, she achieves an optimal expected value of $V = ^1/_3$.

So how should she decide when to bluff? Well when her card is a king, it doesn't matter since both strategies will bet the king, but when her card is a queen then she has to make a one-in-three decision: When should she bet the queen? Well, fortunately, we're playing this with six cards, and we have three queens. One of them is red, the queen of hearts; the other two are black. So the queen can make the decision for her. If she gets the red queen, the queen of Hearts, then she bets it. So that's going to happen $^1/_3$ of the times that she gets a queen. And if she gets one of the black queens, she doesn't bet it.

What about Colin? He plays with the same probability, so when Rose bets, he'll fold $^1/_3$ of the time and he'll call $^2/_3$ of the time. By the way, how could

Colin make his $\frac{1}{3}$-probability decision? He doesn't have a card to look at. If he has a digital watch he could look at the second digit. This is some number from zero to 59. So if he plans to fold $\frac{1}{3}$ of the time, he can just look at the digits, and if that number is below 20, that is from zero to 19, then he should fold. Otherwise he calls. He can literally look at his watch and see if it's the right time to call.

Here's another poker variation that I actually played a bit when I was a grad student. We gave it a funny name, but I later learned that it was actually a classic game called Le Her, which dates back to the 18th century and may have been the first game ever analyzed where the optimal solution employed a mixed strategy. Here's how it goes. The game begins with several players, but eventually it reduces to a two-person game. Let's call the players the dealer and the receiver. The game is played from a deck of 13 cards, ace through king, where ace is the lowest card and king is the highest card. Both players are dealt one card face down. So here let me mix these up a bit. We'll give one card to the receiver, one card to the dealer. The players look at their own cards, and then the receiver must decide whether to keep her card or switch it for the dealer's card, which she doesn't know. Once she has switched her card or not, the dealer then decides whether to keep the card that's now in front of him or switch it for the top card of the deck. Whoever has the higher card wins. Here, let's play a game so it makes sense. So here the receiver has a card. What card is it? A three, a pretty low card. Pretty obvious what she's going to do; she's going to switch it. Now the dealer looked at his card. He has a queen. So the cards are switched. He now knows he's got a lousy three and she has a queen, so what's his decision? It's obvious. He's going to switch for the top card of the deck. It's a king and the dealer wins the game.

The questions are, who has the advantage in the game? What do you think? Would you rather be the dealer or the receiver? And which cards should the receiver keep? What are the cards that she should keep? What should she give away? And if the receiver keeps her card, then the dealer has a real decision to make. Should the dealer keep his card or swap it? Which cards should the dealer keep, and which cards should the dealer swap?

Most people expect that it's the dealer who has the advantage in this game, but here the receiver actually has the edge. Here's the payoff matrix for the row player, row as in receiver. It's a 13 x 13 matrix. The numbers, which are rounded to two decimal places, were calculated by a computer or an overworked grad student; I don't remember which. What do these numbers mean? When Rose plays strategy eight that means that she will keep any card that is eight or higher. When Colin plays strategy nine, what does that mean? Well, it means that if Rose swaps her card, then he makes the obvious decision because he knows what his card is and what her card is. So he's going to keep his card if it's higher, and he's going to swap it if it's lower. But when Rose keeps her card, then playing strategy nine means that Colin will keep his card if it's nine or above.

From our matrix we see that when Rose plays row eight and Colin plays column nine, then Rose wins 55% of the time. That's what the number says. So, since most of the numbers in this chart are above 50%, look at them, it looks like Rose has the advantage. But how do we determine their best strategies? Even though this matrix has 13 rows and 13 columns, we can actually reduce this problem to a 2 x 2 game through something called dominated strategies, which I'll illustrate.

First of all, I claim that Rose should never use strategies one through six, and the numbers tell you that. Why? Because notice that they are all dominated by row 7. No matter what column is played, row seven is better than rows one through six. So because of that, we can remove rows one through six from the matrix as far as Rose is concerned because she wants big numbers, and row seven does better than rows one through six, column by column. By similar logic, the column player prefers small numbers since they represent the row player's probabilities, so looking at the remaining rows, we see that column nine dominates all of the columns to its left. So column nine dominates the previous columns. So we can remove columns one through eight. Row nine, what's left of our matrix, row nine dominates rows 10 through king, so we can ignore those rows. Then column 10, with what's left of our matrix, dominates jack, queen and king, so we eliminate those columns, and finally, row eight dominates row seven, so row seven can go too. We're left with just a 2 x 2 game.

The reduced 2 x 2 game looks like this. Here, let's blow up the 2 x 2 game and expand the numbers to three decimal points. The algebra tells us that the receiver should play strategy eight 80% of the time and strategy nine 20% of the time. What does this mean? It means that the receiver should always swap sevens and below and should always keep nines and above. The only questionable card is eight, and according to our mixed strategy the receiver should keep eights 80% of the time and swap eights 20% of the time. Similarly, the dealer should always swap eights and below, always keep 10s and above, and keep nines 56% of the time, and swap nines 44% of the time. The value of this game is 0.547, so using this strategy, the receiver has a 54.7% chance to win.

Most people are surprised at this result since they expect the dealer to have the advantage. It's true that the dealer sometimes has more information than the receiver, and he can exploit this. For instance, if the dealer has a five and the receiver has a six, and the receiver swaps her six for the five, then the dealer automatically wins without having to take any chances by drawing another card. On the other hand, the receiver has the advantage that she has two completely free chances to get a high card since if she doesn't like her first card, then she can try the dealer's card. On the other hand, the dealer doesn't always get two chances for a good card since, when the dealer starts with a good card, half the time it gets stolen by the receiver. And when the card doesn't get stolen, the dealer's pretty sure that the receiver has a good card anyway.

So far we've only talked about games involving two players. When three or more players are involved, the strategies become vastly more complicated. One of my favorite examples comes from the game show *Jeopardy!* At the end of the show, there are three contestants playing Final Jeopardy, each with a certain amount of money. Let's say that Alice has $8,000, Betty has $7,000, and Charlie has $4,000. Each player has to secretly wager some of their money before hearing the Final Jeopardy question. Whoever has the most money at the end gets to keep their money and gets to play again the next day. So how should the players bet?

In most situations like this, I usually see all three players make the wrong bet. Let's start with Alice. She wants to be in control of her destiny so that if she answers the question right, she wins the game. To protect herself from Betty she needs to bet at least $6,000 so that she has at least $14,000 if she answers correctly. Most of the time I'll see a player in Alice's position bet something like $6,100. But I say she should bet exactly $6,000—exactly 6,000. Why? Well, if there's a tie for first then the rules of *Jeopardy!* actually allow both players to keep their money and play the next day. Now there are really two reasons why Alice should try to let Betty tie. One is that if Alice and Betty have talked beforehand, then presumably Betty would extend the same courtesy to Alice if Alice found herself in second place. The other reason is that since Alice was able to do better than Betty today, she should bet to be better than Betty tomorrow. So now it's Betty's decision. What should Betty bet? Now if she's talked things over with Alice before the game, then she should probably bet all $7,000 in hopes of tying the score if they both answer correctly, and that's what most people do in Betty's situation. But if Alice and Betty have not spoken in advance, then most of the time, Alice will bet more than $6,000. Alice is betting more than $6,000, so Betty's only hope of winning is for Alice to answer incorrectly. If Alice answers incorrectly she'll have, at most, $2,000. So Betty should bet accordingly. Now to protect herself from Charlie, who's probably betting all $4,000, she should bet at least $1,000, and I would say, exactly $1,000, for the same reason as before, so that no matter what she ends up with some number between $6,000 and $8,000. This way she wins in the scenario where Alice is wrong and Betty is right, but she also wins if all three players get it wrong, and that can happen if the question is really tough.

Finally, consider Charlie's position. Now most of the time Charlie bets it all, but that's almost certainly the wrong approach. In order for Charlie to have any chance of winning, Alice must get the question wrong. Since she's betting at least $6,000 she'll have at most $2,000 left. And most people in Betty's situation will bet all $7,000, so if she gets it wrong, she'll be left with zero. So how much should Charlie bet? I'd say $2,000 so that he can win even if he gets the answer wrong.

Like I said, most contestants in Final Jeopardy, smart as they are about trivia, tend to get the math wrong.

By the way, in 1998, one of my very own students, Andrew Hutchings from Harvey Mudd College, was the winner in the College Jeopardy tournament, and since he was a math major, not only did he clean up in categories like All About Calculus, he also made the right betting decisions, which contributed to his ultimate victory.

In this lecture we saw that in a simplified version of poker, bluffing is a fundamental part of the game. Traditional poker and more popular games like Texas Hold'em are vastly more complicated. We'll learn the mathematical essentials of real poker in our next lecture. As you'll see, these ideas can be very profitable if you play your cards right. I'll see you then.

Practical Poker Probabilities
Lecture 5

T his lecture is devoted to the game of poker, one of the most popular card games ever invented. Poker is an extremely complex game because players are faced with many types of decisions. In this lecture, you will learn the mathematics that is essential for successful poker playing. Although this lecture focuses on the game Texas Hold'em, the strategies that you learn can be applied to all variations of poker, including video poker.

Texas Hold'em
- The most popular poker variation by far is called Texas Hold'em. In this game, you can have as many as 10 people playing at the same table. Everyone is dealt two cards facedown, and then there's a round of betting. After that comes the flop, where three cards are turned over. These are common cards that every player is allowed to use in his or her hand. There's a round of betting, and then another common card is revealed. This is called the turn. There's another round of betting, and then a fifth common card is revealed called the river, followed by a final round of betting.

- The players who have not yet folded each have seven cards—their own two facedown cards and the five common cards—to create their best five-card poker hand. Whoever has the best hand wins.

- Before you've seen any cards in the deck, what's the probability that all three cards in the flop have the color red? Each card has a 50/50 chance, or 0.5 probability of being red. If someone offered to pay you seven to one odds that the flop is all red, would that be a fair bet?

- Let's first look at a related question. If someone offered you seven to one odds for flipping three heads in a row then that would be a fair bet because when you flip a coin, each flip would have heads probability 1/2, and the flips are independent, so the chance of getting three heads would be a $1/2 \times 1/2 \times 1/2 = 1/8$. Therefore, the chance of not getting three heads would be 7/8. In this scenario, getting seven-to-one odds would be fair because your losing chances, 7/8, are exactly seven times as big as your winning chance of 1/8.

POKER HAND RANKINGS

Royal Flush	10 ♥	J ♥	Q ♥	K ♥	A ♥
Straight Flush	4 ♣	5 ♣	6 ♣	7 ♣	8 ♣
Four of a kind	K ♠	K ♥	K ♣	K ♦	3 ♠
Full House	10 ♥	10 ♠	10 ♦	A ♠	A ♣
Flush	10 ♠	K ♠	2 ♠	6 ♠	7 ♠
Straight	7 ♣	8 ♠	9 ♦	10 ♠	J ♥
Three of a Kind	5 ♠	5 ♥	5 ♣	J ♦	A ♦
Two Pair	A ♠	A ♥	3 ♣	3 ♠	J ♣
One Pair	Q ♦	Q ♥	2 ♥	8 ♠	9 ♣

- However, coins and cards behave a little differently, so getting three heads in a row is not the same as getting three reds in a row. While coin flips are independent, the card outcomes are not. Because the cards are dealt without replacement, knowing the first card can affect the probability of the second card, and so on.

- The probability that the first card is red is indeed 1/2, but the probability that the second card is red, given that the first card is red, is 25/51 because there are 25 red cards among the remaining 51.

- If the first two cards are red, what's the chance that the third card is red? Because among the remaining 50 cards, 24 of them are red, the third card will be red with probability 24/50. When we multiply these numbers together, we get the probability that all three cards are red: 2/17, which is less than 1/8.

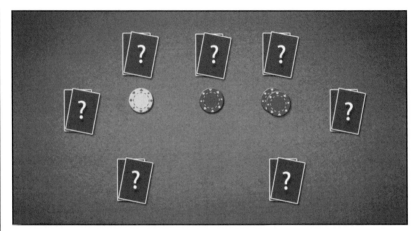

Texas Hold'em setup.

- Because you win with probability 2/17 and, therefore, lose with probability 15/17, then the fair odds of this bet would be 15 to 2, or 7.5 to 1, instead of 7 to 1.

- Suppose that after the flop, you determine that you don't have the best hand, but there are some cards that, if they appear in the next two cards, would give you the best hand. These winning cards are called your outs—as in, there are nine good cards *out* there for you.

- For example, suppose that your hand contains two hearts (a queen and a nine), and there are two hearts on the table, so there are nine hearts out there that will give you a flush. The queen-nine hand has nine outs.

- Suppose you started with the 10 and jack of spades, and the flop is 8 of spades, 9 of hearts, and 10 of clubs. Currently, you would have a pair of 10s, but your hand could get even better. How many cards are left in the deck that are especially good for you? To some extent, this depends on what your opponent has. With 10 or more outs, a more accurate probability is $(3x + 9)\%$.

- Let's say that by your opponent's previous betting, you're pretty sure that he or she probably has you beat with a pair of aces or kings. Under these circumstances, your outs are two 10s (10 of diamonds and 10 of hearts), which give you three of a kind. There are three jacks, which would give you two pair. Receiving an 8 or a 9 would also give you two pair, but those cards would improve everyone else's hand, so they're not counted as outs. Because your hand has an 8, a 9, a 10, and a jack, there are four 7s and four queens that give you a straight. Altogether, there are 13 good cards for you, so you have 13 outs.

- The rule of 2 says that if you have x outs and there's just one more card to be shown, then your chance of winning is approximately $2x\%$. For example, if you have 10 outs, then the chance that one of them shows up on the last card on the river is about 20%.

- If you already have seen six cards—namely, your two cards and four cards on the board—then the chance that you win on the last card is $x/46$ because there are 46 cards you don't know about, x of which are good for you. That's $0.022x$, or about $2x\%$. If you can do the mental math and multiply by 2.2%, then you get an even better estimate. For instance, with 10 outs, you really have a 22% chance of success. We use the rule of 2—or, more accurately, 2.2—when there's one card left to be revealed.

- If there are two cards left to be revealed, the situation immediately after the flop, we use the rule of 4, which says that if you have x outs and two more cards to be shown, then the probability that one of your outs shows up is approximately $4x\%$. For instance, with 10 outs and two cards to be revealed, your chance of success is about 40%.

- This rule makes sense because if you know five cards, two in your hand and three from the flop, then there are 47 cards left in the deck. The chance that the first card is one of your x outs is $x/47$. The chance that the second card is one of your outs, not knowing the first card, is also $x/47$. The chance that either card is good is slightly below $x/47 + x/47$, which is about $4x\%$. With 10 outs, your chance of success is about 40%. The actual probability is about 38.4%, so this estimate is pretty close. With 10 or more outs, a more accurate probability is $(3x + 9)\%$.

Number of Outs	Rule of 4	Exact	Modified
1	4%	4.4%	4%
2	8%	8.4%	8%
3	12%	12.5%	12%
4 (inside straight draw)	16%	16.5%	16%
5	20%	20.3%	20%
6	24%	24.1%	24%
7	28%	27.8%	28%
8 (open ended straight)	32%	31.5%	32%
9 (flush draw)	36%	35.0%	36%
10	40%	38.4%	39%
11	44%	41.7%	42%
12 (inside straight or flush)	48%	45.0%	45%
13	52%	48.1%	48%
14	56%	51.2%	51%
15 (straight flush draw)	60%	54.1%	54%
16	64%	57.0%	57%
17	68%	59.8%	60%

Video Poker

- Video poker is different from typical poker because you're not playing against opponents who are deliberately trying to beat you. There's no need to bluff against the computer. It's just you against the machine, so in many ways, it's like blackjack, where the dealer plays with fixed rules.

- The most popular version of video poker is known as Jacks or Better, which is played like traditional five-card draw poker. You are dealt five face-up cards, and you have to decide which cards to keep and which cards to let go. The machine replaces the cards you let go, and if your resulting hand is good enough, then you win.

- In video poker, you initially pay one unit—for example, $1. The payoff table is a bit misleading in that the payoff represents the amount of money that you get back after you've spent one unit. For example, if you bet $1 and you end up with a pair of jacks, then you get your original $1 back, so you really just broke even. Even though the payoff is pretty stingy, you can actually come close to breaking even in this game by following a few simple tips.

Jacks or Better Payoff Table

Pair of Js, Qs, Ks, or As	1
Two Pair	2
Three of a Kind	3
Straight	4
Flush	6
Full House	9
Four of a Kind	25
Straight Flush	50
Royal Flush	800

- The following is basic strategy for video poker. With two pair or higher—a profitable hand—do the obvious thing. For example, with three of a kind, draw two cards. With a straight, don't take any cards. With one pair, draw three cards. Never keep "kickers" like jacks, queens, kings, or aces. With no high cards—jacks, queens, kings, or aces—draw five cards. With one high card, draw four. With two high cards, draw three.

- Surprisingly, with three or four different high cards, you should only keep two of them. In other words, you should draw three. Which two high cards should you keep? If you have two high cards of the same suit, then keep them because you might get a flush. On the other hand, if you don't have two high cards of the same suit, then keep the two lowest high cards among them—because it increases your chance of getting a straight, and there are more ways to get a straight with a king and a jack, for example, than with a king and an ace.

- There are some exceptions to this basic strategy. First, with four cards in a straight flush, go for the straight flush: Take one card. The exception is if you were dealt a straight or a flush, don't break it up to go for a straight flush unless it could give you a royal flush. With a pair of jacks or higher in your hand, this first exception is the only exception that you need to know from basic strategy.

- For example, if you have three high cards (ace, king, and jack), but two of them are the same suit (the ace and jack of spades), hold onto those two cards. On the other hand, suppose that instead of having a jack of spades, you had a jack of diamonds, then because all three high cards have different suits, then you should hold the two lowest cards—the king and the jack—and discard the rest.

- Assuming that you don't have a pair of jacks or higher, the following are the other exceptions in order of priority. The second exception is if you have four cards in a flush, go for the flush. The third exception is with three cards in a royal flush, go for it: Take two cards.

- Finally, if your hand has no pairs in it—not even a pair of 2s—then take the following chances in order of priority. The fourth exception is if you have an open-ended straight draw, go for the straight. The fifth exception is with three straight flush cards, go for it: Draw two cards. The sixth exception is if you have a 10 and a high card of the same suit, keep the 10 since there's a potential royal flush.

- If you play with these tips, then you only expect to lose about 0.5¢ per dollar bet (the expected value). If you played the game perfectly, the expected value is –0.46¢ per dollar bet. Either way, you're down to about 0.5¢ per dollar bet, which makes video poker about as fair as basic strategy in blackjack, if played properly.

Suggested Reading

Chen and Ankenman, *The Mathematics of Poker.*

Duke and Vorhaus, *Decide to Play Great Poker.*

Guerrera, *Killer Poker by the Numbers.*

Harrington and Robertie, *Harrington on Hold'em.*

Moshman and Zare, *The Math of Hold'em.*

Paymar, *Video Poker.*

Sklansky, *The Theory of Poker.*

Problems

1. Suppose you are playing Texas Hold'em.

    a. What is the probability that the first card of the flop is a low card (2 through 9)?

    b. Use this to estimate the probability that all three cards in the flop are low.

    c. Compute the exact probability that all three cards in the flop are low.

    d. What would be the approximate fair odds for betting that all three cards in the flop are low?

2. You are dealt an 8 and 9 of diamonds in Texas Hold'em. The flop contains 6 of diamonds, 7 of diamonds, and queen of hearts. You suspect that one of your opponents has a pair that is higher than 9s.

    a. How many outs do you have?

    b. Estimate your probability of getting a straight or flush from the next two cards.

c. The next card is the two of clubs. Now estimate your probability of getting a straight or flush on the next card.

d. It's down to you and one other player. You have $10 in chips remaining, and your opponent bets $10, bringing the pot to $40. Should you call this bet?

3. In Jacks or Better video poker with the standard payouts, determine which cards to keep when dealt the following hands:

a. JS, JC, QD, 4D, 9D.

b. AS, QH, JH, 1H, 3D.

c. AS, QH, JH, 3H, 3D.

d. AS, QH, JH, 4H, 3H.

Practical Poker Probabilities
Lecture 5—Transcript

This lecture is devoted to the game of poker, one of the most popular card games ever invented. There are many variations on the game of poker, but most of them are based on five-card poker hands and the following types of hands. Here are examples of each type of hand from most valuable to least valuable. The most valuable kind of hand you can have is called a straight flush. That's five consecutive values, like four, five, six, seven, eight, all of the same suit, like clubs. Now if they happen to be the 10, jack, queen, king, ace of the same suit, that's the best straight flush, called a royal flush. Next we have the four of a kind, as its name suggests, four cards of the same value. Then a full house, that's three cards of one value and two cards of another. Below that, we have a flush, five cards of the same suit; a straight, five consecutive values, like 7, 8, 9, 10, jack. Next, three of a kind, that's obviously three cards of one value; two pair, like two aces, two threes, and something else; and below that, one pair, like a pair of queens and nothing else matching.

Below one pair would be hands like ace high, five cards with no pairs, no straights, no flush, but containing an ace. By the way, here's a simple mnemonic to remember the order of the hands above ace high: one, two, three, straight, flush, two, three, four, straight flush. I'll say it again, but this time look at the hands that each number corresponds to: one, two, three, straight, flush, two, three, four, straight flush. By the way, the reason for this ordering of hands is mathematical. The easier it is to be dealt a type of hand, the less valuable it is. For example, the reason a straight is less valuable than a flush is because if you're dealt five cards at random, there are more ways for it to be a straight than a flush. In case you're interested, here are the number of ways you can be dealt each hand.

The most popular poker variation by far is called Texas Hold'em. In this game, you can have as many as 10 people playing at the same table. Everyone is dealt two cards face down, then there's a round of betting. After that comes the flop where three cards are turned over. These are common cards that every player is allowed to use in their hand. There's a round of betting, then another common card is revealed. This is called the turn.

There's another round of betting, and then a fifth common card is revealed called the river, followed by a final round of betting. The players who have not yet folded each have seven cards, their own two face-down cards and the five common cards, to create their best five-card poker hand. Whoever has the best hand wins.

Here's a typical game. There are eight players, and each has two cards face down. I've dealt them all face up so you can see them, but normally these would all be face down. The person to the dealer's left is called the small blind, and they have to make the initial bet this round. In this game, the small blind must bet 50¢; so 50¢ that the small blind has to do. And the next player, the big blind, has to bet $1, represented by one of these blue chips. Now let's say the ace king raises to $3. The ace-7 folds. The pair of sixes here, and the 10-4 folds also. The pair of sixes calls. By calling that means I'll go $3. The 5-deuce folds, and the king-queen calls.

The small blind, remember the small blind who bet 50¢, has a queen-jack suited. Two queen, queen-jack of spades, so they're going to call. So they'll replace their 50¢ bet with $3, and the queen-9 of hearts, we're going to pay special attention to this hand here, has already put in $1 and so he only needs to put in two more dollars to call, and he does. So now all five players remaining have put $3 in, so the pot has $15 in it. I'll put all these chips over here, $15. Now comes the flop, which is ace of hearts, king of hearts, seven of spades. The queen-jack goes first, but this time he's not compelled to bet. So let's say he checks which means not folding, just not betting. Next the queen-9 of hearts also checks. Then the ace-king bets $8, about half the pot. So there's 10 – 2, $8. The pair of sixes folds. The king-queen stubbornly calls; might not be the right decision, but that's what he does. The queen-jack folds, and the queen-9 of hearts, we're going to pay close attention to this hand, calls, because the queen-9 has four cards to a flush, hoping to get a flush, so we'll put in $8 there. The pot now has $39 in it.

Next comes the Turn card. That's the four of spades. The hearts check, and the ace-king goes all in. That means betting his entire stack, which in this case is just $9. I have a five and four, $9, all in. The king-queen now wisely folds, and now suppose you have the queen-9 of hearts. Would you call to see the next card? There's going to be one more card dealt. Would you call to see it? The pot now has $48. Thirty nine dollars plus the nine that just came in. Are you willing to risk $9 of your money and hope for a flush? We'll answer that question later.

As you can see, poker is an extremely complex game since players are faced with many types of decisions. When should you check, bet, fold, or raise? And if you bet or raise, then how much should it be? Your decisions are based on lots of factors, most important are your cards and what cards have been revealed, but you also need to consider things like your position. Where are you seated at the table? How many chips do you and your opponents have? Who are your opponents? How much do they bluff? What is your perceived image at the table? The math can get very tricky, much more so than any other game we've discussed so far, and very often the right decision can surprise you.

But before we get into anything tricky, let's do some simpler problems to develop your mathematical poker skills. So question, before you've seen any cards in the deck, what's the probability that all three cards in the flop have the color red? Suppose I offered to pay you seven-to-one odds if the flop is all red. Would that be a fair bet? Each card has a 50/50 chance of being red. That is, the probability that the first card is red is a half. And so is the probability that the second card is red and the third card is red. I mean, each card is just as likely to be red as any other. So, if I offered you seven-to-one odds if you flipped a coin three times and got heads each time, then that would be a fair bet, since when you flip a coin each flip would have heads probability $\frac{1}{2}$, and the flips are independent. So the chance of getting three heads would be a $\frac{1}{2} \times \frac{1}{2} \times \frac{1}{2}$, $\frac{1}{8}$. Right? So the chance of not getting three heads would be $\frac{7}{8}$.

In this scenario, getting seven-to-one odds would be fair since your losing chances, $\frac{7}{8}$, are exactly seven times as big as your winning chance of $\frac{1}{8}$. However, coins and cards behave a little differently, so getting three heads in a row is not the same as getting reds in a row. Now what makes coins and cards different is that while coin flips are independent, the card outcomes are not. Since the cards are dealt without replacement, knowing the first card can affect the probability of the second card, and so on.

Here, let's calculate the probability that all three cards are red. Here the probability that the first card is red is indeed $1/2$, but now the probability that the second card is red, given that the first card is red, is 25 out of 51 since there are 25 red cards among the remaining 51. And if the first two cards are red, what's the chance the third card is red? Since among the remaining 50 cards, 24 of them are red, the third card will be red with probability $24/50$. When we multiply these numbers together, we get the probability that all three cards are red, the fraction simplifies to $2/17$, which is less than $1/8$. So what would be the fair odds for this bet? Since you win with probability $2/17$, and therefore, lose with probability $15/17$, then the fair odds would be 15 to 2 or 7.5 to 1 instead of 7 to 1. By the way, there are some casinos and online gaming sites that let you make this seven-to-one bet, but save your money for the real poker game at hand.

Here's a related exercise. What is the chance that all three cards in the flop have different suits? This is called a rainbow. Let's first get a good mental estimate of the answer, then we'll do it exactly. Here's a quick approximation. The chance that the second card has the same suit as the first card is what? Well, there are four suits in the deck, so there's about a one-in-four chance that the second card matches the first card. So the chance that the second card is different is about $3/4$. Then the chance that the next card is of a different suit than the first two would be about $1/2$. So the probability that they're all different is about $3/4 \times 1/2$; that's $3/8$. That's 0.375.

Now let's do that calculation exactly. For all suits to be different the first card could be any suit. Let's say it's a spade. Among the remaining 51 cards, 12 are spades, and 39 are not. So the chance that it's different would be 39 out of 51. If it's a different suit, let's say hearts, then there are now 50 cards remaining, 26 of which are not spades or hearts. So the last card is different with probability 26 out of 50, thus the probability of a rainbow is the product $(39/51) \times (26/50)$. That's 0.398, about 40%, and that agrees with our earlier estimate of about 0.375. What this means is that 60% of the time, at least two of the suits will match, so you might have to worry that one of your opponents will be going for a flush. So if a rainbow occurs 40% of the time, what would be the fair odds for you to bet on it happening? Let's think this out. Since you lose 60% of the time and you win 40% of the time, you would need to be paid 60 to 40, or three-to-two odds, for the bet to be fair and better than three-to-two odds for the bet to be favorable.

Now let's look at a new situation. This time you're dealt an ace-king. This is a strong hand, especially if the flop has an ace or king. So what are the chances that the flop has an ace or a king? Let's do an approximate answer and then an exact answer. There are 50 cards remaining in the deck, and you're interested in six of them, three aces and three kings. Each card in the flop has a 6 out of 50, that's a 12% chance, of being an ace or a king. The chance that you get an ace or king on the first, second, or third card is about 36%. There's a 12% chance, 6 out of 50 that the first card's an ace or king, 6 out of 50 that the second is, 12% that the third one is. This is a slight overestimate because it double-counts the situation where you have two or three aces and kings among these three cards. To get the exact probability, it's easier to answer the complementary problem of determining the probability that there are no aces or kings on the flops. Now for there to be no aces or kings on the flop, the first card has a 6 over 50 chance of being an ace or a king, so the chance that it's not an ace or king is 44 out of 50. That's 88%.

Then if the first card is not an ace or a king, then the chance that the second card is not an ace or a king is $^{43}/_{49}$, about 87.8%. And the chance that the third card is not an ace or a king would be $^{42}/_{48}$. That's 87.5%. Hence the probability that none of the cards are aces or kings is their product, which is about 68%. Thus, if the probability of no ace or king on the flop is 68%, then the chance that it does have an ace or king is 32%, 100% – 68%. This is consistent with our earlier calculation which said that the probability should be a little under 36%. The take-home message is that it's close to a third that you'll get an ace or king here, and, that mental estimates are pretty close and often much easier to do than exact calculations. In fact, having good mental math skills can be a real asset in the game of poker since you're not allowed to bring a calculator to most poker tables.

After the flop, it's actually easier to compute probabilities using the so-called rule of 2 and rule of 4, which I'll explain in a moment. Suppose that after the flop, you determine that you don't have the best hand yet, but there are some cards which, if they appear in the next two cards, would give you the best hand. These winning cards are called your outs, as in there are nine good cards out there for you. For example, in our opening problem, our hand contains two hearts, and there are two hearts on the table. Let's have a look at it here.

We had a queen-9 of hearts and there are two hearts on the table, on the flop. So there are nine hearts out there that will give us a flush. So the queen-9 here has nine outs. By the way, if our opponent also has a flush, we would win this hand since our hand would have the ace, king, and queen so we'd have the best flush.

Here's a trickier example. Suppose you started with the 10-jack of spades and the flop is 8 of spades, 9 of hearts, 10 of clubs. Currently, you would have a pair of 10s, but your hand could get even better. Now how many cards are left in the deck that are especially good for you? Let's count our outs. To some extent, this depends on what your opponent has. Let's say that by your opponent's previous betting, you're pretty sure he has you beat, probably with a pair of aces or kings. So under these circumstances, what are your outs? So there are two 10s out there, the 10 of diamonds and the 10 of hearts, which give you three of a kind; those would be great. There are three jacks, which would give you two pair. By the way, if your opponent had a pair of queens instead of kings or aces, the jacks would be a bad card for you because of the straight possibilities.

What about eights or nines? Receiving an eight or a nine would also give us two pair, but those cards would improve everyone else's hand so they're not counted as outs. But notice that your hand has an 8, 9, 10 and jack. So there are four sevens and four queens that give you a straight. Altogether there are $2 + 3 + 4 + 4$, 13 good cards for you, so you have 13 outs.

Now the rule of 2 says that if you have x outs and there's just one more card to be shown, then your chance of winning is approximately 2x%. For example, if you have 10 outs, then the chance that one of them shows up on the last card on the river, that's about 20%. Why does this rule work? If you already have seen six cards, namely, your two cards and four cards on the board, then the chance that you win on the last card is $x/_{46}$ because there are 46 cards you don't know about, x of which are good for you. That's 0.022x, or about 2x%. By the way, if you can do the mental math and multiply by

2.2%, then you get an even better estimate. For instance, with 10 outs, you really have a 22% chance of success. We use the rule of 2, or more accurate, 2.2, when there's one card left to be revealed.

Now what if there are two cards left? That's the situation immediately after the flop, and that's when we use the rule of 4. The rule of 4 says that if you have x outs and two more cards to be shown, then the probability that one of your outs shows up is approximately 4x%. For instance, with 10 outs and two cards to be revealed, your chance of success is about 40%. Now this rule makes sense if you know five cards, two in your hand and three from the flop, then there are 47 cards left in the deck. What's the chance that the first card is good, it's one of your x outs? It would be $x/_{47}$. What's the chance that the second card is good? Not knowing the first card, it's also $x/_{47}$. So the chance that either card is good is slightly below $x/_{47} + x/_{47}$. That's about 4x%. So with 10 outs, your chance of success is about 40%. Now the actual probability is about 38.4%, so this estimate is pretty close.

Here's a table with typical outs, along with their actual probability of winning. Notice that the rule of 4 is very accurate when the number of outs is nine or less. When there are 10 or more outs, we can get even better accuracy. If you want to remember just one extra rule, using 3x plus 9%. Using 3x + 9 whenever x is 10 or higher gives us a more accurate prediction. This stays within 1% of the exact answer for all practical values of x. So with 10 outs, the 3x + 9 rule predicts a 39% chance of improving your hand. With 13 outs, let's see, $3 \times 13 + 9$, that's 48%.

Let's see how these rules get applied in actual play. At the very beginning of this lecture, we faced a situation where we had four hearts to a flush. The queen-9 of hearts, the ace-king of hearts on the board, and there's one card to go. We had nine outs, so the rule of 2 says our chance of winning is 2×9, 18%. The rule of 2.2 says it's closer to 20%, so let's go with 20%. With a 20% chance, should you pay $9 to see the last card? That's what it comes down to. The 20% chance, should you pay $9 to see the last card? Well it all depends if you're given the appropriate odds to take the bet. Since you are an 80% chance to lose and a 20% chance to win, you would need to get 80 to 20 odds—that's four-to-one odds to make it worth your while. Now, is anyone giving you these odds? Well, yes. The pot itself has $48 in it, so you are risking $9 to gain $48. Those are pot odds of 48 to 9, and that's better than four to one, so yes, you should take the bet. If the pot only had, say $25 in it, then 25-to-9 odds would not be good enough. It would be worse than four-to-one odds. If the pot had $60 in it, 60-to-9 odds, well that would be way better than four to one, so it would be an easy call. Alright, let's see what the next card is. It's not a heart. Too bad. You lose the hand, but, in the long run you will be a winner when you call with appropriate pot odds.

So what are the best two cards to be dealt at the beginning? Your intuition would say a pair of aces, and you would be right. It's a solid favorite against all other hands, and it wins 85% of the time when it goes heads up against a random hand. Here are the 10 best hands and their probabilities of beating random cards.

The term ace-king suited means a hand like the ace and king of spades. Whereas an expression like ace-king off-suit would have unmatching suits, like say the ace of spades and the king of hearts. So how are these percentages calculated? There are programs that can look at any starting scenario like ace of spades, king of hearts versus two of diamonds, two of clubs, and determine which is the better hand simply by examining all possible five-card combinations that can follow it. The number of ways this can be done by the way is $(48 \times 47 \times 46 \times 45 \times 44) / (1 \times 2 \times 3 \times 4 \times 5)$. That's over 1.7 million. Now that's a large number, but very manageable for a computer. In fact, you can go online and search for poker hand calculator and find many free resources. You can learn a lot just by playing around with these calculators.

Now here's an interesting question. Suppose I gave you the choice of picking as your initial two cards a pair of twos, a jack-10 suited or an ace-king off-suit—ace of clubs, king of spades. Which one do you like most? Which of those three would you prefer? Most people would choose the ace-king, but, when we match this up against a pair of deuces we see that the deuces beat the ace-king about 53% of the time. Why does the pair of deuces beat the ace-king? Well, I'll give you two answers. One, the computer says so and we believe computers. Answer two, notice that at the moment the pair of twos is a better hand than the ace-king, right? It seems it's a wimpy pair, and this is two very high cards, but if the game ended here, the pair of deuces beats the ace-king. For the ace-king to win it probably needs an ace or a king to show up among the next five cards. We saw earlier that the ace-king misses the flop 68% of the time. Okay? We calculated that earlier.

What about the next two cards? The rule of four says that with six outs, with six remaining aces and kings, an ace or king will appear about 24% of the time. So it's going to miss the next two cards 76% of the time. So the probability that the ace-king never sees another ace or a king is about 0.68×0.76 which is about 52%, which is almost exactly what our calculator said, that the pair of deuces beats the ace-king about 53% of the time.

So you might be tempted to choose the pair of twos, but if you do then I, if I'm your opponent, and I'm playing this game too, I'll pick the jack-10 suited because where the poker calculator tells us that the jack-10 suited beats a pair of twos 53% of the time. Now why this does better than that is it has additional potential for getting straights and flushes that make it a better hand against the pair of twos. It appears that the jack-10 suited is the best of the three hands. Right? Because ace-king is worse than a pair of twos, and a pair of twos is worse than a jack-10, but not so fast. Let's see how the ace-king does against the jack-10 suited. If nothing special happens to either hand, then the ace-king beats the jack-10. At the moment this is a better hand than that. Furthermore, the presence of the ace and king cuts down on the number of straights for the jack-10. As a result, according to our poker calculators, the ace-king off-suit beats the jack-10 suited 59% of the time.

In other words, the ace-king is favored to beat the jack-10 suited, the jack-10 suited is favored to beat the pair of twos, and the pair of twos is favored to beat the ace-king. These are called nontransitive probabilities, and we'll see more of them in a later lecture. But I wanted you to see them now in a very real situation. This is one of the many reasons why poker is such a fascinating game to play and analyze.

Let's put all these concepts together to look at another simple problem with a surprising answer. Suppose you're playing in the following situation. You have six chips remaining and you're the big blind. The small blind over here bets one chip, and you, being the big blind, are forced to bet two chips even though you have a lousy hand. How lousy? It's the two of spades and the seven of hearts. It's probably the worst hand since both cards are low, and they can't be part of the same straight or flush. The next player bets six chips and scares off all the other players, including the small blind. You only have four chips left, and you have to decide whether to call with your remaining four chips, or should you fold. Now while you're deciding, the big better says, look, I see you're low on chips and I feel sorry for you, so I'll show you my cards. I'm not bluffing. I really have a strong hand, and he shows you that he has an ace and a king. Knowing that he has an ace and a king and you have a lowly 7-deuce, should you call his bet? Believe it or not, the answer is yes. Now before I show you the math that justifies this, let me say something about poker culture.

Poker players give funny nicknames to various pairs of cards. For example, these two cards are called Motown, as in jacks and five. These two cards are called the dog, namely K-9, and the nickname for the ace and the king off-suit is the tennis player, Anna Kournikova, because of her initials and the fact that these cards often look better than they play. The ace-king hand, although strong, only beats random hands, believe it or not, about $^2/_3$ of the time. We saw that on our chart earlier. And according to our hand calculator, the 7-2 hand that you hold here, nicknamed by the way, whip, as in worse-hand-ln-poker, still wins against the ace-king about 33% of the time. So what do the pot odds have to be in order to call this bet? Sixty-seven to 33. You lose 67% of the time; you win 33% of the time, in other words, two to one. Now since the pot has nine chips, six from the raiser, two from you, one from the small blind, and you only have to risk four chips to win nine, right? You have four chips to risk to win nine, the pot is giving you nine-to-four odds, and that's better than the two-to-one odds because nine to four is better than eight to four. So you can call the bet. I should point out that for this argument to work, it was important that either you or your opponent was out of chips after this bet since otherwise there'd be more betting.

By the way, in this lecture we have focused on the poker game of Texas Hold'em, but the ideas that we've presented here apply to almost all variations of poker, including video poker. Video poker is different from typical poker since you're not playing against opponents who are deliberately trying to beat you. There's no need to bluff against the computer. It's just you against the machine. So in many ways, it's like blackjack where the dealer plays with fixed rules.

Now let's look at the most popular version of video poker known as Jacks or Better. It's played like traditional five-card draw poker. You are dealt five face-up cards like so, and you have to decide which cards to keep and which cards to let go. The machine replaces the cards you let go, and if your resulting hand is good enough, then you win. So if you were dealt this hand, what cards should you keep? The pair of fours or maybe just keep the king, or maybe, you should go for the flush. Don't answer yet since I haven't explained how the payoffs work in this game. Now in video poker you initially pay one unit. Let's say $1, and here are the payoffs for the various hands you can end up with.

I should warn you that the payoff table is a little bit misleading in that the payoff represents the amount of money that you get back after you've spent one unit. For example, if you bet $1 and you end up with a pair of jacks, then you get your original $1 back, so you really just broke even. If you get two pair, then you get back $2, but you've really only made $1 profit. Sometimes casinos call this kind of payoff two for one, which is not as generous as two to one, where you would make a $2 profit on a $1 bet. Even though the payoff is pretty stingy, you can actually come close to breaking even in this game by following a few simple tips. I call this basic strategy for video poker. Rule number one, with two pair or higher, a profitable hand, do the obvious thing. Like with three of a kind, draw two cards. With a straight, don't take any cards. Rule number two, with one pair, draw three cards. Never keep kickers like jacks, queens, kings or aces. So in this hand, with a pair of sevens and a jack, queen, ace, just keep the pair of sevens and discard the rest. With no high cards, let's say, no jacks, queens, kings or aces, draw five cards; just try it all again. With one high card, draw four. With two high cards, draw three. But surprisingly, with three or four different high cards, you should only keep two of them. In other words you should draw three. Now which two high cards should you keep?

If you have two high cards of the same suit, then keep them because you might get a flush. On the other hand, if you don't have two high cards of the same suit, then you keep the two lowest high cards among them. Why the lowest? It increases your chance of getting a straight, and there are more way to get a straight, say, with a king-jack, than with a king-ace. So for example, if your cards were these, what should you do? We have three high cards, ace, king, and jack, but two of them are the same suit, the ace and jack of spades, so let's hold onto those two cards, and that's what we would do. On the other hand, let's suppose instead of having a jack of spades, we had a jack of diamonds, then since all three high cards have different suits, we should hold the two lowest cards, the king and the jack, and discard the rest.

 That's the basic strategy. Now here are the exceptions. With four cards in a straight flush, go for the straight flush. Take one card. The exception is, if you were dealt a straight or a flush, don't break it up to go for a straight flush unless it could give you a royal flush. So for example, let's say, here's a hand. We have the 8, 9, 10, jack of spades, and the jack of hearts. Now even though we have a pair of jacks here, we're going to go for the straight flush. We'll discard the jack of hearts. We'll hold onto the other cards and go for the straight flush. With a pair of jacks or higher in your hand, rule 1 is the only exception that you need to know from basic strategy.

So now, assuming that you don't have a pair of jacks or higher, then here are the other exceptions in order of priority. If you have four cards in a flush, go for the flush. Here we have the Fibonacci hand: the two, three, five, eight of hearts, and a king, a 13, of clubs. Now, since this is not a paying hand, you should discard the king, hold the other cards, and go for the flush. How about our original problem? Suppose you're dealt a pair of fours and a 7-10-king of hearts, including the four of hearts. What should you do? Basic strategy says to keep the pair of fours. But this hand is an exception since we don't have a pair of jacks or better, then instead, we should go for the flush and discard the four of clubs. But if we, instead, started with, let's say, this hand, now we have a pair of kings which is a paying hand, so we should keep the kings and discard the three other hearts.

Exception number three, with three cards in a royal flush, go for it. Take two cards. For example, in this hand I have three cards of the royal flush. I have a 10, jack, ace of diamonds, so it's not a paying hand. Let's go for the royal flush. We'll hold on to those diamonds and discard the pair of eights.

Finally, if your hand has no pairs in it, not even a pair of twos, then take the following chances in order of priority. Exception number four: if you have an open-ended, straight draw, go for the straight. So for instance, in this hand we have the 7, 8, 9, 10, and a king. Basic strategy says that you should keep the king and draw four, but the right play is instead to discard the king and go for the straight instead.

Exception number five: with three straight flush cards go for it. Draw two cards. So here, let's see, I have a five, six, eight of diamonds. They can be part of a straight flush so we'll hold onto these and discard the jack and the queen. Exception number six, if you have a 10 and a high card of the same suit, here keep the 10 if there's a potential royal flush. So in this hand here, normally we don't hold onto 10s, right, because it's jacks or better. But here,* for the chance of getting a royal flush, we're going to hold onto the 10 and the queen and discard the others. Let's see what happens here. Let's deal these cards and see what we get. A royal flush! I win! That's great.

Clearly, there's a lot to remember, almost as much as basic strategy for blackjack, but the good news is that, unlike blackjack, you are allowed to bring a cheat sheet with you to play. If you play with these tips, then you only expect to lose about 0.5¢ per dollar bet. Literally, this strategy has an expected value of -0.54¢ per dollar bet. If you play the game perfectly, the expected value is -0.46¢ per dollar bet. So either way you're down to about 0.5¢ per dollar bet. That makes video poker about as fair as basic strategy in blackjack, but it can also be as dangerous as blackjack too. According to my sources in the industry, the strategies that most people use in video poker are far from optimal, losing about 4¢ per dollar bet, and thus you lose your money about 10 times faster than playing the optimal strategy.

One last note, the numbers that I've given assumes the payoff structure that we described in the beginning, for example, where a flush pays six for one. If you bring any of these numbers down, that can greatly reduce your expected value. For instance, if flushes only pay five for one, then that lowers your expected value down by about 1¢ per dollar bet, and now you'll lose on average 1.5¢ per dollar bet, so be sure to choose your machines carefully.

As we've seen, poker can be very complex, and we've barely scratched the surface. In our next lecture, we transition from cards back to dice where I'll teach you to play Backgammon, another game where a mathematically trained player has a decisive edge.

Expert Backgammon
Lecture 6

B ackgammon, one of the world's oldest games, trains you to make decisions under uncertainty, a skill that's useful in many of life's circumstances. In this lecture, you will learn the rules of the game, the basic strategy for winning, and the ideas behind the strategy. You will see how math enters the game—from figuring out the safest way to move your checkers to the all-important doubling cube, which makes the game even more interesting.

Backgammon: The Basics

- Backgammon is a dice game played between two players, represented by black and white pieces, or checkers. The player using the black checkers moves his or her checkers clockwise while the player using the white checkers moves them counterclockwise, with the goal of bringing all of the checkers into a quadrant called the inner board or home board. Once all of checkers are in a player's home board, he or she can start taking checkers from the board. Whoever removes all of their checkers off the board first is the winner.

- To start the game, both players roll one die, and whoever gets the higher number goes first using that roll. If both players roll the same number, then they keep rerolling until the dice are different.

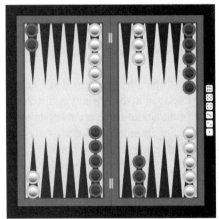

Backgammon initial setup.

- When rolling both dice during the game, if you roll a 3 and a 1, you can move one of your checkers three spaces forward and another checker one space forward—you don't have to just move the total number of four spaces with one checker. Checkers are not allowed to move backward.

- When you have two or more checkers on one spot—which is called a point in backgammon—then you own that point, and your opponent is not allowed to land on it. There is no limit to the number of checkers that can go on a point.

- When you roll doubles in this game, it's like getting four of that number. For instance, if you roll double 6s, you get four 6s to play. Rolling doubles is usually a good thing. The probability of rolling doubles is 1/6. (If you throw two dice, one at a time, after the first die lands, the chances are 1/6 that the second die is going to match the first.)

- When a checker is on a point all by itself, it's called a blot, and if the opponent lands on it, it is hit and is sent all the way back to the starting point. The hit checker is placed on the bar, which is in the middle of the board. When a player has checkers on the bar, he or she must bring those checkers back into the game before moving any of the other checkers.

- When it is the player's turn to roll the dice, if his or her checkers that are on the bar are being blocked from entering the game by the other player's checkers, then his or her turn is over. (We say that the player has just "fanned" or "danced.")

- Although backgammon eventually becomes a race, each player's plan should be to try to build a blockade called a prime in front of the other player's entry point so that when the other player has checkers on the bar, there's nothing he or she can roll to get back on the board. In this case, we say that the other player is closed out and can't move until the player with the blockade opens up one of the entry points.

- The best opening rolls in backgammon are those that make a point as part of a blockade: 3 and 1, 4 and 2, 6 and 1, or 5 and 3. The roll 6 and 4 could be used to make the 2 point, but most good players don't do that because the 2 point and the 8 point can't be part of the same blockade.

Backgammon: Playing the Game

- Backgammon is a game of dice, and all dice probabilities are easy to calculate. When rolling two dice, there are 36 possible—equally likely—outcomes. A roll like 6-2 can happen two ways: with a 6 and 2 or a 2 and 6, but a roll like double 4s can only happen one way. In general, a specific roll of doubles, like double 4s, has a 1/36 chance of happening, and a specific non-doubles roll, like 6-2, has a 2/36 chance of happening.

Total Roll Values for Two Dice

	1	2	3	4	5	6
1	2	3	4	5	6	7
2	3	4	5	6	7	8
3	4	5	6	7	8	9
4	5	6	7	8	9	10
5	6	7	8	9	10	11
6	7	8	9	10	11	12

- If you need a total roll of 8 to hit your opponent's checker, then in backgammon terminology, we say that your checker is 8 pips away.

- In general, if you can hit your opponent in his or her home board or outer board on your first roll, then it's almost always right to do so.

- An indirect shot is a shot that requires a combination of both dice to hit your opponent's checker—so the checker is a distance of more than six pips away. On the other hand, when a checker is a distance of six away or closer, then it's called a direct shot because it can be hit with just a single die.

- How many dice rolls use the number 1? The answer is that 11 of the 36 rolls, about 30% of them, contain the number 1. Likewise, there are 11 rolls that contain a 2, and so on.

- If your opponent has a blot that is 4 pips away, how many rolls hit the blot directly with a 4 on one of the dice? There are 11 dice rolls that contain a 4 on one of them. Add to that the numbers with a total of 4—there are 3 of those. Don't forget to count double 1s, when you get to play 1 four times. That gives you a total of 11 + 3 + 1 = 15 shots on your opponent's blot. Hence, the probability that you hit the blot is 15/36. Being able to count shots can often help you determine the right play to make.

Rolls That Hit

	1	2	3	4	5	6
1	X		X	X		
2		X		X		
3	X			X		
4	X	X	X	X	X	X
5				X		
6				X		

- A double direct shot is a shot that can be hit by all 2s and all 5s, for example. As you know, direct shots get hit 11 ways plus combinations. With double direct shots, there are 20 shots plus combinations. For example, there are 20 dice rolls that contain a 2 or a 5 on one of the dice. There are 16 rolls that don't use a 2 or 5 anywhere; therefore, there are 36 − 16 = 20 numbers that do.

- Essentially, both players are trying to bring all of their checkers to their zero point. If a checker on the 6 point has to travel six points, then it has to travel a distance of six pips. A checker on the 4 point has to travel four pips, etc. We measure each player's race by doing what's called a pip count.

- Once players have all of their checkers in their home board, they can start removing them from the board, a process known as bearing off. When bearing off, you're essentially moving your checkers to the zero point.

- There's only one other rule for bearing off: Once there are no more checkers on the 6 point, then 6s can be used to take off checkers from the next largest point. Once the 6 and 5 points are cleared, then 6s and 5s can be used to clear checkers from the next largest point, and so on. Rolling double 6s is virtually always the best roll when you're trying to take off checkers quickly. As usual, the two players take turns rolling the dice, and whoever takes off all of their pieces first is the winner.

- If one player takes off all of his or her checkers before the other player removes any of his or hers, then that's called a gammon, and that player wins twice whatever the game was worth. If the game was worth 1 point—for example, in a tournament match—then winning a gammon earns you 2 points. If the first player earns a gammon while the other player still has a checker inside of the first player's home board, then that's called a backgammon, and the first player wins triple the stake.

The Doubling Cube
- A relatively recent development introduced to backgammon in America around the 1920s that makes the game even more interesting is called the doubling cube, which is used to raise the stakes in backgammon—much like raises do in poker.

- A doubling cube has the numbers 2, 4, 8, 16, 32, and 64 on it. It usually sits off to the side of the board. During a game of backgammon, if you feel that you have a much stronger position than your opponent, then before it's your turn to roll, you can offer to double the stakes by picking up the doubling cube, placing it in front of you with the number 2 face up, and saying, "I double."

- Your opponent has two options: drop (pass) or take the cube. If your opponent drops, which is like folding in poker, then the game is over, and you win. On the other hand, if your opponent takes the cube, then he or she puts the cube on his or her side of the board. Now, whoever wins the game gets 2 points. Then, it's your turn. You roll the dice and the game continues, but now the cube is on your opponent's side of the board, and you can't touch it.

- Later, if the tables turn and your opponent has a much stronger position than you do, then your opponent can redouble you to four, making the game worth 4 points. At this point, you can either drop or take. If you drop, then you lose 2 points, and if you take, then you will put the cube over in front of you on your side of the board so that you could potentially use it later. You could turn it to 8, for instance.

- The doubling cube takes some of the luck out of the game because the person being doubled has to decide if his or her chances are good enough to justify playing for higher stakes. How good do your chances have to be to take the double? Assume you're in a situation where neither side is likely to win a gammon—maybe the game has become a straight race, for instance—then in order to take the double, your chances need to be at least 25%.

- In practice, your doubling cube action can also depend on factors like your ability to use the cube if you turn the game around or your chance of getting gammoned. For instance, if the game is a pure race, you can often take with a 22% chance of winning because you probably have a better than 25% chance of being able to reach a position where you can double your opponent out. This allows you to take with a little less than 25% chance. On the other extreme, if you're in a position where you never win a gammon, but all of your losses are gammons, then your winning chances would have to be at least 50% in order to take the cube.

- Sometimes it can be tricky to estimate your winning chances, but the more you play, the better you become at doing this. A decent rule of thumb is you should double your opponent if you're comfortably ahead of the game, and you should take a double if you can see a clear way to turn the game around that doesn't require too much luck on your part.

Suggested Reading

Clay, *Backgammon in a Week.*

Magriel, *Backgammon.*

Trice, *Backgammon Boot Camp.*

Woolsey, *How to Play Tournament Backgammon.*

Woolsey and Beadles, *52 Great Backgammon Tips.*

Problems

1. The following questions apply to the game of backgammon.

    a. What are the chances of hitting a checker that is 3 pips in front of you?

    b. What are the chances of hitting a checker that is 5 pips in front of you?

    c. What are the chances of hitting a checker that is 12 pips in front of you?

    d. Suppose there are three blots in front of you that are 3 pips, 5 pips, and 12 pips away. What are the chances of hitting at least one of them?

2. When playing backgammon, you have two checkers on the bar, and your opponent has a two-point board (say, owning the five and six points). What are the chances that in your next roll:

    a.   both checkers come in?

    b.   both checkers stay on the bar?

    c.   one checker comes in and one checker stays on the bar?

3.   The backgammon game is almost over. You have two checkers left on your two point. Your opponent has one checker left on her four point and one checker on her one point. You own the doubling cube.

    a.   What is the probability of taking both of your checkers off on this roll?

    b.   If you don't use the doubling cube, what is the probability that your opponent wins in this position?

    c.   If you double, should your opponent take?

    d.   Is it correct for you to double?

Expert Backgammon
Lecture 6—Transcript

Harvey Gillis, a successful CEO of a venture capital firm, once wrote about the following experience:

> The drama was unfolding. The choices were complex and I was sure that the result of making a mistake could be deadly. Attacking was risky; but so was doing nothing. A setback at this point could spell defeat for the entire campaign. The volatility of the situation made the decision even more difficult. Perhaps I could stall, buying myself some time or deferring a frontal assault by the enemy? Without a precise model, the choice was unclear; but I had to act. I would just have to rely on strategic principles and my limited experience to make the decision.

Now you might think that I'm describing the war room of a major military conflict, or a final showdown of two business competitors, or an incredibly important investment decision, or even a medical team's handing of a malignant tumor. Not so. This was an ordinary encounter between two backgammon players.

More than any game I can think of, backgammon trains you to make decisions under uncertainty, a skill that's useful in all walks of life. I certainly enjoy other games involving strategy or chance including chess, bridge, blackjack, and poker, but for someone who wants to put their math skills to good use, I can't think of a better game than backgammon. The game takes just a few minutes to learn, and there's enough luck in the game that even a new player can beat a great player in a single game, although as a significant underdog, but in the long run, the more skillful player will come out ahead.

Backgammon is one of the world's oldest games. Sets have been found that are about 5,000 years old. But despite its history, you can get very good at backgammon in a very short amount of time. I remember when I learned backgammon in middle school, having just read one book on the subject made me a much better player than all my friends.

In this lecture, I'll teach you the rules of the game, the basic strategy for winning, the best way to play the opening rolls, and the ideas behind them. I'll show you how math enters the game through figuring out the safest way to move your checkers, to the all-important doubling cube, which makes the game even more interesting.

So let's quickly go over the rules of the game. Backgammon is a dice game played between two players, black and white. The game starts in this position. Black moves his pieces clockwise with the farthest checkers back here. They start back here; they move to here, to here, and to there. Black wants to bring all of his checkers into this quadrant called black's inner board or home board. Likewise, this is called black's outer board. This quadrant is white's outer board and this quadrant is white's inner board or white's home board. Once all of black's checkers are in his home board, he can start taking the checkers off the board. White moves counterclockwise, with the farthest checkers here in black's home board. She wants to bring all of her checkers from here, to here, to here, to here into her home board and then start taking them off. Whoever removes all their checkers off the board first is the winner.

So how do the pieces move? To start the game, both players roll one die, and whoever gets the higher number goes first using that roll. If both players roll the same number, then they keep re-rolling until the dice are different. For example, if black rolls a three and white rolls a one, then the opening roll is a 3-1, and black gets to go first. In a game like Monopoly, you would call this roll a four because you only care about the total, but in backgammon it's called a 3-1 because you can move one of your checkers three spaces forward and another checker one space forward. Checkers are not allowed to move backwards. So for example, you could play this roll lots of ways, including 3—1, 2, 3—then 1. Or you could play it, say, 3—1, 2, 3—and then another checker, 1, like that. But the best way to play it would be 3 and then 1. The reason that this is the best play is because when you have two or more checkers on one spot, on a point—we call these points—then you own that point, and your opponent is not allowed to land on it.

Now if we number the points on the board 1, 2, 3, 4, 5, 6, 7 and so on, then this play is said to make black's five point. So right now, black owns his five point and his six point in his inner board, as well as his eight point and 13 point and 24 point. Now if white's next role is 6-5 then white could play, for instance, six and then five. That would be legal. Suppose, instead, that white's next roll was 5-4, then white would not be able to move at either of these checkers. Because 1, 2, 3, 4 is blocked and 1, 2, 3, 4, 5 is blocked. Those checkers there would be blocked. With a 5-4, white would probably do something like this, bring two checkers here, five and then four. Here let me take these off; I don't need those anymore.

Now before we go further, I need to say something about rolling doubles. In backgammon when you roll doubles, it's like getting four of that number. For instance, if you roll double sixes, you get four sixes to play. Rolling doubles is usually a good thing, so let's answer the question, what is the probability of rolling doubles? The answer is one in six, and we'll see this a lot, and I'll show you two ways to understand why.

Imagine that you throw two dice, one at a time. So we've got two dice here. When the first die lands, whatever it is—it's a two—the chances are one in six that this die is going to match it. That's one way to see why rolling doubles is one in six. Another way to get the one in six is to create a table, listing all possible outcomes. Let's say you have a red die and a yellow die, each with six possibilities. Then there are 6 × 6, 36 equally likely outcomes, as displayed on this table, with six rows and six columns. Among the 36 entries, six of them represent doubles. We've got double 1, 2, 3, 4, 5, and double six. Thus, the chance of rolling doubles is six out of 36, or one in six.

Let's get back to our game. Let's suppose that black's next roll was double fours, so black gets four fours to play. Now look at white's checker over here on white's nine point. When a checker is on a point all by itself, it's called a blot, and if the opponent lands on it, it is hit, and it's sent all the way back. So when black rolls double four, the best play is to hit white's blot like so, so black goes four, and then four. I put the white over here, and then black has two more fours to play. Let's say four and four. So that's the best way to play double fours. The hit checker is placed here on the bar. This is called the bar. But really you should think of it as being here, like on the zero point if one existed. When a player has checkers on the bar, they must bring in those checkers, the checkers on the bar have to come in, before you're allowed to move any of the other checkers. Notice that in this position, black owns the four point, the five point, and the six point. So if white rolls a 6-1, now we count 1, 2, 3, 4, 5, 6. White can't use the six to go here, so white is forced to come in with the one and then white can play a six wherever is legal; probably would play it here like so.

Let's say instead, white was on the bar and rolled a number like 3-2. Now, she could come in, either on the two or come in on the three, probably the best play would be to come in on the three and then move two, like so. But, let's put white back on the bar, if white's roll was a 6-5, then white will not be able to come in with the six because it's blocked; it cannot come in with the five because that's blocked, and her turn is over. We say that white has just fanned or danced.

Although backgammon eventually becomes a race, and I'll talk more about the end game later in this lecture, black's plan, here's plan A, is to try to build a blockade— called a prime—in front of white. So here's what black is trying to do, to go, say, have checkers here and, say, here and there, building a nice solid blockade. Notice that in this position, black has what's called a five-point prime, 1, 2, 3, 4, 5, and the only roll that white can escape with would be a 6-1. With a 6-1, white could roll a one, go one, and then six. That would escape. Or if black reaches this situation, here's let's say black gets to here, now black has a six-point prime, and now there's nothing that white can do to get past this wall. Or, better still, if black reaches this situation, now white is on the bar and can't get in. There's nothing white can roll to get in. We say that white is closed out, and white can't move until black opens up one of these points.

With these strategies in mind, let's look at the best way to play the opening rolls in backgammon. The best opening rolls are those that make a point as part of a blockade. That would be 3-1, which we saw before, or, 4-2, four, two, or 6-1. That goes six and one or 5-3, five and three. What about rolls that don't make a point? Oh, by the way, the roll 6-4, you might ask about that, 6-4. We generally don't do that. It could be used to make the two point, but most good players don't do that since the two point and the eight point can't be part of the same blockade. How do most people play? Most people play the 6-4 this way by running this checker 6 + 4 or possibly this way, coming out with a six and bringing this checker down with the four. Likewise, the 6-2 and the 6-3 are played similarly. You could either come out with a 6-2 or the 6-3 or you could play six and two or six and three. Obviously, with a roll like 6-5 you would run all the way, six and five, like that. By the way, there's no limit to the number of checkers that can go on a point.

We've now seen all rolls that use a six. How about those that use a five? Let's look at the roll 5-2. Now many beginning players will play it this way, five and two, because it's completely safe, but a much better play is this, a much better play would be to come down five and then two. White can only hit this block with a roll of 6-4, and that's not very likely. And if that blot is missed, then black has a pretty good chance of making a good point next turn. Likewise, with a roll of 5-4, let's see, where are we here? A 5-4, you could play five and four, like that, or alternatively, come down with the five and play the four like that. Since black would very much like to make white's five point, so it's trying to do that. Similarly with a play of 5-1, black's best play is probably five and then one, splitting the back checkers in hopes of making the four point, the five point, or the seven point soon.

When both numbers are small, then it's usually best to bring one checker down from here, called the midpoint, and split the back checkers. So for instance, a 4-3 you could play four and three, like that. For a 4-1 you'd bring the four down and play one like that. For a 3-2 you could play three and two; bring them both down, or, if you want, you could go two here and three there. And finally, with a 2-1, you could bring the two down and split the one, or, a more aggressive play is to come down two here and bring the one down like that. Great. You now know how to play the opening roll like an expert.

What about the rest of the game? In the rest of this lecture, I'll show you many aspects of backgammon where a little knowledge of mathematics can go a long way. Backgammon is a game of dice, and the good news is that all dice probabilities are easy to calculate. As we've seen before, when rolling two dice there are 36 possible, equally likely outcomes as shown with their totals included. Notice that a roll like 6-2 can happen two ways, with a six and two or a two and six. But a roll like double fours can only happen one way. In general, a specific roll of doubles, like double fours, has a $\frac{1}{36}$ chance of happening and a specific non-doubles like 6-2 has a $\frac{2}{36}$ chance of happening.

Let's suppose that black gets an opening roll of 5-4 and plays it this way, five and four. What are white's hitting chances? What are the chances that white can hit black's blot? To hit this checker, white needs a total of eight. Right? Because there's the one point, there's the nine point. White needs a total of eight. In backgammon terminology, we say that this checker is eight pips away from white. From our table, we see that there are five dice rolls with a total of eight. It's either two ways to roll a 6-2, two ways to roll a 5-3, and just one way to roll double fours. But there's another roll that can hit black's blot. Do you see it? If white rolls double twos, then white can use all four twos, that's eight pips of that roll, to hit black's checker. So white with a double two could go two, two, two, two, and hit black's checker. By the way, in general, if you can hit your opponent in his home board or outer board on your first roll then it's almost always right to do so. So altogether white hits black, how many times did we say? Six times out of 36, or a $\frac{1}{6}$ chance.

This problem was an example of an indirect shot because it was eight pips away, and therefore, it required a combination of both dice to hit it. On the other hand, when a checker is a distance of six away or closer, then it's called a direct shot because it can be hit with just a single die. For example, suppose black opens with a roll of 2-1 and plays it this way, two and then one, and some strong players will do that. Black's blot is on the five point. It's just four pips away from white. So it can be hit by dice rolls that have a total of four, as well as by rolls that have a four on either of the dice. So, what are white's chances of hitting black?

Now before we answer this question let's first do an easier one. How many dice rolls use the number one? The answer is 11, and not because of the number 11 has two ones in it. I'll give you three good reasons why. Answer one, look at the table and count them. We see that 11 of the 36 dice rolls use the number one. Answer two, which you can do in your head, there are six dice rolls where the first die is one, and there are six rolls where the second die is one, and one of the rolls, double ones, has been counted twice. Hence the number of rolls is $6 + 6 - 1$, which is 11. Answer three, take the indirect approach and ask how many rolls do not have a one in it? For this to happen, the first die has five choices, so we have five choices for this not to be a one. We have five choices for this die not to be a one, and therefore, there are 25 rolls without ones. If there are 25 rolls that don't have a one, then the number of dice rolls that do have a one is 36 – 25, which is again, 11. We've now conclusively shown that 11 of the 36 rolls, about 30% of them, contain the number one.

Likewise, there are 11 rolls that contain a two. Eleven numbers that contain a three, and so on—four, five, six. You'll use the number 11 a lot.

Now let's look at the chance of black hitting white's checker here on the five point. Notice that this blot is four pips away. So how many rolls hit the blot directly with a four on one of the dice? You should know automatically that there are 11 dice rolls that contain a four on one of them. Add to that the numbers with a total of four. You see? There are three of those—hey, that kind of looks like a four. I've never noticed that before. And don't forget to count double ones. You get to play one four times. So that gives us a total of 11 + 3 + 1, 15 shots on this checker. Hence, the probability that white hits the blot on the five point is 15 out of 36. Notice that there's also a two out of 36 chance that white can hit the blot here on the 11 point, but the shot that does already hit the checker here. With a 4-6, you'd already hit. So black still has a 15 out of 36 chance of getting hit.

Being able to count shots can often help you determine the right play to make. Here's a position from a recent game of mine. Black has just rolled a 6-3, and is forced to leave a shot somewhere. Getting hit would be very bad for black, so he wants to play this roll as safely as possible. Black has two real plays to consider. He could play it this way, three and six, which would allow white to hit with fives. Or, he could play it this way, six and three, which would allow white to hit with ones and eights. Let's count the number of shots in each play. Starting with the first play, if we go three and six, now white can hit with any direct five. There are, as usual, 11 of those, plus, there are combination shots that add up to five, and there are four of those. So this play gets hit 15 times. The second play, 6-3, gets hit with ones and eights. Now we know, of course, there are 11 ways to hit with a one, plus there are six ways to roll an eight. We saw that before, namely, 6-2, 5-3, double four, and double two. So this plays leaves 17 shots, so we should make the first play which only left 15 shots.

By the way, there's a third play that we didn't consider. For example, black could play six and three, like that. How many shots does that leave? This is a double-direct shot since it can be hit by all twos and all fives. Remember how I told you to memorize that the direct shots get hit 11 ways plus combinations? With double-direct shots, there are 20 shots plus combinations. For example, there are 20 dice rolls that contain a two or a five on one of the dice. Why are there 20 numbers? You can either count them from our table, easy as tic-tac-toe, or you can mentally ask how many rolls don't have a two or five in it. Then, each die has four choices. Right? There are four numbers that aren't a two or five on the first die; four numbers that aren't a two or five on the second die. That's 16 rolls that don't use a two or five anywhere. Therefore, there are 36 – 16, 20 numbers that do.

Don't forget about combination shots. Are there are any combination shots here that add up to two? Well, yes, double ones, but that number is blocked here by this point, so those won't count. How about combinations that add up to five? There's 1-4 and 2-3, but we've already counted 2-3 among the numbers that hit with a two, so we only have to add to that the 1-4 combination, that's another two shots. So we had 20 direct shots plus two combinations, that's 22 shots. Thus, overall, we see that playing this way was really bad. It left 22 shots. The best way of playing was this way, which only left 15 shots. So that's the way to play. It's also, probably, the best roll strategically since if the blot is not hit here, then black has a good chance of playing the next roll or two safely. Alright? So black would like to break contact and just bring his checkers home quickly, since if he doesn't get hit, he has an excellent chance of winning the race. On that note, let's talk about the race.

Let's suppose that white rolls double sixes and plays here—six, six, six, six. White misses the shot, but her chances improve, her racing chances improve. Now since it's highly unlikely that either side is going to leave a shot for the other to hit, the game has essentially become just a race.

The question is, who's winning the race? Now I'll say more about how the checkers are taken off the board pretty soon, but essentially, both players are trying to bring all of their checkers to their zero point. So if a checker on the six point has to travel six points, has to travel a distance of six pips, a checker on the four point has to travel four pips, etcetera. We measure each player's race by doing what's called a pip count. Here black has a pip count of 92. Here's how I count that. We have $6 + 4 + 3$. That's 13×3 is $39 + 4$ is $43 + 10$ is $53 + 39$ is 92. I'm a pretty fast pip counter. Similarly, we can show that white has a pip count of 98. Black is on roll and has fewer pips to go, so black has the racing lead. I would estimate that black wins about $^2/_3$ of the time.

Let's suppose that a few rolls later the position looks like this and it's black's roll. Since black has all of his checkers in his home board, he can start removing them, a process known as bearing off. When bearing off, you're essentially moving your checkers to the zero point. The best way to explain is by example. Suppose black rolls a 6-5, then black must bear off the checker on the six point. So there it goes 1, 2, 3, 4, 5, 6, and it's off. With the five, he can either move a checker from the six point down to the one point or he can bear off a checker from the five point. Since the goal is to remove the checkers as quickly as possible, black should definitely take the five off. Note that black cannot use the five to take off any of the lower checkers on the four point, three point, or two point.

There's only one other rule for bearing off, though. Once there are no more checkers on the six point, then sixes can be used to take off checkers from the next largest point. Once the six and five point are cleared, once there's nothing on them, then sixes and fives can be used to clear checkers from the next largest point, from the four point, say, and so on. Thus if black's next roll is double six, which is virtually always the best roll when you're trying to take off checkers quickly, then he must take off four checkers as follows: six, six, six, and six, like that. As usual, black and white take turns rolling the dice, and whoever takes off all their pieces first is the winner. By the way, if black takes off all of his checkers before white removes any of hers, then that's called a gammon, and black wins twice whatever the game was worth. So if the winner gets $1, then winning a gammon earns you $2. If the game was worth one point, say in a tournament match, then winning a gammon earns you two points. Finally, if black earns a gammon and white still has a checker inside of black's home board, then that's called a backgammon, and black wins triple the stake.

So you now know how to play Backgammon as it's been played for centuries. The only part of the game I have not yet explained is a relatively recent development introduced to the game in America around the 1920s, and it makes the game even more interesting. It's called the doubling cube. The doubling cube is used to raise the stakes in backgammon, much like raises do in poker. Here's an example of a doubling cube. It has the numbers 2, 4, 8, 16, 32, and 64 on it. It usually sits off to the side of the board, usually like in the middle here. It might start off here maybe with the 64 showing like this, or off to the side like that. Now let's say that during our game, I feel that I have a much stronger position than yours. Then before it's my turn to roll, I can offer to double the stakes. I do this by picking up the doubling cube, placing it in front of you with the number two face up, and I say, I double. And in this case, black might say to white, Okay, I double. Now when I do this, you have two options, white here has two options. White can either drop or take the cube. If you drop or pass—that's the same thing—then the game's over. I win one point, and we can start another game. You can think of dropping like folding in poker.

On the other hand, if you take the cube, then you put the cube on your side of the board. You might put it like right over there, right in front of you, and now whoever wins the game gets two points. Then it's my turn. I roll the dice and the game continues. But now the cube is on your side of the board, and I can't touch it. But if later the tables turn and you have a much stronger position than I do, then you can redouble me to four. Now you say, Okay, let's make this game worth four points, and I can either drop or take. If I drop, then I lose two points, and if I take, then I'll put the cube over here in front of me, and now the cube is on my side of the board, so I could potentially use it later on. I could turn it to eight, for instance. By the way, if the game is worth four points and someone wins a gammon, then that person would win eight points.

The doubling cube takes some of the luck out of the game, since the person being doubled has to decide if their chances are good enough to justify playing for higher stakes. How good do your chances have to be to take the double? Let's assume we're in a situation where neither side is likely to win a gammon, maybe the game has become a straight race, for instance. Then in order to take the double, your chances need to be at least 25%. Why is that? Let me justify this answer three different ways, once with algebra, once with hindsight, and once with the logic of poker. You can decide which explanation you like the best. Let's suppose your chance of winning the game is P. This is the algebraic approach. If you take the double, then what is your expected value? Well now you're going to either win two points with probability P, or you're going to lose two points with probability 1-P. Thus if you take the double, then your expected value is $(P \times 2) + (1 - P) \times (-2)$, and that's equal to 4P-2. On the other hand, if you drop the cube, then you automatically lose one point, so your expected value would be -1. You should take the cube when the expected value for taking is greater than the expected value for dropping. That is to say, you should take if 4P-2 is greater than -1. That happens when 4P is bigger than one. That is, when P is bigger than a $1/4$, 25%.

Here's another way to see that doesn't require any algebra. Imagine that you had a 25% winning chance, and you face this doubling decision 100 times. If you drop the cube each time, then you would be down 100 points, but if you took each time, then you would expect to win two points 25 times. You'd win 25% of the time, so you'd win two points 25 times ,and you'd lose two points 75 times, and that would give you a net total of $(25 \times 2) + (75 \times -2)$. That's 50-150 which is -100. That's the same as if you had dropped each time. Thus if you expect to win more than 25 out of 100 games, then you're better off taking. You're still expecting to lose, but you'll lose, on average, less by taking than by dropping.

Finally, let's derive the 25% figure using the logic of poker. Let's look at the number line from -2 to 2. When you're being doubled, you're given a choice. If you drop, what's your profit? Your profit is -1. If you take, then you'll either wind up with 2 or -2. You'll have two if you win, you'll have -2 if you lose. If you decide to play and lose you're down two points, but that's only one point worse than dropping. But if you take the double, then by winning two points, that is three points better than dropping. Playing on has a downside of one—you go from -1 to -2. But it has an upside of three—you're going from -1 to 2. So you are essentially being given pot odds of three to one. So for this to be worthwhile, your winning chances need to be at least one in four. So now I've hopefully convinced you three different ways that you need a 25% chance of winning in order to take the doubling cube.

In practice, your doubling cube action can also depend on other factors like your ability to use the cube if you turn the game around or your chance of getting gammoned. For instance, if the game is a pure race with a few rolls to go, you can sometimes take with a 22% chance of winning since you probably have a better than 25% chance of being able to reach a position where you can double your opponent out. This allows you to take with a little less than 25% chance. On the other extreme, if you're in a position where you never win a gammon, but all of your losses are gammons, then your winning chances would have to be at least 50% in order to accept.

Sometimes it can be tricky to estimate your winning chances, but the more you play, the better you become at doing this. Also there are books and computer programs and apps that can greatly improve your ability to estimate these numbers, but if you don't want to get too quantitative, here's a decent rule of thumb. You should double your opponent if you're comfortably ahead of the game, and you should take a double if you can see a clear way to turn the game around that doesn't require too much luck on your part.

Now Backgammon may be a game that has a lot of luck in it, but since you make many decisions, you have some control over how much of the luck works for you and how much of it works against you.

Here's a situation where you can easily apply the 25% rule. It's the last roll of the game. If black can bear off both checkers this turn, he wins, otherwise, he loses. What are his chances of winning? Let's count. What are black's winning rolls? Well, black certainly wins if either die has a five or a six in it, since the big numbers bear off the five and the small number will bear off the one. How many rolls is that? Well as we saw earlier, there are 20 such numbers. It's just like hitting a double-direct shot. There are 20 dice rolls that have a five or a six in it. Is there anything else that will get black off this turn? Well, let's see, black doesn't get off when both numbers are less than five, except for some doubles. Namely, double fours will do the trick, double threes will do the trick, and even double twos will do the trick, two, two, two, two. So, black altogether has 20 numbers with a five or a six in it and three doubles—double four, three, and 2. That gives us 23 winning rolls, so his chance of winning is 23 out of 36. So black is a favorite in this position, and since it's the last roll of the game and the cube can never be used as a weapon against him, he should double the stakes. He should say, okay, let's make this worth two points.

Since white wins 13 times out of 36, if black wins 23 times, then white wins 13 times out of 36, and that's way better than 25%; 25% is 9 out of 36, then white has an easy take. So it's correct for black to double, and it's correct for white to take.

Here's another common position. This is called a two-roll position. Black has four checkers on the ace point; white has four checkers on the ace point. It's black's roll, and black is clearly the favorite because it's black's roll, so black doubles, so, should white take? Well, again, what are white's chances? Now white can only win if black does not roll doubles, because if black rolls doubles he wins the game right away, and then white must roll doubles, so the chance of this happening of black not getting doubles and white does get doubles is five out of six times one out of six. That's five out of 36. Since five out of 36 is way less than nine out of 36, 25%, then white should definitely drop. In fact, even it's a three-roll position, like that, we call that three rolls because we've got five checkers, so it's a three-roll position. Then white's winning chances are a little less than 25%. It's about 22%. So this would still be a drop.

Now the four-roll position is a little more interesting. Here I'll give black eight here and white–it doesn't matter if white has seven or eight, it's really the same thing from here. Then the four-roll position is more interesting. Here it can be shown using dynamic programming calculations like we did in blackjack, that black should double and white should take. Now there's enough time left in the game for white to get that lucky roll of doubles. If it's a five-roll position or higher—I'll give black two more and white two more like here. Then it's still the case that black has a double and white has a take, but though black has a double, black doesn't have a redouble. In other words, if the cube's in the middle, black can double to two. But if black owns the cube, black should not redouble to four. Black should wait until it's a four-roll or three-roll position before redoubling.

Here's a useful rule of thumb that I use when the game is a straight race, where both sides have 50 or more pips to go. For example, earlier we saw a position where black had 92 pips and white had 98 pips. Should black double, and if so, should white take? In general, what kind of lead do you need to double, and when can your opponent take? Here's what I call the 10% rule. Throw away the last digit of your pip count. That's 10% of your pip count. One less than that is your doubling point. Two more than that is your opponent's take point.

Here's an example to show what I mean. Suppose you have a pip count of 92. Stripping the last digit gives us nine. So with an eight-point racing lead you should double. What that means is if your opponent has less than 100, you should wait. In our example, white has 98 pips, so even though black is winning, he should not double. If he does double, then white would have an easy take. In fact, white can take if the lead is 10% plus two or smaller. Thus if black has 92 pips, then white can take with a deficit of $9 + 2$, 11 pips. In other words, with a pip count of 103 or smaller, white can take.

When I'm looking for an enjoyable game of backgammon and want to learn how to play better at the same time, I bring out one of my favorite backgammon apps like XG Mobile on my iPad or iPhone. It uses the software Extreme Gammon, which is probably the best player in the world right now. When you play against the computer, you can have it tell you when it thinks you've made a mistake, how serious the mistake is, and what it thinks is the best move. It'll also give you hints on doubling decisions too. It's an amazing learning tool.

As we've seen, there's a ton of mathematics lurking underneath the game of backgammon. But the game can be enjoyed by anyone, even if neither player is using any math at all. I recommend joining a club or the US Backgammon Federation, and I guarantee that the more you play and practice, the better you'll become.

In our next lecture, I'll show you some games and puzzles that you can be an expert in with almost no practice at all if you know the secret. Just one disclaimer, I take no responsibility for any scams or get-rich-quick schemes that you may come up with after viewing that lecture. So I'll see you there if you dare.

Games You Can't Lose and Sneaky Puzzles
Lecture 7

There are many games that seem very innocent and fair, but where you actually have a big advantage. The focus of this lecture is on scams and hustles that arise in games and puzzles. In this lecture, you will learn about games with nontransitive probabilities, involving cards, coins, dice, and even bingo cards. You will also learn how averages can be misleading by learning about Simpson's paradox. The strategies presented in this lecture may keep you from being exploited by a devious adversary.

Nontransitive Probabilities

- There is a dice game that uses four dice, but they are not ordinary dice. Die A has two 6s and four 2s. Die B has all 3s on it. Die C has four 4s and two 0s, and die D has three 5s and three 1s. Each of two players rolls a die, and whoever rolls the higher number is the winner. Player 1 chooses a die, and player 2 selects a different die.

- Die A is tempting because it has the largest number and the largest total, but if player 1 chooses die A, then player 2 should choose die B. Notice that because player 2's roll is guaranteed to be 3, he or she will win whenever player 1 rolls a 2, which happens 4 times out of 6. Thus, die B beats die A with probability 2/3. The notation is as follows: $P(B > A) = 2/3$.

- If player 1 picks die B instead, then player 2 should choose die C, which wins whenever player 2 rolls a 4—because player 1 has to roll a 3, and that happens 2/3 of the time. Therefore, die C is going to beat die B 2/3 of the time.

- Die D beats die C 2/3 of the time. Die D can beat die C in two ways: If die D is a 5, which happens half the time, then it's guaranteed to beat C, or if die D is a 1 and C is a 0, then D will beat C. The probability that die D is 1 and C is 0 is $(1/2)(1/3) = 1/6$, so the probability that die D beats die C is $1/2 + 1/6 = 2/3$.

- If player 1 chooses die D, then player 2 should choose A. Player 2 has two ways of winning: Either player 2 rolls a 6, which happens 1/3 of the time (because two of the six numbers are 6s), or player 2 can roll a 2 and player 1 can roll a 1. In that case, there's a 2/3 chance of player 2 rolling a 2, and there's a 1/2 chance that player 1 rolls a 1, so $(2/3)(1/2) = 1/3$. The probability that die A beats die D is $1/3 + 1/3 = 2/3$.

- To summarize, die A loses to die B, die B loses to die C, die C loses to die D, and die D loses to die A—each with probability 2/3. This situation is what mathematicians call nontransitive probabilities.

- At first glance, this sounds impossible. Most competitive situations are transitive. If A is faster than B and B is faster than C, then A is faster than C. We encounter nontransitive situations in games like rock-paper-scissors, but when it shows up in other games, like dice games and poker, it's very unexpected.

Roulette

- In the game of roulette, every bet on average loses about 5.3¢ per dollar bet. Suppose that you like to bet $1 on your favorite number—for example, 17. If 17 shows up, then you win $35; otherwise, you lose $1. That's one of the ways that roulette is played.

- Let's say that you decide to bet on your favorite number (17) 35 times in a row. What are your chances of showing a profit after 35 bets? You may be surprised to learn that your chance of showing a profit is around 60%.

- If you win once, then you made a profit because you have one big win of $35 and 34 losses of $1. We need to figure out the chance of winning at least one of your 35 bets. To do that, answer the opposite question: What are the chances of losing all 35 bets—of not showing a profit?

- Each bet has a 1/38 chance of winning and, thus, a 37/38 chance of losing. Because the outcomes are independent, the probability that you lose all 35 bets is $(37/38)^5 = (0.9736...)^5 \approx 0.39 = 39\%$. Hence, the probability that you don't lose all your bets—that is, the probability that you win at least one bet—is about 61%.

- The problem is that when you are profitable, you're usually only $1 profitable. Sometimes you win more, but when you lose, which is nearly 40% of the time, you always lose $35. Sometimes you win twice, and very occasionally you win three times, but on average, after 35 bets, you will be down about $2. You can't beat this game.

Bingo

- Bingo is not quite as fair as it seems. In a typical Bingo game, everyone gets a five-by-five card filled with numbers from 1 to 75. Numbers are drawn one at a time in random order, and the winner is the first person who gets a "bingo," consisting of five numbers in a row, column, or diagonal.

B	I	N	G	O
7	25	44	57	62
15	22	40	50	70
11	30	FREE SPACE	46	74
2	28	37	55	68
10	27	39	59	75

- If more than one person gets a bingo at the same time, then the prize money is shared between them. You would think that any bingo card is just as good as any other, but that's not always the case.

- To prove this point, let's simplify the game. If every card just had one number and all the cards were different, then indeed each card is just as good as any other. That would just be the same as a raffle.

- However, suppose that each card has two numbers. Let's say you have the following domino-shaped cards.

A	B	C	D	E
[1 2]	[3 4]	[1 5]	[3 1]	[4 1]

- The numbers 1 through 5 are drawn in random order, and whoever gets both of the numbers first is the winner. Does any one card seem to be better than the others?

- If the prize were $120 and the game were fair, then each card would have an expected value of $120/5 = $24. However, if we do the math, the expected values of these cards are 21, 40, 21, 19, and 19, respectively.

A	B	C	D	E
[1 2]	[3 4]	[1 5]	[3 1]	[4 1]
21	40	21	19	19

- Card B has an enormous advantage. So, if everyone paid $24 to play this game, then B has an expected profit of $16, while everyone else will lose, on average, $3 or $5.

- Why does B do so much better than the rest? Notice that all the other cards need the number 1 to win, and sometimes they have to share their prize, but B wins whenever the number 1 is drawn after the 3 and 4, and this happens 1/3 of the time. That makes sense because among the numbers 1, 3, and 4, 1 is just as likely to be the first, second, or third of these three numbers.

- Moreover, B never shares the prize. Hence, B's expected value is 1/3 of $120, which is $40. In fact, by the same logic, B wins 1/3 of the time—even if there were more cards that all had 1 in them.

- When the cards get larger, the game becomes more complicated, and a full five-by-five card game would be way too difficult to analyze. What happens when the cards have three numbers? Suppose that two players agree to play bingo with the following L-shaped cards.

A	B	C
3	4	1
1 2	3 2	4 2

- On these three cards—A, B, and C—the numbers 1 through 4 are chosen in random order, and A beats B if a 1 and 2 or a 1 and 3 appears before a 2 and 3 or a 3 and 4.

- For example, if A plays B and the numbers come out in order 2, 4, 1, 3, then A has the bingo, so A would win. On the other hand, if the numbers came out 1, 4, 3, 2, then both players get a bingo at the same time, so this situation would be a tie.

- This is another nontransitive game—where A is favored to beat B, B is favored to beat C, and C is favored to beat A. To see why A beats B, notice that the numbers 1, 2, 3, and 4 can be arranged 24 ways (4 choices for the first number, 3 choices for the next, 2 choices for the next, 1 choice for the next, or 4! = 24 ways).

- In 12 of those 24 ways, A beats B, and in 10 of those 24 ways, B beats A. In 2 of those 24 ways, it would be a tie. Therefore, A has a 12-to-10, or 6-to-5, advantage over B. By the same logic, if we exclude card A, then we see that B has a 6-to-5 advantage over C, and C has a 6-to-5 advantage over A.

- Suppose you walk into a Bingo hall and watch a game until it ends. Is the winning card more likely to be a horizontal bingo or a vertical bingo? Intuitively, you would think it would be just as likely for someone to have a horizontal bingo or a vertical bingo. However, it's actually more likely—in fact, about twice as likely—for the winning card to come from a horizontal than from a vertical bingo.

- This bingo result is closely related to a classic conundrum known as the birthday paradox. Suppose you walk into a room with 22 other people. What are the chances that two or more people in the room have the same birthday? Most people think it's pretty low, but there's actually more than a 50% chance that two people in that room have the same birthday.

Simpson's Paradox

- Is it possible for there to be two baseball players, A and B, for which A has a better batting average than B one year and the next year, but when we combine the two years, B does better than A? Not only is it possible for this to happen, it actually has happened.

- The batting records for Derek Jeter and David Justice in 1995 and 1996 are a great example. In both years, Justice had the better average, but when we combine the two years, Jeter has the better average.

	1995	1996	Combined
Jeter	12/48 = .250	183/582 = .314	195/630 = **.310**
Justice	104/411 = **.253**	45/140 = **.321**	149/551 = .270

- In fact, Justice even outperformed Jeter in the 1997 season, but when we combine all three years, Jeter has the better average.

Jeter batted .300, and Justice batted .298: 385/1284 = .300 versus 312/1046 = .298.

- Mathematicians call this Simpson's paradox, and it arises in many places even outside of games and puzzles. Simpson's paradox cannot happen if both players have the same number of at bats each season, but it can happen when the denominators are very different, like in this example.

	1995	1996	1997	Combined
Jeter	12/48 = .250	183/582 = .314	190/654 = .291	385/1284 = **.300**
Justice	104/411 = **.253**	45/140 = **.321**	163/495 = **.329**	312/1046 = .298

Suggested Reading

Bewersdorff, *Luck, Logic, and White Lies.*

Diaconis and Graham, *Magical Mathematics.*

Gardner, *The Colossal Book of Short Puzzles and Problems.*

Gardner, *Perplexing Puzzles and Tantalizing Teasers.*

Haigh, *Taking Chances.*

Problems

1. Look at the magic square below.

   a. If you choose a random number from the first row and your opponent chooses a random number from the second row, who is more likely to have the higher number?

   b. Find a nontransitive situation from the rows of the magic square. (A similar situation arises with the columns, too!)

4	9	2
3	5	7
8	1	6

2.

You have three six-sided dice (A, B, and C) with the following numbers:
A = (6,3,3,3,3,3), B = (5,5,5,2,2,2), and C = (4,4,4,4,4,1).

    a.   Find P(A > B).

    b.   Find P(B > C).

    c.   Find P(C > A)

    d.   From the above probabilities, if your opponent chooses die A, which die should you choose to maximize your probability of winning?

3. Choose your favorite baseball team, and your opponent will choose hers. Each team will play about 160 games in the season. Your opponent's score at the end of the season is the sum of her scores after each game. (So, if in the first five games, your opponent's team scores 1, 1, 2, 3, and 5 runs, then her total will be 12 at that point.) You get the product of the scores. (So, if your teams scored 1, 1, 2, 3, and 5 runs, then your product would be 30 at that point.) Who is favored to win this bet?

4. Your friend has two American coins in his hand totaling 30 cents, but one of them is not a nickel. What coins does he have?

Games You Can't Lose and Sneaky Puzzles
Lecture 7—Transcript

Psst. Hey buddy. Come here. I got an offer you can't refuse. Do you want to know who'll win tomorrow's baseball game? I have a mathematical model that will predict the winner. Give me $10, and if I'm wrong, I'll give you your money back. What do you think? You look skeptical. Alright. Since I'm so sure of my prediction, if I'm wrong, I'll give you $15 back. So if my prediction is wrong, you'll make money. Either way, you can't lose. Would you take this offer?

Here's my sophisticated mathematical model. I flip a coin. Look at it from my perspective. I'm right half the time. When I'm right, I keep your $10. When I lose, I return $15, but $10 of that was yours to begin with, so I'm only down $5 when I'm wrong. So half the time, I'm up $10, half the time I'm down $5. So my expected value is $2.50. I win on average $2.50 per prediction, just by flipping a coin.

By the way, if I know something about the teams that allows me to make a correct prediction more than 50% of the time, then my expected value goes up, and thus yours will go down even more. In fact, there are some good mathematical models from making sports predictions, and by the end of this lecture, I'll give you a pretty accurate method for predicting the score of a baseball game, before it begins. But, the focus of this lecture is on scams and hustles that arise in games and puzzles. Naturally, I don't recommend that you actually use these strategies to take advantage of others, but it may keep you from being exploited by a devious adversary. And besides, most of the information is fun and mathematically interesting.

The simplest piece of advice is that if a deal seems too good to be true, then it probably isn't. The author Damon Runyon probably put it best when he said:

> One of these days in your travels, a guy's going to come up to you
> and show you a nice brand new deck of cards on which the seal is
> not yet broken and this guy is going to offer to bet you that he can
> make the jack of spades jump out of the deck and squirt cider in

your ear. But son, do not bet this man for as you're standing there, you are going to end up with an earful of cider.

Let's change the situation. Suppose you get an unsolicited email one day, and it says that a particular stock will go up in the next week. Sure enough a week goes back and the stock price goes up. Then you get another email from the same person, and it says that another stock price will go down in the next week, and sure enough it does. Five weeks go by and every week the prediction is right. After the fifth week, they email you saying that if you want future picks from them, then you should pay to subscribe to their service. Should you do it?

If they really are as good as they seem, then such information would be very valuable, but it's possible that you're being scammed in the following way. Suppose that in their first week, they sent out 32,000 emails. In half of them, they say that a certain stock will go up and the other half they say it will go down. They will give the correct advice, then, to 16,000 people, and those people will get an email the following week. The rest are ignored. For those 16,000 people, they give half of them one piece of advice and half of them the opposite advice. The 8,000 people who get the right advice are sent email the following week, and so on. So after five weeks, exactly 1,000 of those 32,000 people have been given correct advice each time, and you might have been one of those lucky 1,000. So even though from your perspective this company seems to know what they're doing, they just might be flipping a coin so be careful.

By the way, we see this in other real-life situations. An investment company shows how all the funds that it offers have performed over the last few years, but the funds that have been most unsuccessful have probably been closed. Or when you see movie reviews in advertisements, you almost only see the very positive ones mentioned. The negative reviews are generally not advertised so much.

Alright. Here's another game that I'd like to play with you. It uses four dice, but these are not ordinary dice. This die which, I'll call die A, has two sixes and four twos. Die B has all threes on it. C has four fours and two 0s and D has three fives and three ones. Each of us will roll a die, and whoever rolls the higher number, is the winner. Since I'm a gentleman, I'll let you choose whichever die you like, and I'll select a different die. Which die would you like? Die A is tempting since it has the largest number and the largest total. But if you choose die A, then I'll choose die B. Notice that since my roll is guaranteed to be three, I will win anytime you roll a two, which happens four times out of six, thus B beats A with probability $^2/_3$.

Maybe you prefer to pick B instead, but if you pick B, then I'll choose C, which wins whenever I roll a four, right, since you have to roll a three, and that happens $^2/_3$ of the time. Right? I've got four fours and two 0s. So C is going to beat B $^2/_3$ of the time. So maybe C is the right choice, but I claim that D beats C $^2/_3$ of the time. Let's see why; this takes more explanation. D can beat C in two ways. Either if D gets a five, which happens half the time, then it's guaranteed to beat C, or, if D is a one and C is a 0, then D will beat C. What's the probability that D is one and C is 0. Well that has probability $^1/_2 \times {}^1/_3$, which is $^1/_6$. So the probability that D beats C is $^1/_2 + {}^1/_6$, and that is equal to $^2/_3$.

Alright, so that settles it; you should pick D right? But not so fast. If you choose D, then I'll choose A. Again, I have two ways of winning. Either I roll a six, which happens $^1/_3$ of the time because two of the six numbers here are sixes, or, I can roll a two, and you can roll a one. And what's the probability of that? Well there's a $^2/_3$ chance of me rolling a two. There's a $^1/_2$ chance that you roll a one, so, $^2/_3 \times {}^1/_2$ is $^1/_3$. So the probability that A beats D is $^1/_3 + {}^1/_3$ is $^2/_3$. To summarize, we have A loses to B; B loses to C; C loses to D; and yet D loses to A, each with probability $^2/_3$. This situation is what mathematicians call nontransitive probabilities.

At first glance this sounds impossible, right? Most competitive situations are transitive. If A is faster than B and B is faster than C, then A is faster than C. We encountered nontransitive situations in games like rock-paper-scissors. Rock loses to paper; paper loses to scissors; scissors loses to rock, but this was established by the rules of the game. But when it shows up in other games like with dice games and poker, it's very unexpected.

By the way, the dice we just used were the invention of Bradley Efron who's a professor of statistics and the humanities at Stanford University. The following dice are the invention of Allen Schwenk, a mathematician from Western Michigan University. It leads to an even sneakier scam. This time I have three dice with various numbers on them. The dice are red, white, and blue. This time you can choose your dice as well as mine. What could be fairer than that?

Here's the trick. These are very special nontransitive dice. As an exercise, it can be shown that red will usually lose to white. White will usually lose to blue. And blue will usually lose to red. But, if you roll two dice of the same color—two reds, two whites and two blues—then the situation is completely reversed. The red total is favored to beat the white total; the white total is favored to beat the blue total; and yet the blue total is favored to beat the red total. In fact, when you roll three dice of the same color, the probabilities switch back again. We can take advantage of this nontransitivity by allowing you to choose your color and mine, but I didn't specify how many dice we would use. So if, say, you chose red and gave me white, then I'd ask each of us to roll one die. But if you gave me red and chose white for yourself, then I'd ask us to roll two dice, very sneaky.

My favorite example of nontransitive probabilities comes from a game called Penney Ante, invented, curiously enough, by a mathematician named Walter Penney. As we know by now, if you flip a penny three times, there are eight equally likely outcomes. Now, which pattern do you like best? Choose any pattern you'd like, then I'll pick another. You then flip a coin until one of our patterns appears. Whoever pattern shows up first is the winner. Sound fair enough? Let's suppose you picked the pattern head-head-head. Then I'll pick the pattern tail-head-head, and I'm an enormous favorite. Why?

Look at the sequence of coin flips, and look for when the sequence head-head-head first appears. Since this is the first head-head-head, it had to be preceded by a tail. Because otherwise you would have had an earlier head-head-head. Hence, my sequence tail-head-head must come before yours. In fact, unless the sequence of coin flips immediately starts with head-head-head, which happens only $1/8$ of the time, then my sequence tail-head-head is guaranteed to occur before yours. Thus tail-head-head beats head-head-head $7/8$ of the time. In fact, no matter what sequence you choose, I can find another sequence that's favored to come first. Here's the rule. If you chose sequence A-B-C, where each letter stands for a coin flip, then I choose sequence B'-A-B, where B' denotes the opposite of B.

In other words, turn over the second coin, then put it before the first two coins. Let me give you an example. If you chose tail-head-head, then I would choose tail-tail-head. Here's a table that shows each situation along with the second player's probability of winning. Take a look here. Let's look at, say, you chose tail-tail-head, then I would choose head-tail-tail. And our table shows that I would win $^3/_4$ of the time. I won't derive the probabilities here, but notice that in every case your probability of winning is at least $^2/_3$, which is huge. Technically, you can lose in any given game, but if you play enough games, then it's virtually certain that you will win in the long run.

Here's a dangerous gambling strategy that can cost you a lot of money if you're not careful. In the game of roulette, every bet, on average, loses about 5.3¢ per dollar bet. Now suppose you like to bet $1 on your favorite number, say 17. If 17 shows up, then you win $35, and otherwise you lose $1. That's one of the ways that roulette is played. Let's say that you decide to bet on your lucky number, 17, 35 times in a row. What are your chances of showing a profit after 35 bets? What do you think? Is it very high, close to 100%; pretty high, around 60%; exactly 50%; pretty low, around 40%; or very low, close to 0%? What do you think? Take a guess. You may be surprised to learn that your chance of showing a profit is B, around 60%. Let's verify that answer.

Notice that if you win once, then you made profit. Since you have one big win of $35 and 34 losses of $1. So even if you just win once out of those 35 you show a profit. So what we need to figure out is the chance of winning at least one of your 35 bets. Let's do that by first answering the opposite question. What are the chances of losing all 35 bets, of not showing a profit? Each bet, we know, has a $^1/_{38}$ chance of winning and thus a 37 out of 38 chance of losing. And since the outcomes are independent, the probability that you lose all 35 bets, bet number one, two, three, four, all the way up to 35, is $^{37}/_{38}{}^{35}$,, which is about 39%. Hence, the probability that you don't lose all your bets, that is, the probability that you win at least one bet, is about 61%. Right? 100%-39%, 61%, as promised. Now before you all start running off to Las Vegas to use this strategy, let's see what's really going on.

The problem is that when you are profitable, you're usually only $1 profitable. Sometimes you win more, yet when you lose, which is nearly 40% of the time, you always lose $35. Sometimes you win twice, and very occasionally you win three times, but on average, after 35 bets, you will be down about $2. You can't beat this game.

In contrast to our last example, here's a gambling strategy that you wouldn't think works, but actually does. In fact, it's so amazing that you could make a magic trick out of it. It's played with five cards, two kings and three deuces. Kings are winners and deuces are losers. The cards are mixed up, and you have to say how much you'll bet before seeing any of the cards. Since there are two winning cards and three losing cards, it sounds like an unfavorable situation, but here's a winning strategy. I'm not even going to see what these cards are. I promise you that what I'm going to do is I'm going to first bet $16. After that, I'm going to use the following betting rule. After a win, I will bet 50% less, and after a loss I'll bet 50% more. So let's do an example. We've shuffled these cards, and let's see what we got. The first card that comes out is a king. That's a winner. So that's a win. Good. Now what did the rule say? After a win, I'll bet 50% less. So my second bet is going to be $8. Let's see what it is. It is another king. That's another win. That's good. But what does that mean? Now my next bet after a win, I bet 50% less, so my next bet is going to be how much? Half of eight, $4. What happens here? I fear I know what happens here; it's a deuce, so I'm going to lose. And now, after a loss, we bet 50% more. So 50% of four is two. So if I bet 50% more, my next bet will be six. What happens there? We lose. We know that. After a loss we bet 50% more, and it's another loss, so 50% more of six, that was nine. Right? And we lose there too. So altogether my total wins here, 16 + 8 is $24. My total losses, 4 + 6 + 9 is $19. So my profit here was $5. Even though I had two wins and three losses, I came up with a profit of $5. That's pretty amazing. Of course, I could've told you that from the very beginning because I had a prediction here that said your profit will be exactly $5. How did I do it? Do I have a different prediction on every page here? No. Amazingly, no matter how the cards are arranged, you always end up with a profit of $5. To prove this, I claim that if you bet in the way that I told you, then a win followed by a loss will result in the same thing as if you had a loss followed by a win. Now that's not at all obvious, so let's see why that's true.

Suppose you bet \$N somewhere, anywhere, and it's followed by a win, then a loss. Look what happens. Since you won your \$N bet, the next bet will be half of that, it'll be $^N/_2$ dollars, which you lose. So these bets, you've won \$N, you lost $^N/_2$, dollars, your profit will be $^N/_2$ dollars, and what will your next bet be? Well after you've lost $^N/_2$ dollars, your next bet will be 50% more. So $^N/_2$ plus half of that, $^N/_4$ is $^{3N}/_4$ dollars. So remember those numbers. With a win followed by a loss you are ahead $^N/_2$ dollars, and your next bet is $^{3N}/_4$ dollars. On the other hand, suppose you bet \$N, and it's followed by a loss, then a win. After your \$N loss, your next bet will be $^N/_2$ dollars more. After you lose, you bet $^N/_2$ dollars more, and you win that bet. So these two bets earn you a profit of $^N/_2$ dollars, just as before. And what's your next bet going to be? Well following a win, you bet half as much. And so if you were betting $^N/_2$, then on your next bet you're going to add $^N/_4$ to that, so you're going to bet $^{3N}/_4$ dollars just like before. So either way you're going to be ahead $^N/_2$ dollars, and your next bet will be $^{3N}/_4$ dollars.

What this means is that no matter how the cards are arranged, no matter how those cards are shuffled, a win followed by a loss is the same as a loss followed by a win. So for instance, I could swap a loss followed by a win is the same as a win followed by a loss; a loss followed by a win is the same as a win followed by a loss. Essentially, it has the effect of moving these kings all the way up here, so every scenario is equivalent to the scenario of two wins followed by three losses, which coincidentally, was what we saw here. So, no matter how those cards were arranged, you will have a profit of \$5.

Here's another game that you may have played before that's not quite as fair as it seems, the game of Bingo. In a typical Bingo game everyone gets a five by five card like this one filled with numbers from 1 to 75. Numbers are drawn one at a time in random order, and the winner is the first person who gets a Bingo consisting of five numbers in a row, column, or diagonal. If more than one person gets a Bingo at the same time, then the prize money is shared between them. Now you would think that any Bingo card is just as good as any other, but that's not always the case. To prove my point, let's simplify the game a bit. Now if every card just had one number, and all the cards were different, then indeed, each card is just as good as any other. That would just be the same as a raffle. But now suppose each card has two numbers. Say we had the following domino-shaped cards. The numbers one through five are drawn in random order, and whoever gets both of the numbers first is the winner. Now does any one card here seem to be better than the others? Perhaps card A, which is the only card with the number two? Or maybe C, which has the only five? If the prize was $120, and the game were fair, then each card would have an expected value of $120/_5$, $24. And yet, if we do the math, the expected values of these cards are 21, 40, 21, 19, and 19. As you see, card B has an enormous advantage. So, if everyone paid $24 to play this game, then B has an expected profit of $16 while everyone else will lose on average $3 or $5.

Now why does B do so much better than the rest? Notice that all the other cards need the number one to win, and sometimes they have to share their prize, but B wins whenever the number one is drawn after the three and four, and this happens $1/_3$ of the time. That makes sense since among the numbers one, three, and four, one is just as likely to be the first, second, or third of these three numbers. Moreover, B never shares the prize. Hence B's expected value is $1/_3$ of $120, which is $40. In fact, by the same logic, B wins a third of the time even if there were more cards that all had one in them. But now card B looks a little too conspicuous. When the cards get larger, the game becomes more complicated, and a full five-by-five card game would be way too hard to analyze.

But to show you how interesting things can get, let's look at what happens when the cards have three numbers. Suppose you and I agree to play Bingo with L-shaped cards here. I've got cards A, B, and C, and the numbers one through four are chosen in random order, and A beats B if a one and two or a one and three appears before a two, three or three, four. Let me do an example. So if A plays B—we won't pay attention to C here—and the numbers come out two, four, one, three, then let's see what happens with a two, both players are happy; with a four, B is happy; and then the one comes out; and A has the Bingo. A has the line across, so A would win in this game. On the other hand, if the numbers came out one, four, three, two, then we have one, four, and then both players have three and notice that they both get a Bingo at the same time, so this situation would be a tie.

So you and I are going to play, and I'll give you your choice of card. Which card do you think is best; take your pick, A, B, or C? Hopefully by now you've developed a healthy suspicion of my generous offers. This turns out to be another nontransitive game where A is favored to beat B, B is favored to beat C, and C is favored to beat A. To see why A beats B, notice that the numbers one, two, three, and four can be arranged 24 ways. Why 24? Four choices for the first number, three choices for the next, two choices for the next, one choice for the next—four factorial, 24 ways. Here they are. Notice that in 12 of those 24 ways, if you actually verified this, you'd see that A would beat B, and in 10 of those 24 ways B would beat A, and in two of those 24 ways it would be a tie. Therefore, A has a six to five advantage over B. 12 to 10 is the same as six to five. And by the same logic, if we exclude card A, then we see that B has a six-to-five advantage over C, and C has a six-to-five advantage over A—quite the paradox.

Here's an amazing fact about the real game of Bingo. Suppose you walk into a Bingo hall and watch a game until it ends. Is the winning card more likely to be a horizontal Bingo or a vertical Bingo? Intuitively, you would think it would be just as likely for us to have a horizontal Bingo or a vertical Bingo. Right? And yet, it's actually more likely for the winning card to come from a horizontal than from a vertical. When I first heard this, I didn't believe it, yet it's true. Let me try to give you a plausible explanation for this.

Suppose we just focus on the third row and the third column of a Bingo card, which, by the way, is the most probable location for a Bingo because of the free space. Everybody starts with a coin on the free space. I will admit that on your card it is just as likely that you win horizontally as vertically, but let's say the room has 1,000 Bingo cards. The chances are pretty good that someone else has the same four vertical numbers as you do, but it's highly unlikely that anyone else has the same four horizontal numbers as you do. Why is that? Notice that the number of ways to create your four horizontal numbers is 15^4. That's 50,625. Where do those numbers come from? Fifteen choices for the B number; 15 choices for the I; 15 for the G; and 15 for the O. So there's 50,000 different ways of writing down those four numbers. But for the vertical column, for column N, the numbers have to be different, and the order doesn't really matter. Anybody that has your four vertical numbers is going to get a Bingo at the same time as you. There's 44, 40, 37, 39. It doesn't matter what order they're in; somebody has those same four numbers. They essentially have the same column as you do. The number of ways of picking those four numbers is $^{(15 \times 14 \times 13 \times 12)}/_{24}$, the number of ways of arranging those four numbers because order doesn't matter, and that gives you 1,365 essentially different N columns.

So, to summarize, with 1,000 cards it's pretty unlikely, less than a 2% chance, that someone has your horizontal numbers. But there's a better than 50% chance that someone else has your vertical numbers. In fact, with 1,000 Bingo cards, you can expect there to be on average about 980 different possible horizontal winners, but on average there will only be about 520 different possible vertical winners. So when a Bingo is called, it's more likely to be from a horizontal card, than a vertical one, and when there's a vertical winner, it'll often be tied with another card. In fact, we had a computer run a simulation on 100,000 games of Bingo. Each time we generated 1,000 cards at random, then played Bingo to see if the winners were only horizontal or only vertical or something else, like a diagonal win or both a horizontal and vertical win. Here were the results.

Based on our simulation, it appears that the winning Bingo was about twice as likely to be horizontal than vertical.

This Bingo result is closely related to a classic conundrum known as the birthday paradox. Suppose you walk into a room with 22 other people. What are the chances that two or more people in the room have the same birthday? Most people think it's pretty low, and yet, it's more than 50% chance that two people in that room have the same birthday. Here's the reason why. Let's figure out the probability that there are no birthday matches in the room, then we'll subtract that answer from 100%. Imagine that 23 people walk into the room one at a time with me going in last. We'll denote the first person with a one. Then the next person enters the room. The chance that the second person's birthday matches person one is one out of 365, so the chance that it's different is $^{364}/_{365}$. Now if both birthdays are different and a third person enters the room, then the chance that it matches one of the first two is two out of 365, so the chance that it's different is $^{363}/_{365}$. Then a fourth person enters the room, and the chance that his is different from the first three is $^{362}/_{365}$. Finally, when I walk into the room, assuming that there have been no matches so far among those 22 people, the chance that my birthday is different from those 22 others is $^{(365-22)}/_{365}$. That's $^{343}/_{365}$. And when we multiply all these probabilities together, we get about 49%. By the way, the result is still true even if we allow February 29 as well. Hence, if the probability that all the birthdays were different is 49%, then the probability that at least two people have the same birthday is about 51%.

With 30 people the chance of a birthday match is 71%. With 40 people the chance is 89%; and with 50 people the chance is 97%; and with 100 people it's 99.99997%. The chance of no matches is less than one in 30,000. People are often surprised to hear this, but I think they're thinking of the wrong problem. For example, with 100 random people, the chance that one of those people in the room has your birthday is less than $^{100}/_{365}$, which is 27%. More exactly, the probability that they're all different from you would be $^{364}/_{365}{}^{100}$, and one minus that gives you 24%. But if you have 101 people, if every pair of them shakes hands, then the number of handshakes is $^{(101 \times 100)}/_{2}$, that's 5,050. So there are 5,050 interactions in that room, each of which has a probability of about $^{1}/_{365}$ of a birthday match. So the odds of at least one match with 5,050 of these interactions, each of which has a $^{1}/_{365}$ chance of a birthday match, is overwhelming. In fact, with 101 people, if everyone compared birthdays, the expected number of pairs of people with matching birthdays is $^{5,050}/_{365}$, which is about 14. By the way, our calculations assume that every birthday has the same probability, but if that assumption is wrong, say due to seasonal differences or the occasional citywide power outage, then that only increases the chance of a birthday match.

With the time we have remaining, I want to show you some simple puzzles with sneaky answers. These are what you might call gotcha puzzles. I'll be giving the answers right away, so you may want to use the pause button before I reveal the secret.

Here's a warm-up problem. If you have 11 coins and three cups, can you distribute the coins in the cups so that each cup contains a different number of coins and the numbers are all odd? Well sure. And I said this is an easy one. We'll put seven in the first cup, we'll put three in the second, and we'll put one in the third. Easy, right? Now for the real problem. Can you place 10 coins in the cups? You got rid of one. Ten coins in the cup so that each contains a different odd number of coins, so they all have to be different, and they all have to be odd. Now a mathematician will tell you that's impossible since three odd numbers have to add up to an odd number, so it can't be done with 10 coins because 10 is an even number. And yet, the mathematician would lose this bet because it can be done. Do you see it? I'm going to place seven coins in my first cup. I'll put one coin in the second cup. I'll put two in the third cup—hold on. Then I'll place the second cup in the third cup, like that. Now each cup has an odd number of coins. Seven, three, and one, even though we're just using 10 coins.

Alright. Here's a cute little number puzzle. Starting with the false equation, $32 + 8 = 17$, can you move one of the digits to make it a true equation? I don't want you to like move the one and turn that into a not equal sign. I want you to move a digit and make it a true equation. Here's a hint; move the digit two. You don't have to move it very far either, just move it up slightly, and you get a true equation. $3^2 + 8 = 17$.

Now here are some cute puzzles involving toothpicks. Using 16 toothpicks arranged like so, we have five unit squares. The challenge is to move just two of the toothpicks so that you're left with exactly four squares of the same size and no extraneous pieces. This is not a trick question. It's just hard to see. You may want to pause and look at it for a while. I'll give you a hint now. It involves these two toothpicks. If you move these two toothpicks like so, we now have four unit squares.

Now let's remove four more toothpicks so we only have 12. The challenge is to find a way to arrange these 12 toothpicks to create six squares of the same size. You can move as many of the toothpicks as you'd like, but no breaking of pieces allowed. Six unit squares from these 12 toothpicks. How are you going to do that? This one really seems impossible, but it can be done if you think outside the box. Or you maybe you should just think inside a box, or may just think about a box. And if you do, we have 12 toothpicks arranged in such a way that it contains exactly six unit squares, one on each side of the cube.

Alright. If you didn't like that one, you're going to hate the next one. From these 11 toothpicks can you move five of them to get nine? No problem. Ready? One, two, three, four, five. There's your nine.

Here's a problem that comes from the game of baseball. Is it possible for there to be two players, say, A and B, for which A has a better batting average than B one year and the next year, but when we combine the two years, B does better than A? Not only is it possible for this to happen, it actually has happened. Here are the batting records for Derek Jeter and David Justice in 1995 and 1996. Notice that in both years, Justice had the better average, but when we combine the two years, Jeter has the better average. In fact, Justice even outperformed Jeter in the 1997 season, yet when we combine all three years, Jeter has the better average. Jeter has batted 300 and Justice batted 298. You might say, what about Justice? But mathematicians just call it Simpson's paradox, and it arises in many places, even outside of games and puzzles. Simpson's paradox can't happen, cannot happen, if both players have the same number of bats each season, but it can happen when the denominators are very different like in our examples.

In our next lecture we will begin focusing our attention on puzzles beginning with those where you move things around by jumping pieces, sliding tiles, or pushing buttons. But before we go, I promised near the beginning of this lecture that I would show you a mathematical method for predicting the score of a baseball game before the game even starts. It's extremely accurate. Are you ready for it? Always predict the score 0 to 0. After all, that's the score of the game before the game even starts. Gotcha!

Solving "Impossible" Puzzles
Lecture 8

In this lecture, you will learn how mathematics plays an interesting role in solving and understanding various puzzles. You will explore some classic puzzles, including the Fifteen Puzzle, an electronic game with lights, and peg solitaire, many of which have been driving people crazy for centuries. On the surface, they seem very different—involving sliding blocks, blinking lights, or jumping pegs—but they do have some common features that apply to many other puzzles as well.

The Fifteen Puzzle

- A classic puzzle called the Fifteen Puzzle is also sometimes referred to as the Rubik's Cube of the 19th century. In its classic form, the numbers 1 through 15 are displayed in a four-by-four square, and a blank square allows the tiles to move.

- You start with a randomly scrambled position, and your goal is to get it back to the original order. To solve the puzzle, you basically get the numbers in the right place one at a time—with just an occasional twist.

The Fifteen Puzzle

1	2	3	4
5	6	7	8
9	10	11	12
13	14	15	

- Starting from a random position, you first want to move tiles 1 and 2 to their goal positions. Next, you want to bring 3 and 4 to their positions. To do this, first bring 3 to the upper right corner then bring 4 below it. After that, bring 3 and 4 to their goal positions. Once the numbers 1 through 4 are in their final positions, they won't move for the rest of the puzzle.

- The next row is pretty much the same. First, you bring the 5 and 6 to their proper positions. Then, bring the 7 and 8 to their proper positions. The first two rows are now finished, and you'll never have to touch them again.

- The next tiles you place are not 9 and 10, but 9 and 13. First, bring the 9 and 13 next to each other on the bottom row. Then, bring the 9 to its proper place and the 13 to the place below the 9. Next, you want to move the 10 and 14 next to each other and then to their final positions, in which the 14 ends up below the 10.

- Finally, you're left with the 11, 12, and 15 in some order. If the original puzzle was solvable, then they can simply be rotated to reach the goal position. World chess champion Bobby Fischer was able to do this puzzle consistently in under 25 seconds.

- The Fifteen Puzzle was invented by Noyes Chapman, a postmaster from New York, and was later popularized by the puzzle maker Sam Loyd, who offered $1,000 to anyone who could solve the original Fifteen Puzzle but with tiles 14 and 15 swapped. Loyd's money was safe because it turns out that this puzzle has no solution.

An Electronic Game with Lights

- In an electronic game, there is a three-by-three box of lights. At the start of the game, some of the lights are on and some are off. The lights are all buttons, and we can label the buttons as numbered: 1, 2, 3, 4, 5, 6, 7, 8, and 9. Buttons 2, 3, 5, and 8 are lit, and the rest are not. Your goal is to turn off all the lights by pressing the right combination of buttons.

Box of Lights

1	2	3
4	5	6
7	8	9

- There are three types of buttons: corner buttons (1, 3, 7, and 9), edge buttons (2, 4, 6, and 8), and the middle button (5). Pressing a corner button will toggle the corner and the three surrounding lights, turning each one from on to off and off to on. For example, pressing button 1 will toggle the lights in cells 1, 2, 4, and 5—turning 1 and 4 on and 2 and 5 off. Pressing button 1 again brings each button back to its original position.

- The following are more examples: Pressing button 3 toggles lights 2, 3, 5, and 6. Pressing button 7 toggles 4, 5, 7, and 8. Pressing button 9 toggles 5, 6, 8, and 9.

- Pressing an edge button toggles the edge and two of its surrounding neighbors. For example, pressing button 2 toggles the lights in cells 1, 2, and 3. The other rows don't change. Pressing button 2 again brings each back to its original position. Similar rules apply for pressing buttons 4, 6, and 8.

- Finally, pressing button 5, the middle button, toggles the middle and the four edge lights: 2, 4, 6, and 8. Pressing 5 again brings each back to its original position.

- The goal is to press a sequence of buttons so that you go from the initial position to the position where all lights are out—hopefully, using as few buttons as possible. The solution is far from obvious.

- When pressing buttons, does the order matter? For example, if you press the buttons 1, 2, 3, 4 in that order, will you get the same position if you press the buttons in a different order—for example, 2, 4, 1, 3? The answer is not immediately clear.

- To clarify this situation, it's time to introduce what mathematicians call mod 2 arithmetic. With mod 2 arithmetic, there are just two numbers—0 and 1. For the most part, addition works in the usual way: $0 + 0 = 0$, $0 + 1 = 1$, and $1 + 0 = 1$, but $1 + 1$ does not equal 2 because the number 2 is not in the original number system (which only allows 0 and 1). As a result, with mod 2 arithmetic, $1 + 1 = 0$.

- One way to make sense of mod 2 arithmetic is to think of 0 as representing any even number and 1 as representing any odd number. Then, the mod 2 addition table is really just the following: Even plus even equals even, even plus odd equals odd, and odd plus odd equals even.

- With the electronic game, mod 2 arithmetic comes in handy. First, every position can be represented by a vector of zeroes and ones, where 0 means that a light is off and 1 means that a light is on. For example, the beginning position would have vector representation $\mathbf{b} = (0, 1, 1, 0, 1, 0, 0, 1, 0)$, where we have a 1 in positions 2, 3, 5, and 8.

- Each button can also be represented by a vector. For example, pressing button 2, which toggles the lights in positions 1, 2, and 3, can be represented by the vector $\mathbf{v}_2 = (1, 1, 1, 0, 0, 0, 0, 0, 0)$. Pressing button 2 is just like adding the vector $\mathbf{v}_2$.

- For example, if we take the beginning position and press button 2, we get a new position where lights 1, 5, and 8 are on. If we take the vector representing the original position with 1s in positions 2, 3, 5, and 8—$\mathbf{b} = (0, 1, 1, 0, 1, 0, 0, 1, 0)$—and add the vector $\mathbf{v}_2$, which has 1s in positions 1, 2, and 3—$\mathbf{v}_2 = (1, 1, 1, 0, 0, 0, 0, 0, 0)$—and do that addition (mod 2), then the new vector $\mathbf{b} + \mathbf{v}_2$ will have ones in positions 1, 5, and 8—$(1, 0, 0, 0, 1, 0, 0, 1, 0)$—just like the lights.

- Similarly, pressing button 1, which toggles lights 1, 2, 4, and 5, is equivalent to adding the vector $\mathbf{v}_1$ with 1s in the first, second, fourth, and fifth positions (and similarly for the other buttons).

- By the way, pressing a button twice in a row leaves a position unchanged, and we can also see that from vectors. Because order does not matter, no solution would require you to press the same button twice in a row. In other words, if a puzzle has a solution, then it has a solution where every button is pressed at most once.

- Strictly speaking, finding a solution to this game is a problem from linear algebra, the mathematics of vector equations. Starting from the beginning position, represented by the vector **b**, you need to add some of the vectors v_1 through v_9 to reach the vector of all zeroes, which is the position where all lights are off.

- Instead of using linear algebra, there is a quick way to solve this problem in your head without the need to write down a single equation. Recall that when you solve this puzzle, the order that you press the buttons does not matter. Therefore, you can always solve the puzzle in the following order: First, decide on the edge buttons, then decide on the corner buttons, and then decide on the middle button.

Peg Solitaire

- Peg solitaire is typically played on a board that looks like a giant plus sign. Every spot, except for the central one, is occupied by a peg or sometimes a marble. Pieces can jump over other pieces horizontally or vertically, provided that there is an empty space on the other side, and the piece that's jumped over is removed from the board.

- The goal of the puzzle is to jump your pieces in such a way that all you are left with at the end is one piece, preferably in the middle of the board. Curiously, the middle square is practically the only place that a single peg can end up.

- To solve the puzzle, begin by making your initial move toward the center, or "bottoms up." To clear most of the pegs from the board, use the following mnemonic: right, up, left, then move it up. Repeat this four times, rotating the board 90° after each time you make this set of moves.

- After rotating the board the last time, you are left with what looks like a house, which is made from the remaining pegs. You are going to clear the rest of the pegs by going to the attic in the house, and one of the pegs is going to do a grand tour and annihilate most of the pegs, ending up with a T formation. At that point, the puzzle is pretty easy to solve.

Peg Solitaire

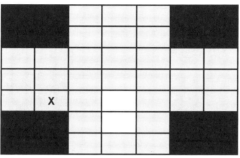

Right

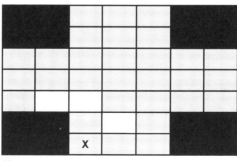

Right

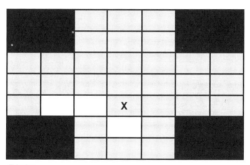

Up

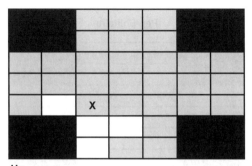

Up

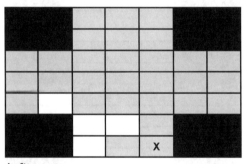

Left

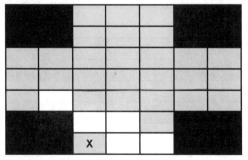

Left

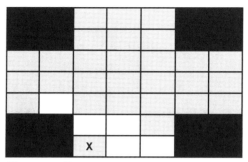

Then move it up

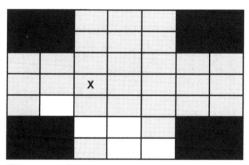

Then move it up

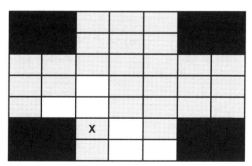

Then move it up

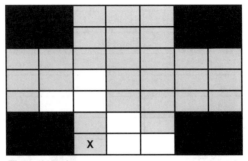

Then move it up

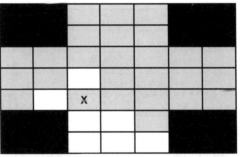

Now rotate the board counterclockwise and repeat 3 more times

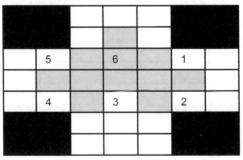

The House Tour

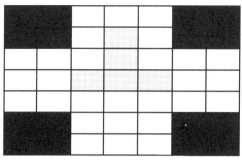

T Formation

Suggested Reading

Ball and Coxeter, *Mathematical Recreations and Essays.*

Beasley, *The Ins and Outs of Peg Solitaire.*

Beasley, *The Mathematics of Games.*

Hess, *Mental Gymnastics.*

Gardner, *The Colossal Book of Short Puzzles and Problems.*

Hoffman, *Puzzles Old and New.*

Slocum and Sonneveld, *The 15 Puzzle.*

Wells, *Book of Curious and Interesting Puzzles.*

Problems

1. In the electronic game presented in the lecture, suppose the initial position looks like the following.

ON	ON	OFF
OFF	ON	ON
ON	OFF	OFF

Which of the edge buttons (2, 4, 6, or 8) should you press? What will you do after that?

2. Consider the following Fifteen Puzzle position.

3	14	15	9
2	6	5	13
8	7	12	4
10	1	11	

    a. How many "oddballs" does it have?

    b. Based on your answer to a.), determine if the Fifteen Puzzle position is solvable.

3. In the triangular peg solitaire with 15 pegs, where the first hole is unoccupied and all other holes are occupied, is it possible to reduce the puzzle to a single peg in the second row?

Solving "Impossible" Puzzles
Lecture 8—Transcript

In this lecture, we will explore some classic puzzles, many of which have been driving people crazy for centuries. On the surface, they seem very different, sliding blocks, jumping pegs, and blinking lights, but they do have some common features, and I'll mention one of them here. Although none of these are what you'd call number puzzles, we'll see that each of them deals with odd and even numbers in their solution or analysis. I thought of calling this lecture Odd Puzzles Can Be Even More Interesting, but I changed my mind. Now let's get started.

Let's begin with a classic puzzle. You might even call it the Rubik's Cube of the 19th century. It's called the Fifteen Puzzle, and I'm sure you've seen one of these before in some form or another. Sometimes there's a picture that gets scrambled up in which you have to restore the picture. In its classic form, you have the numbers one through 15 in a four by four square and a blank space that allows the squares to move. Now here's an electronic version that works on the iPad. You start with a randomly scrambled position, and your goal is to get it back to the original order. I'll say more about the mathematics and history of the puzzle later, but let me first teach you how to solve the puzzle. The solution is pretty intuitive. You basically get the numbers in the right place one at a time with just an occasional twist. Let me first outline the solution method for you, and then we'll solve a random puzzle.

Starting from a random position, you first want to move the tiles one and two to their goal positions. That's pretty easy. Next, you want to bring three and four to their positions, but if you bring the three here, then you probably aren't going to be able to get the four into its proper place. So instead, you bring the three here and the blank here. So you have the three here, the four here, and the blank here. After that we can bring the three and four to their proper places like so. The numbers one through four are now in their final positions, and they won't move for the rest of the puzzle.

The next row is pretty much the same. First, you bring the five and six to their proper positions. Then bring the seven over here and the eight over there, with a blank over here, and then you bring them home, like so. The first two rows are finished, and you'll never to touch them again. We're starting to run out of maneuvering room. The next tiles we place are not nine and 10, but nine and 13. We want to bring them here, but if we start by putting the nine there, we won't be able to squeeze the 13 into the corner, so first bring the nine and 13 next to each other like so. Then bring them home. Almost done. Next we want to move the 10 and 14 to their final positions, but to do that we first need to bring them here and then to here. Finally, we're just left with the 11, 12, and 15 in some order. If the original puzzle was solvable, then they can simply be rotated to reach the goal position, like so.

World chess champion Bobby Fischer was able to do this puzzle consistently in under 25 seconds. I'm happy if I can finish it in under two minutes, so let's give it a try. Here we go. I'll talk through it as I do the problem. One is already in the right position, so I first have to bring the two over like so. Next, we want to bring the three and the four over to there. Okay, the three is where it needs to be. Now let's get the four underneath it like so. Three, four are done. Now let's move that five up where it wants to go. Now we have to get the six next to it. Alright. Let's take the long way to get there. Alright. There we are. The seven is where it needs to be. That's great. Let's put the eight underneath it. Now we have seven and eight. Now we need to get nine and 13 next to each other. There they are. We can now slide them to where they belong. Good. Finally, we need to get the 10 and the 14 next to each other. Let's space them out here first, and now we can put the 10 and 14 like so. Great, 11, 12, 15, we're done. Hey, I broke one minute. That's a personal best.

The Fifteen Puzzle was invented by Noyes Chapman, a postmaster from New York and later popularized by the puzzle maker, Sam Loyd. Loyd offered $1,000 to anyone who could solve the following puzzle. Starting from the original Fifteen Puzzle position, can you rearrange the tiles to reach this position where tiles 14 and 15 have been swapped? Loyd's money was safe because it turns out that this puzzle has no solution. The reason has to do with even and odd numbers. Let me explain.

The numbers one, two and three can be arranged in six ways, right? Three factorial ways. Let's look at the arrangement one-three-two. I have the cups here one-two-three. Let's look at the arrangement one-three-two like so.

Notice that we can bring it back to the original order by performing one swap. Right? I go from one-three-two to one-two-three in one swap, whereas if I started with the arrangement two-three-one, then that's going to require two swaps, like I could swap the one and the two, then the two and the three, like so.

Here's a table of all six arrangements. Mathematicians call these permutations, along with the number of swaps needed to bring them back to the original order. Here they are. Now let's look at one-three-two again. Now, there are a lot of other ways we can use swaps to bring it back to the original order. Like for instance, I could do one move here, and then another move here, and then finally another swap here. That took me three swaps. There are other sequences of moves that take three swaps or five swaps or seven swaps. What's interesting, or should I say, what's odd, is that no matter how hard you try, you can't straighten out one-three-two in an even number of swaps. The number of swaps has to be an odd number so we call one-three-two an odd arrangement.

Looking at all six arrangements again, we can label them as odd or even as follows. Notice half of them are even, half of them are odd. So just like every number can be labeled as odd or even, every arrangement of objects, whether it be three objects, 16 objects, or whatever, can be labeled as odd or even. So to bring your arrangement back to its original order, an odd arrangement requires an odd number of swaps, and an even arrangement requires an even number of swaps.

Let's go back to the Fifteen Puzzle. Here's a brand new arrangement. Every position is some arrangement of 16 objects. Namely the numbers one through 15 and the blank. Now Loyd's puzzle is clearly an odd arrangement since it's just one swap away from the original order, just swapping 14 and 15 gives you Loyd's arrangement, so that's clearly an odd arrangement because one is an odd number. If there's a solution to Loyd's puzzle using legal moves, it must be an odd number of legal moves. But notice this: Every legal move is actually a swap that involves the blank square and an adjacent square. As I'm moving this you can really think of every move as a swap with the blank tile and some other tile, but notice that the blank square begins in the lower right corner, and it ends in the lower right corner. Thus, the blank square must travel an equal number of moves to the left as moves to the right. And the blank square has to make an equal number of up moves as down moves, so the total number of moves, all of which are swaps, must be an even number.

In order for a puzzle to be solvable, it has to come from an even arrangement. Thus Loyd's problem here is impossible since it came from an odd arrangement. Now, as it turns out, we can solve any position that comes from an even arrangement of the numbers one through 15. So for example, if we swap 14 and 15 and also, say, four and nine, then the algorithm we learned will successfully solve it. But if we start from any odd position, then our process would eventually lead us to the Loyd position, and we would be stuck. We saw earlier, with the arrangement of three numbers, that half the arrangements were odd and half of them were even, and that's true in general. So if someone physically removed the tiles of a Fifteen Puzzle, just shook them out here and put them back at random, then there would only be a 50% chance that the puzzle would be solvable. In fact, when I was preparing for the course, one of the apps that I purchased had that very flaw. Half the time the puzzle it gives you is unsolvable. How frustrating. Some apps, like the one we use here from the company AppAnnex, are smarter and only give you solvable puzzles. By the way, how can you tell if a given arrangement of pieces will be solvable or not?

After moving the blank square to the bottom, right-hand corner, you can determine if an arrangement is even or odd by counting for each square how many lower numbered squares come after it. If it has an odd number of smaller numbers that come after it, we call that square an oddball, at least I do. A legal arrangement has to have an even number of oddballs. So, for example, in the goal arrangement there are no oddballs. We have the numbers 1, 2, 3, 4, 5, 6, 7, 8, 9, 10, 11, 12, 13, 14, 15 in their natural order, so it's never the case that a lower number comes later than an earlier number. And so since zero is an even number, then that's fine. This is a legal arrangement, of course. Whereas with the Loyd arrangement, we have one oddball, namely the number 15. So this arrangement is impossible. Because after 15 comes 14. That's one number that's smaller than it.

Here's a random position from my app. The number 12 has all 11 of its smaller numbers coming after it, so that makes 12 an oddball. Whereas, let's look at the number six in the diagram here; what numbers come after it, 11, 3, 4, and 14. Three and four are smaller than six, so six has an even number of smaller numbers coming after it, so six is not an oddball. The number 10 has seven of its smaller numbers coming after it so it's an oddball, too. You can check for yourself that none of the other numbers are oddballs. Since this puzzle has exactly two oddballs, it is solvable. But if we swapped any two of those numbers, then we would have an unsolvable puzzle.

Now in the Fifteen Puzzle you could tell that you were making good progress towards a solution as more and more of the squares were brought to their proper place, but that's not always the case with puzzles, especially electronic ones like we have in our next example.

I have here a three-by-three box of lights. At the start of the game, some of the lights are on and some of the lights are off. Actually, these lights are all buttons, and we can label the buttons as numbered one, two, three, four, five, six, seven, eight, nine. So this position here, you could say, has buttons that are lit, buttons two, three, five, and eight. Those are on, and the rest are off. Your goal is to turn off all the lights by pressing the right combination of buttons. Now there are three types of buttons: corner buttons, buttons one, three, seven, and nine; edge buttons two, four, six, and eight; and the middle button, button five. Pressing a corner button will toggle the corner and the three surrounding lights. For example, pressing button one will toggle these four lights—the lights in cells one, two, four and five. Notice right now we have off, off, on, on. Well, after I press button one, it's going to look like on, on, off, off. And if I press button one again, it's going to bring us back to the original position. Whereas pressing button three toggles lights two, three, five, and six. Pressing button seven will toggle these four lights, and button nine will toggle those four lights, like so.

Pressing an edge button will toggle the edge and two of its surrounding neighbors. For example, pressing button two up here will toggle the lights in Cells one, two, and three. So right now, the first row looks like off, on, on. Then after pressing button two, it looks like on, off, off. The other rows don't change. Pressing button two again would take us back to where we were. Similarly, button four toggles lights one, four, and seven, so these lights get toggled. Right now they're all off, and then, after I press button four, they're all on. Pressing four again brings us back. Similar rules apply for pressing button six, which toggles these three lights and pressing button eight, which toggles those three lights. Finally, pressing button five, the middle button, toggles the middle and the four edge lights, two, four, six, and eight, so pressing five would take us from here, to there, and back again.

So, those are the rules. Our goal is to press a sequence of buttons so we go from the initial position to the position where all lights are out. Poof! Hopefully using as few buttons as possible. The solution is far from obvious. Before I give it to you, let me ask you another question. When pressing the buttons—let's go back to our original position—does the order matter? For example, if I take a position like this one and press the buttons one, two, three, four in that order, will I get the same position if I press the buttons in a different order, say two, four, one, three? What do you think? Same or different outcomes? The answer is not clear.

To clarify this situation, it's time to introduce what mathematicians call mod 2 arithmetic. With mod 2 arithmetic, there are just two numbers, 0 and 1, For the most part, addition works in the usual way, $0 + 0$ is 0; $0 + 1$ is 1; $1 + 0$ is 1, but $1 + 1$ is not two since the number two is not in our original number system. We only allow 0 and one. As a result, with mod 2 arithmetic, we have $1 + 1 = 0$. One way to make sense of mod 2 arithmetic is to think of 0 as representing any even number and one as representing any odd number. Then, the mod 2 addition table is really just saying, even plus even is even; even plus odd is odd; and odd plus odd is even. Let's see how mod 2 arithmetic comes in handy with this puzzle.

First of all, every position can be represented by a vector of zeroes and ones, where 0 means that a light is off, and one means that a light is on. For example, our beginning position here would have vector representation (0-1-1), (0-1-0), (0-1-0), where we have a one in positions two, three, five and eight. Now each button can also be represented by a vector. For example, pressing button two, which toggles the lights in positions one, two, and three, right, pressing button two affects lights one, two, and three, I claim that pressing button 2 is just like adding the vector V2, which consists of (1-1-1), (0-0-0), (0-0-0). So let's see that in action. For example, if we take our beginning position and press button 2, we get a new position where lights one, five, and eight are on. Notice if we take the vector representing the original position with ones in positions two, three, five and eight, and I add the vector V2, which has ones in positions one, two and three, and I do that addition mod 2, of course, then the new vector $B + V2$ will have ones in positions one, five, and eight, just like our lights. We have lights in the first, fifth, and eighth position.

Similarly, pressing button one, which toggles lights one, two, four, and five, is equivalent to adding the vector V1 with ones in the first, second, fourth, and fifth position and similarly for the other buttons. By the way, we've seen that pressing a button twice in a row leaves a position unchanged, but we can also see that from vectors. For instance, if we press button one twice, that's just like adding the vector $V1 + V1$, which is the vector of all zeroes. So pressing a button twice in a row literally adds nothing to your position. So now that you see that pressing a button is the same as adding one of the nine vectors, V1 through V9, I'll ask you again, does the order that you press the buttons matter? For instance, if you press button one then button two is that the same as pressing two then one? Well pressing one then two is the same as adding the vector $V1 + V2$, but notice that's the same as adding $V2 + V1$, so what that tells us is the order doesn't matter, and that's true for any two buttons. This fact was not at all obvious, at least to me, until we used vectors to represent the buttons.

Alright. So let's hear it for vectors and mod 2 math. And by the way, since order does not matter, no solution would require you to press the same button twice. You'd never press a button twice in a row. You wouldn't have to do it, so you would not press them far apart either because you could rearrange those button presses so that they were twice in a row. In other words, if a puzzle has a solution, then it has a solution where every button is pressed at most once. But how do we find a solution?

Strictly speaking, this is a problem from linear algebra, the mathematics of vector equations. Starting from your beginning position represented by the vector B, you need to add some of the vectors V1 through V9 to reach the vector of all zeroes. The vector of all zeroes is the position where all lights are off. A linear algebra student can take the initial vector and the button vectors and find a unique solution by solving a system of equations, but let me show you a quick way to solve this problem in your head without the need to write down a single equation.

Recall that when we solve this puzzle, the order that you press the buttons does not matter. So since it doesn't matter, I will always solve the puzzle in the following order. I will first decide on the edge buttons, then I will decide the corner buttons, and then finally I will decide the middle button. Now you'll admit that if I can do steps one and two correctly, then the third step, deciding on the middle button, is trivial since I will either be done with the puzzle or I will have to press button five.

For instance, in the original puzzle here, once I choose the correct edge and corner buttons, bam, bam, bam, all the lights are off, and there is nothing left to do. If the lights were not out, here let me press button five, then we would be in this position, and we would only have to press button five to finish, like so. But, how do we decide the edges and corners? Let's look at the corners. Now I claim that if I can solve the edges, then the corners are also easy—extremely easy. Here's why. After I press the correct edge buttons, the only buttons remaining for consideration are one, three, five, seven, and nine. Let's look at corner number one here. Which of the remaining buttons will affect light one? Now button one will definitely toggle it, but none of the remaining buttons will. Button three does not affect that. Number five does not affect it, seven and nine—none of those affect it. So, if light one is on, then you are going to have to turn it off because in the end we want everything off. So if it is off, leave it alone. If it's on, you must press it now. The same is true for the other corners. So in step two, you simply turn off the lights at every corner. So in the original position, once I correctly choose the edge buttons, bam, bam, then the corners are easy. The only lit corner is corner seven, so when we press it, we are done.

If we can figure out the edge buttons, then we are home free. But how do we figure out the edge buttons? For example, how do we decide whether or not to press button two? To do this we look at the rectangle surrounding button two. Consider the following question: for each of the buttons one through nine, how many lights are toggled inside the rectangle? I have written the answer for each button here. For example, button one toggles these four lights, all of which are in the rectangle. Button five toggles five lights, but only four of them are in the rectangle, that is why we have a four there. Button eight toggles three lights, but none of them are in the rectangle. That is why the 0 is there.

Do you notice anything interesting about button two? It toggles three lights inside the rectangle, and it is the only button that toggles an odd number. In the end, we want no lights on in that rectangle, so here's what we do. Count the lights in the rectangle surrounding button 2. We see that in our position here that there are presently three buttons lit inside of that rectangle, right? That's an odd number. In the end, we need to have an even number; we need to have zero lights lit in that rectangle. So, since all the other buttons will change the number of lights in that rectangle by an even amount, if we want to get from an odd number of lights in that rectangle to an even number of lights in that rectangle we must press button two now. The other edge buttons can be determined in a similar way. For example, with button four, we look at the rectangle that surrounds it and see that right now it has three lights lit inside of that rectangle. Since we want to have an even number, we are going to have to press button four to change the parity of its rectangle from odd to even.

On the other hand, when I look at the rectangle for button six, we see that it has four lights lit. That's an even number, so we leave button six alone. How about button eight? Tell me what we should do here for eight. Eight's rectangle has two lights lit. That is an even number, so, do we press it or leave it alone? It is even so we will leave it alone. So which of the four edge buttons are we going to press? Buttons two and four. Let me do so quickly, bam, bam. All that is left is pressing button seven, and we are done.

Let us do one more example. Create a random position. That looks nice. How do we do this? First we are going to decide the edge buttons, then we will do the corner buttons, and then we will do the middle buttons. To do the edge buttons we have to look at the rectangles for buttons two, four, six and eight. Button two has a rectangle that looks like this, and I see it has four lights lit, so we're going to leave button two alone. Rectangle four has four lights lit. We will leave that one alone. The rectangle for button six has three lights lit so we are going to want to press six, and the rectangle for button eight has four lights lit, so we are going to leave that one alone. So the only edge button we need to press is button six, so let us do that. Next, we press the corners that are lit. I only have two lit corners. We will do that, bam, bam. Well, we are not done yet, so that means we have to press the middle button. When we do that, we're done.

The last puzzle I would like to do was a favorite of mine of my childhood called peg solitaire. It's typically played on a board that looks like a giant plus sign. Every spot except for the central one is occupied by a peg, or sometimes a marble. Pieces can jump over other pieces horizontally or vertically, provided there is an empty space on the other side, and the piece that's jumped over is removed from the board. For example, in this puzzle our first move can either be a horizontal jump like this, or it can be a vertical jump like that.

The goal of the puzzle is to jump your pieces in such a way that all you are left with at the end is one piece, preferably in the middle of the board. In fact, one puzzle maker says that if you can end up with one piece, you are outstanding, and if it is in the middle of the board, then you are a genius. Let me first show you a quick solution to this puzzle, then I'll show you that, contrary to the puzzle maker's claim, ending up with one peg outside the middle hole should not make you outstanding.

Here's the solution to the puzzle. Begin by making our initial move towards the center or as I like to say, bottoms up. Now, here's the mnemonic I use to clear most of the pegs from the board. As a professor, you write lots of papers, especially early in your career as you seek tenure and promotions. And no matter how many papers you've written, it seems that there's always one more write-up left if you want to move up in the profession. So repeat after me: Right, up, left, then move it up. And we're going to repeat this four times. So we go right, up, left, and then move it up. It is this peg here. How do we move it up? By bringing this down and jumping up. Alright. If you didn't get it, that's okay. We're going to do it three more times. I rotate the board, and one more time we go right, up, left, and move it up, just like so. We rotate again, right, up, left, and move it up. Last chance, rotate, and we have right, up, left, and move it up. And when we do, and I'll rotate it one last time, we have a house, or a Space Invaders character. Whatever you like.

Now we're going to clear the rest of the pegs by going to the attic in the house, and this piece is going to do a grand tour all around and annihilate most of the pegs. Here we go. We're going to jump here, and then here, and then here, and then here, and then here, and then here, ending up in this T formation. And now the puzzle is pretty easy to solve. We jump this way, that way, this way, and we're done. Got it? You are now officially a genius.

Curiously, as we're about to see, the middle square is practically the only place that a single peg can end up. I'll prove it to you by labeling our board with the symbols x, y, and z, like so. Now I'm going to give you some simple rules for adding the symbols x, y, and z together, and you'll see why we want to do this in a minute. Now here's my addition table. Take a look at it. Notice that when we add two letters together we get the third one. For instance, $x + y = z$, or $z + x = y$. When you add a symbol to itself, you get zero. For instance, $x + x$ is 0, and as usual, adding zero to something leaves it unchanged. For instance $0 + y$ is y.

Now what do x, y and z represent? When we did mod 2 arithmetic we saw that 0 and one could be thought of as even and odd numbers. With x, y, z arithmetic we think of each symbol as representing a pair of even or odd numbers. Here x would be the even-odd pair, y is odd-even, z is odd-odd, and 0 is even-even. Then everything is nice and consistent. For example, the statement $x + y = z$ really says (even-odd) + (odd-even) = (odd-odd), which makes sense. For instance $(2-1) + (5-2) = (7-3)$. And a statement like $x + x = 0$ is saying that (even-odd) + (even-odd) is (even-even). Anyway, trust me when I say that the symbols x, y, z, and 0 form a consistent mathematical system called the Klein four group. I'll point out one last useful fact. I claim that $x + y + z$ is 0. We can verify this because $x + y + z$ is the same as $z + z$ which is 0.

So how do these symbols help us understand peg solitaire? For any peg solitaire position, we define its signature to be the sum of the symbols of all of the occupied squares. For example, the T formation that we saw earlier has signature $x + y + z + x + z$. That's $0 + y$, which is y. How about the house position? Exploiting the fact that $x + y + z$ is 0, I see three x, y, z triples, each of which sums to 0, so we could ignore those. So the signature here is $x + z$, which is y.

What about the signature of the original position? If we replace each x, y, z with 0, we get massive cancellation, and all that we're left with is x + z, which is y. It seems as if every position has a signature of y. Do you see why? Look at the x, y, z pattern on the board; this one here. Notice that every three consecutive squares contain an x, and a y, and a z, like say in this position here, or here, or there. Every time you perform a jump, you are replacing two pegs from occupied squares with one peg from an unoccupied square. For instance, if you jump from x over z you must land on a y. But that won't change the signature at all since x + z is equal to y. Consequently, the signature of the board will never change, and since the signature started at y, it will forever be y. Thus, if we can reduce the puzzle down to a single peg, then it must be on a square with label y. And yet, not every square with a y is a possible ending point for a single peg. Now why is that?

For example, I claim that we cannot wind up with a single peg on this square. Why is that? Because if we could, if there was a sequence of moves where a peg ended up on that square, then by symmetry, we could also have performed a sequence of moves that would allow a single peg to finish on this square. And since it's impossible for a single peg to finish on a z square we can't finish on that y square either. By the same logic, you can disqualify most of the other y squares as landing spots, except for these five. And yet, how could the final peg land in one of these end squares? How could we get something to end up in this square? Only if the last two pegs were situated like this, but if that's the case, then those pegs could have just as easily jumped to the center. And if getting a peg in the center earns you a genius rating, you'd be foolish to jump the peg anywhere else. So, why should a solution of one peg away from the middle earn you an outstanding rating? I don't know.

A couple of years ago, I was at a friend's house, and I noticed a puzzle he had in his living room that he had picked up in his travels. It looked like peg solitaire, but it had four extra squares on it. Just like in the original puzzle, all the squares were occupied except for the middle square. My friend said that he was never able to solve the puzzle. Then he said, hey, you're a mathematician. Maybe you can figure it out. I brought out a piece of paper and labeled the board with xs, ys and zs, just like before, with the four new squares included. Let's see why my friend was having such trouble.

It was still the case that every three consecutive squares in a row or column had an x, a y, and a z in it, so the signature would not change. So what is the new signature? Well previously the signature was y, so the new signature, which has these four new squares on it, would be $y + x + y + z + y$, and since $y + y$ is 0, and $x + y + z$ is 0, the signature of the new board is simply 0. Consequently, it would be impossible for a single peg to land anywhere since that would change the signature to x or y or z. Hence, the puzzle was impossible. My friend was grateful, and my reputation was saved.

In this lecture, we've seen how mathematics plays an interesting role in solving and understanding various puzzles. Although the puzzles we considered were very different, their solution methods had some common elements which apply to many other puzzles as well. One thing to look for when solving a puzzle is what computer scientists sometimes call a macro. A macro takes rules of your game and looks for efficient combinations of those moves that help you solve your problem. In the Fifteen Puzzle, once we found an efficient way to solve the top row, we could repeat that process for the second row, and the last two rows were finished in a similar fashion. And in peg solitaire we found that the right-up-left-and-move-it-up macro could be performed four times and reduce our puzzle to a much more tractable problem.

Another common theme that appeared in all of our puzzles was the exploitation of parity. Now, for instance, in the Fifteen Puzzle we saw that there were odd arrangements and even arrangements. The analysis of our electronic game was all about mod 2 arithmetic, and even with peg solitaire, we found that the symbols x, y, and z, and 0 represented pairs of even or odd numbers. With games of chance, we spoke often about determining the best odds and trying to break even, and so it is with puzzles that it often pays to look at odds and evens too.

Let me end with one last impossible puzzle, frequently found in restaurants while waiting for your pancakes. It's peg solitaire played on a triangular board, like so. Starting with one empty hole on the top, your goal is to eliminate all pegs but one, preferably left in the top hole. Here's the solution along with my mnemonics. After our initial jump, that is from here to there, the next four moves will all use this point somehow. After this sideways jump, my daughter said that this sort of looks like a snail. So now, the snail will lose its tail on the pail. Alright, what do I mean by that? So the snail loses its tail on the pail, and now we aim for an A minus, and I'll tell you what I mean by that in a moment, by jumping from the corner followed by a double jump. So I jump here and a double jump—jump, jump. And now I have an A minus the top two. Alright? Finally we create a diamond by jumping up from here, up from there, and now we clear the rest. One, two, three, and we're done. Time for some pancakes.

In our next lecture, we'll take on, perhaps, the most famous puzzle of all time. So be there or be square, or maybe I should say, be there and be cubed.

Mastering Rubik's Cube
Lecture 9

R ubik's Cube, perhaps the most famous puzzle of all time, combines
mental dexterity with physical agility. In this lecture, you will learn
some of the mathematics behind Rubik's Cube. In addition, you
will learn a method that's very easy to learn that will allow you to solve the
puzzle quickly and accurately every time. You probably won't be able to
solve the cube immediately after learning the algorithm used in this lecture,
but you can most likely learn it with a few hours of practice.

Rubik's Cube: The Math

- Rubik's Cube could well be the most famous puzzle ever invented.
  You start with a cube with six different-colored sides, then after
  a few twists, the cube is in a random mess. Most people find it a
  hopeless task to bring the cube back to its proper order.

- Traditionally, the sides of Rubik's Cube have stickers that come in
  six colors: red, orange, yellow, green, blue, and white. In fact, for
  all official Rubik's Cubes, the colors have the white face opposite
  the yellow face, the red face opposite the orange face, and the blue
  face opposite the green face. The opposite faces differ by the color
  yellow: White is opposite yellow; red is opposite orange; blue is
  opposite green.

- Because the cube has dimensions three by three by three, it should
  consist of 27 little pieces, sometimes called cubies. If you actually
  counted, you'd find 26 cubies because there's one cube, the one in
  the very center, that has no color—so there are just 26 pieces that
  you can see.

- There are three types of pieces. Every face has a center piece,
  which has just one sticker on it. For instance, the white center and
  the yellow center are on opposite sides of each other, and nothing
  you can do to the cube can change that. The same goes for the other

centers: The red center is opposite the orange center, and the blue center is opposite the green center. When the cube is mixed up, it is impossible to have two centers on the same face.

- There are two other kinds of pieces: corners and edges. There are eight corner pieces, and there are 12 edge pieces, which have two stickers on them. No matter how you twist the cube, a corner piece can only move to another corner position and an edge piece can only move to another edge position.

- How many different Rubik's Cube positions are possible? The answer depends on what is meant by a "possible" position. For example, if we completely disassembled the cube and stripped it to its interiors and its six center cubes, then how many ways could we put it back together? Starting with the corners, there are eight choices for which piece goes in a corner. Once you pick a piece to go in the first chosen corner, then there are seven choices left that you can make for which piece goes in the next corner. Then, you have six choices for which corner piece goes in the next corner, and so on, down to the last corner.

- The number of ways to choose the locations of the corner pieces is 8!, or 40,320. Once you have placed them in the corners, then there are three ways of orienting the piece. You could perform those orientations 3^8—or 6,561—ways. Similarly, the 12 edge piece positions can be placed in their positions 12! ways, which is nearly half a billion ways, before you oriented them. Furthermore, the edge pieces can be oriented in 2^{12}—or 4,096—ways.

- When you multiply all of those numbers together, you find that there are $8! \times 3^8 \times 12! \times 2^{12} = 519,024,039,293,878,272,000$ (over 500 quintillion) ways that the cube can be reassembled. It turns out that exactly 1/12 of these positions can actually be achieved from the starting position, so the number of starting positions is really only about 40 quintillion: $(8! \times 3^8 \times 12! \times 2^{12})/12 = 43,252,003,274,489,856,000$.

- Another way to say this is that if you randomly assembled a cube, the chances that it would actually be solvable would only be 1 in 12. With the Fifteen Puzzle, every legal position had to be an even arrangement of the numbers 1 through 15. As it happens, the only achievable positions of a Rubik's Cube are even arrangements of the pieces.

- For instance, if you took a final position and swapped any two of the pieces, you would have an unsolvable position—no matter how you oriented the pieces—because you would be going from an even position to an odd position. Because 1/2 of all arrangements are even, this cuts the number of achievable arrangements in half. Furthermore, once you choose the orientation of 11 of the edge pieces, then orientation of the 12th edge piece is also forced.

- Suppose you were in the middle of solving the cube and you accidently dropped it on the floor, causing one of the edge pieces to come out. And suppose that you didn't know how it was placed before it came out, and you put it back in the cube. It matters which way you put the piece back in because if you put it in the wrong way, then the puzzle becomes unsolvable. This cuts down the number of achievable arrangements by 1/2 again.

- Finally, once you've oriented seven of the corner pieces, that forces the orientation of the eighth piece, and because each corner has three potential orientations, only 1/3 of its orientations are achievable. If you multiply $(1/2) \times (1/2) \times (1/3)$, you get $1/12$, which is the fraction of reassembled cubes that are legally achievable or solvable.

Rubik's Cube: The Algorithm
- General note: For the entire process, you will have the yellow side facing up and the white side facing down.

- Notation:
  - The move U means to turn the up face (always yellow) in the clockwise direction (one quarter turn).

○ Likewise, R means to look at the right face and turn it clockwise (AWAY from you).

○ L means to look at the left face and turn it clockwise (TOWARD you).

○ F means to turn the front face clockwise.

○ B means to turn the back face clockwise.

○ D means to turn the downward face (always white) clockwise (you won't need this move).

○ A move like U' means to turn the up face counterclockwise.

○ A move like F^2 means to turn F twice.

• Rubik's Cube has 8 corner cubes (with three colors), 12 edge cubes (with two colors), and 6 center cubes (with one color that never moves). Saying "the yellow side" means the side with the yellow center.

Step 1 (Daisy)
• There are four edge cubes with the color white. One at a time, bring these four edge cubes to the yellow side (upward facing) with the white colors facing up. This forms a "daisy" with a yellow center and four white petals.

Step 2 (Easy)
• Rotate the up side until the edge cube white/red has the red part lined up with the red center. Then, rotate the red face 180° so that the edge cube is now on the bottom (white) face with the white facing down. Do this with all four colors. When you are done, you will have a white cross on the bottom. Those four edge cubes on the bottom are now in their final position. At the end of each subsequent step, they will stay where they are now.

Step 3 (The 1-2-3 Move)

- Look for a corner cube with white on it. The most convenient place to find one is on the top "rim" (but not on the up face). This corner cube will have another color on its rim—for example, green. Twist the top face (U) so that the green part of this cube is on the green side, and orient the cube so that the green side is facing you. The white part of the corner cube will now be either on the right side or on the left side.

- If it's on the right side, then with your right hand, perform the 1-2-3 move by doing RUR': 1) Twist the right side away from you, then 2) twist the top toward you, then 3) twist the right side toward you. If the corner cube is on the left side, then do the same move with your left hand (L'U'L): 1) Twist the left away from you, then 2) twist the top toward you, then 3) twist the left side toward you. This move puts the corner piece on the bottom where it belongs.

- If the white corner is on the up face, then twist the top face so that that white piece is above a corner on the bottom that has not yet been solved. Then, perform 1-2-2-3 (twisting the up face twice instead of once), and that will put the corner piece on the top rim, which you can then solve as above.

- If no white corner is on the top rim, but it's on the bottom rim, then do the 1-2-3 move, and that will move it to the top rim.

- Doing this for all four white corner cubes will complete the bottom layer.

Step 4

- Find an edge piece from the top face that has no yellow on it. Note that piece's "rim" color (not the top color on the yellow face) and twist the top so that the rim color matches its center. Note the "top" color of that piece. Its matching center will be either the right face or left face. If it's the right face, then perform U with the right hand, and then perform 1-2-3 with the right hand. If it's on the left face, then perform U' with the left hand. Then, perform 1-2-3 with the

185

left hand. Either way, you have now dislodged a white corner cube from the bottom to the top. Restore that white corner cube to the bottom (using the process outlined in step 3). You now have placed the original edge piece in its final position.

- If you find yourself in the situation where all of the edge pieces on top have yellow on them, then orient the cube so that one of the non-yellow edge pieces on the second level is facing you. Then, do a 1-2-3 move, restore the white corner, and you will now have that non-yellow edge piece on top so that you can apply the previous paragraph.

- Do this for all four edge pieces that don't have yellow on them. After you finish this step, the bottom and middle level will be completely solved.

Step 5 (FURU'R'F')
- Look for two yellow edge cubes on the top face that are diagonally touching. Along with the yellow center, orient the cube so that they are in the "nine o'clock" position. Then, perform FURU'R'F'. This will produce a yellow cross on the top face (maybe with some yellow corners facing up, too).

- If you do not have two yellow edge cubes that are diagonally touching, then perform FURU'R'F' once or twice to create the nine o'clock position, and then do it one more time to create the yellow cross.

Step 6 (The Fun Move)
- You will now finish the top face so that everything on top has yellow facing up. Currently, the center and all four edge faces are yellow facing up. If all four corners have yellow face up (unlikely), then you can skip this step. If exactly one corner has yellow face up, then orient the cube so that the yellow corner is on the bottom-left corner of the top face. Next, perform the "fun move," which is all done with the right hand: RUR'URU^{2}R'. (In your mind, you can think of it as: out, twist, in, twist, out, twist, twist, in.) You may have to repeat this move to get all four corners yellow.

- If zero or two corners have yellow face up (three is impossible), then orient the cube so that a yellow sticker is in the top-left corner of the FRONT cube. Perform the fun move once or twice to get one yellow cube on the top face, and then proceed as detailed in the previous paragraph.

Step 7 (The R'F Move)

- The only remaining unsolved part of the cube is the top rim. If one side of the top rim has two matching corner colors, then orient the cube so that it's on the back side. (Otherwise, the orientation doesn't matter.) Next, perform R'FR'B²RF'R'B²R². If there were no matching colors the first time, then there will be now. Proceed as above, and you will be done; everything will be finished except for three or four edge cubes on the top rim.

Step 8 (The FURL Step)

- If there are only three edge cubes out of position, then one side of the cube will be completely solved, and this is your last step. Orient the cube so that the pristine face is on the back side. Next, perform the following move once or twice: FFUR'LFFRL'UFF. In your mind, you can think of it as: FFU; both sides down for R'L; dial around for FF; both sides up for RL'; and that's "en-uff" UFF.

- If there are four edge cubes on the top rim that are out of position, then perform the above move, and there will only be three cubes out of position. Performing the move (as above) one more time will solve the cube.

- If you practice this method, you can comfortably solve the cube in under five minutes, and if you use your fingers very efficiently, you can do it in about one minute. It can take about 180 twists to perform, so to do it in three minutes requires that you spend about one second per twist.

- What's the fewest number of moves needed to solve the cube? It was recently proved, in 2010, that every cube is never more than

20 twists away from being solved. That number can't be lowered because there are some positions that provably require at least 20 moves to complete, such as the superflip, which is known to require 20 moves.

- People who are speed cubers use algorithms that are different from what is used in this lecture. They move their fingers incredibly fast, and their methods combine several steps at once. The world's fastest solvers can do a randomly scrambled cube in under 10 seconds.

Suggested Reading

Beasley, *The Mathematics of Games.*

Frey and Singmaster, *Handbook of Cubik Math.*

Harris, *Speedsolving the Cube.*

Joyner, *Adventures in Group Theory.*

Slocum, Singmaster, Huang, Gebhardt, and Hellings, *The Cube.*

Questions to Consider

1. Have a friend scramble your Rubik's Cube and see if you can solve it. How long did it take?

2. From the original position, how many times do you need to perform the move R^2U^2 until you get back to the original position? (You need to have the cube in your hands to do this one. I don't think you can do this problem in your head.)

3. Perform these instructions and see what you get.

    a. $F^2 B^2 R^2 L^2 U^2 D^2$.

    b.   U D' R L' F B' U D'.

    c.   F U F R L^2 B D' R D^2 L D' B R^2 L F U F.

Mastering Rubik's Cube
Lecture 9—Transcript

The Rubik's Cube could well be the most famous puzzle ever invented. You've probably seen one before. You start with a cube with six different colored sides, then, after a few twists, the cube is in a random mess. Most people find it a hopeless task to bring the cube back to its proper order. In this lecture, we'll learn some of the mathematics behind the Rubik's Cube, as well as a method that's very easy to learn that'll allow you to solve the puzzle quickly and accurately every time. Now I need to warn you that you won't be able to solve the cube after just watching this lecture once straight through. I know very few people who can learn all the steps in just 45 minutes, but you can learn it in about two hours if you pause and practice along the way. Traditionally, the sides of the Rubik's Cube have stickers that come in six colors: red, orange, yellow, green, blue, and white. In fact, for all official Rubik's Cubes, the colors have the white face opposite the yellow face; the red face opposite the orange face; and the blue face opposite the green face. Notice that the opposite faces differ by the color yellow. White is opposite yellow. Red is opposite orange and blue is opposite green.

Let's talk a little bit about the mathematics surrounding the Rubik's Cube. First of all, since the cube has dimensions 3 by 3 by 3, it should consist of 27 little pieces, sometimes called cubies. And in fact, here I've taken one cube and I've disassembled it, and we can even break it up even more, like that. If you actually counted, you'd find 26 cubies because there's one cube, the one in the very center, has no color. So, really, there are just 26 pieces that you can see.

There are three types of pieces. Every face has a center piece which has just one sticker on it. For instance, here is the white center piece. Here is the yellow center. Notice that the white center and the yellow center are on opposite sides of each other, and nothing you can do to the cube can change that. Ditto for the other centers. For instance, even in this mixed-up cube here, we still have the white center, over here, opposite the yellow center. The red center here is opposite the orange center, and the blue center is opposite—here's the blue center—is opposite the green center. When the cube is mixed up, you can never have two centers on the same face, right?

That would be impossible. So if I refer to the yellow side that means the side of the cube that has the yellow center. So this is the yellow face. Whatever else is on it, this is the yellow face and this here is the blue side and so on.

There are two other kinds of pieces: corners and edges. There are eight corner pieces, right? So here's a typical corner piece that has three stickers on it. Or let's look at the big cube. Here are the eight corners: one, two, three, four, five, six, seven, eight. And there are 12 edge pieces. All those other pieces are called edge pieces, and they have two stickers on them. Naturally, no matter how you twist the cube, a corner piece can only move to another corner position, and an edge piece can only go to another edge position, which brings us to our first math question. How many different Rubik's Cube positions are possible?

The answer depends on what you mean by a possible position. For example, if we completely disassembled the cube, like we did over here, and striped it to its interiors and its six center cubes, then how many ways could we put it back together? Well, starting with the corners—so here's a corner piece— there are eight choices for which piece, let's say, goes in this corner. So let's say I pick this one to go in this corner, and I'll take another corner piece to go in this corner, and I have seven choices for that, and then six choices for what corner piece is going to go in that corner, and so on, down to the last corner. So the number of ways to choose the locations of the corner pieces, right, I have eight choices for the first corner piece, seven choices for the second, six choices for the third, and so on, is eight factorial—40,320 ways. And once we've placed them in the corners, once I know that this piece wants to go in this corner, then there are three ways of orienting the piece. So this piece has three orientations, so looking over here in a big cube, we have three colors that could go here. It could be the red. It could be the white or the blue. So each corner piece has three possible orientations. So we could perform those orientations $3 \times 3 \times 3 \times [3 \times 3 \times 3 \times 3 \times 3]$. 3^8 ways, 6,561 ways. Similarly, the 12 edge pieces can be placed in their positions 12! ways before we oriented them, and that's nearly half a billion ways right there. And those edge pieces can be oriented in 2^{12} ways, 4,096 ways.

When we multiply all those numbers together, we get that there are $8! \times 3^8 \times 12! \times 2^{12}$; that's over 500 quintillion ways that the cube can be reassembled.

But how many of them are actually achievable from the starting position? It turns out that exactly $\frac{1}{12}$ of these positions can actually be achieved, so, the number of starting positions is really only about 40 quintillion.

Another way to say this is that if you randomly assembled a cube—let's say I dropped this cube and it broke into a whole bunch of pieces, and then I just randomly put it all back together, the chance that it would actually be solvable would only be 1 in 12. Now, where does the number $\frac{1}{12}$ come from? Remember when we talked about the Fifteen Puzzle, we said that every legal position had to be an even arrangement of the numbers 1 through 15. Well, as it happens the only achievable positions of a Rubik's Cube are even arrangements of the pieces. For instance, if I took this final position, and I swapped any two of the pieces, we would have an unsolvable position, no matter how we oriented the pieces because I'd be going from an even position to an odd position. And since $\frac{1}{2}$ of all arrangements are even, this cuts down the number of achievable arrangements in half. Furthermore, once we choose the orientation of 11 of the edge pieces, then the orientation of the 12th edge piece is also forced.

So for example, suppose you were in the middle of solving the cube, and you accidently dropped it on the floor, and one of the edge pieces came out. And you don't know how it was, and you put it back in the cube. Well, it matters which way you put the piece back in, since if you put it in the wrong way, then the puzzle becomes unsolvable. So this cuts down the number of achievable arrangements by $\frac{1}{2}$ again. Finally, once you've oriented seven of the corner pieces, that forces the orientation of the 8th piece, and since each corner has three potential orientations, only $\frac{1}{3}$ of its orientations are achievable. So, if we multiply $\frac{1}{2} \times \frac{1}{2} \times \frac{1}{3}$ we get $\frac{1}{12}$, which is the fraction of reassembled cubes that are legally achievable or solvable.

But enough with the math. Let's learn how to solve the Rubik's Cube. Naturally, if you have a Rubik's Cube handy, you'll want to go get it and be prepared to use the pause button a lot. We will solve the cube in just eight steps. These steps were taught to me by Tyson Mao, a former world champion cube solver. This algorithm is not the one that you would use to be a world champion, but it's very easy to learn, and with practice, you can solve any cube in under three minutes. I taught both of my daughters this method when they were nine years old, and my older daughter can consistently do it in under 90 seconds. She's faster than I am, by the way.

So here's an outline of our solution strategy. We solve the cube in eight steps. First, we have the Daisy, then the Easy, and the 1-2-3 move. Those three moves are going to solve for us the bottom layer of the cube. Then step four, we'll do the middle layer—that's the belt that goes around the middle of the cube. And then with steps five, six, seven and eight, with such some fun names as FURU'R'F', the Fun move, the R'F move, and the Furl move, we'll have the entire top layer solved.

Alright. Here are the ground rules. For most Rubik's Cubes, the white face and the yellow face are on opposite sides; white face, yellow face. We will solve the entire cube with the white face on the bottom and the yellow face on the top. So if your cube has something other than yellow opposite the white face, then that color's face will always be on the top. You're now ready for step one: the Daisy. Now, as always, we keep the yellow face on the top. Our goal is to give this yellow center four white petals. That is, the four white edge pieces, so it looks like a daisy. The first place I look for my white edges is on the middle layer. Now, let's see. I have a white one right here. I just bring that to my top. That's my first daisy petal. This could be my second daisy petal, but you know what? That's too easy. I want to teach you something. Let's look on the bottom for one here. So here's a daisy petal. I'm going to first bring it to the middle layer, like so. So now it's on the middle layer, and once something's on the middle layer, you can turn it up, and there it is. Let's look for another one. Anything on the middle layer? I've got one on the middle layer right here. Now I would turn that one right up, but I'd lose this white daisy piece, so let's move that daisy petal out of the way, so that now when we move it up, there it is. And one more. Anything on the bottom layer? No. Let's see. Look at that. There's one right here at the very bottom. Let me move it in position. Let's get those other daisy petals out of the way. Rotate that 180° and we're done.

Now pause and practice this step many times until you're comfortable that you can get all four white edge pieces to the top layer. This is the only step where you really have to kind of play around with it for a while. So this is a good time to pause and stop and play with this on your own until you can get all four daisy pieces to the top. The next step is actually easier.

After the daisy step, step two is so easy, I call it the Easy. Now every petal of your daisy is an edge piece with two colors. Right? Here I have white and orange, white and blue, white and red, white and green. What we now do is we twist our cube, always keeping the yellow on the top. We twist our cube in such a way that the green here finds its center. So watch. I'll twist and look, the green has found its center. Once it finds its center, we twist that entire face 180°, so right now it's pointing at 12 o'clock. After I twist it 180° it's pointing to six o'clock. Here let's do another face. Look, the orange has already found its center. So let's twist that. I call this dialing down. Let's dial down. And now we're here. I have the blue and the red already lined up, but if they weren't lined up, if they were in this situation, I would just go hunting around until I found the center, twist it, dial it down— just like that. It doesn't matter whether you do this clockwise or counterclockwise. And finally, with the white-red piece, notice the reds are matching. If they weren't you would adjust it so that they were, and dial it down. And now once you've done that, take a look at what you have on the bottom. You have a white cross. Not only do you have a white cross, every piece is where it's supposed to be. Right?

We have the white-blue where it should be, the white-red where it should be, the white-green, and the white-orange. You can almost think of it as the cube is wearing socks. When you look around it you see that it's wearing socks. So practice step two. It's quick. Then we'll finish the bottom layer in step three.

We're halfway done with the bottom layer. The white edge pieces are in place. Now it's time to get the white corners in their proper positions. Alright. Let's first find a white corner piece. Now the best place to look for them is on the top rim. Not the top face; I'm not so interested in the white one over here, but on the top rim like the one over here. We just have this one over here.

So now twist the top face. Notice that every corner piece has another color— in this case orange—that's also on the top rim. So you see we have a white-orange piece here. We're going to twist the top so that the orange color finds its center. So let's say I have white-orange here. If I twist the top just like so, then the orange has found its center. The orange square should now be diagonally next to the orange center, and the white square attached to it will still be on the rim, either on the left side or on the right side. So go ahead and point to the white square with your index finger. Like here, there's my white square, and I'm going to mark it with one of these stickers so we can see it later, a little happy face.

If you're pointing with your left hand, then the next move will use your left hand. If you were pointing with your right hand, the next move will use the right hand. The move that we're going to learn, I call it the 1-2-3 move. Now with the pointing hand—in my case it's my left hand—I'm going to twist that side of that cube away from me. Alright. So here, first I go one like that. Now two, with your index finger twist the top face towards you. Alright. I'm twisting the top face towards me. Notice that I'm now staring at that old white sticker. It is staring me in the face, or I'm staring at its face, that's step two. And finally, step three, I bring that white square down by twisting the side of the cube towards me, like that. And now, that white corner cube is in its proper position. Not only do I have a white there, you'll notice that we have green matching green and the orange matching the orange. Was that too fast for you? That's okay we have three more corners to go.

Again, if we're lucky, we'll find another white corner on the rim. I've got a couple of these here on the rim. Let's see, I have a white-red here. Let's twist the top until the red finds its center, just like that. Red-red diagonally touching, and the white piece is on the side. Let's do another sticker so you can watch what happens to that white piece. We're going to do the 1-2-3 move again. Now this time I'm pointing with my right finger, so I'm going to use my right hand. So one, I twist it away from me, then two, I twist it towards me—you see I'm staring at that face again, alright—and then, three, we're going to bring that down. We bring it down, and now that face is in its proper position. You can tell it's very happy.

Let's do it again, two more corners. I look around the rim. There's a rim, white and blue. I want it to find its center so let's twist it so that the blue matches its center. The white is on the side. The white will always be on the side, either on your right side or on your left side. You don't want to have a white facing you here. You're not going to want to have that white in the back. You want it on the right side or left side. Here it's on my right side again, so with my right hand I do one, two—there's that white sticker—and down like this, three.

Let's look around, look around. I have one more to go. It's white and blue. Look, it's already in its white position. Now I get to use my left hand in order to put that in the proper position, so here we go with the left hand we do one, away from me; two, I twist the top towards me; three, down. And now the bottom layer is solved.

Now that was easy. Maybe it was too easy because there was a complication we didn't actually experience, so let me set that up for you. Suppose there aren't any white pieces on the top rim, but you do have a white piece on the top face, like here, so nothing on the rim. So in that situation all you do is you twist the top. You want to get that white piece above one of the unsolved positions. Doesn't matter which one it is, just it can't be over something that's already been solved. So find something that isn't white preferably. The white is now directly above the orange. And now with my right hand— because it's on my right side—I'm going to do, not the 1-2-3 move, but the 1-2-2-3 move.

When I go 1-2-2-3, watch. We go one, two, two, three. Now that didn't solve the bottom, but that white piece is now on the rim. A mathematician would say we've reduced this to a problem that we know how to solve. Let's now fix it. The white has a blue neighbor, the blue finds its center. And let's see. It's here. The white is on the right, so with my right hand I'll do 1, 2, 3, and that gives me the completely solved bottom. There's only one other situation to be aware of. If you don't have any whites on the top rim or even on the top face, then all you do is, let's say you had a white that was in position here, do a 1-2-3 move, and that will bring that offending white piece to the top rim. Once it's on the top, you know how to solve that position.

It's essential that you practice step three, and steps one and two, for that matter, until you can confidently solve the bottom layer, and I encourage you to do so now. If you get stuck, don't be afraid to rewind me, and I'm happy to explain it to you again.

You now know how to solve the bottom layer, and from now, on every time we finish a step, the bottom layer will still be in its pristine state. Let me show you one of those steps right now. You won't really need it until step six, but it's so easy to learn and so fun to do, that I call it the Fun move. While I teach you the move, I will also display some notation along the way. I won't really explain the notation now, but I want you to start seeing it now so it'll make more sense when we need it in step five. It's done entirely with the right hand, and all you do is twist the right face. By the way, I'm making sure my yellow is still on top here. All you do is you twist the right face and the top face as follows. Now watch and listen closely. I'm twisting the right face and the top face. We sometimes call the top face the up face as well. Here we go. We twist, out, twist, in, twist, out, twist, twist, in. Here, you try it. You go out, twist, in, twist, out, twist, twist, in. Notice that after the move, the bottom layer is still pristine, no matter how you've oriented it, out, twist, in twist, out, twist, twist, in. Alright.

This time I'll do it with numbers. These are the numbers that we used in the 1-2-3 move. It goes 1, 2, 3, 2, 1, 2, 2, 3. One last time. This time I'll have the notation displayed. Remember, we're twisting the right face and the up face. It goes out, twist, in, twist, out, twist, twist, in. Isn't it fun? Now practice this a few times and eventually you'll learn it. You'll learn it kinesthetically. Your hands will just learn it, so you don't even have to pay much attention while you do it. Once you've got that down it's time for step four.

Alright. I'm going to peel off the happy face stickers right now since we won't need those until later. By the way, I've known some people who solve the Rubik's Cube by peeling off the stickers of their cube and rearranging those. I just have to warn you if you find that step three wasn't working for you, it's possible one of your kids has already peeled off some stickers and put them in the wrong places, and that can create problems.

Now we've completed the bottom layer, right? Completely done. It's now time for the middle layer. Now there are no corners in this middle layer, right? It's just the belt that goes around it. So we just have to do four edge pieces. We do these one at a time. We begin by looking at the top layer for any edge piece that doesn't use the color yellow. Say I have a green and orange, I have a red and green, and I have two things that have yellows on it. I like red and green. Let's do that. So I have a red-green edge piece. The first thing you do is you twist the cube until the color on the rim—that would be the green piece,—finds its center. So here it is. We find its center. And now on the top there's red. What do I do with red? Red will either be on this side or that side. Is it here? No. It must be there? So with that I'll point to the red side. In fact, I'm going to give it a slap. Mentally or physically slap the left side, and now, your first step is you twist the top in the direction of the slap. With my index finger I'm going to twist the top towards me. And now what you do is with that same slapping hand, you perform the 1-2-3 move from last step. We go 1-2-3. Now, uh-oh, we lost a white from the bottom, but that's not a problem. The white is back here on the rim so we're going to fix it. We'll fix it by the white has a red neighbor. The red finds its center. And we fix it with the 1-2-3 move, 1, 2, 3. Notice, not only is the bottom now fixed, but that red-green edge piece that we started with is now in its perfect position. If you didn't catch it, that's okay. We have three more edge pieces to do it.

Here's another one with green and orange. Now I got lucky. The green had already found its center. If it wasn't, if it was here, I would have twisted it so that the green finds its center. Its neighbor on top is orange. Orange is on the right side. I'll slap it with my right hand, and in the direction of the slap I'll twist the top just like that. Now I do the 1-2-3 move with my slapping hand, with my right hand. Here we go. One, two, three, oh-oh, we lost a white, but that's okay. We'll fix it using the 1-2-3 move with my left hand. It's always with the opposite hand that will fix it for you. One, two, three, and now that piece, the orange-green piece, is where it belongs.

Let's look again, we have a blue-orange piece right here. Blue-orange piece. Actually, you know what? Let me show you an example. Because what would happen if all the pieces had yellow on them and we still weren't done? Like let's say we found ourselves here with a blue-red piece and everything up on top had yellow, but these weren't in the right position. Then all you do is you do a 1-2-3 move. No slapping required. Just do a 1-2-3 move, one, two, three, and then fix it. Say okay, I'll fix that white piece, one, two, three, and now you've brought that blue-red piece from where it used to be a problem over here. It's now up here on the top. So we sort of kick it up to the top, and that works. Let's do it. The blue-red piece, the blue finds its center. It has a red neighbor. With red I slap, twist the top. We do one, two, three, fix it with the other hand, one, two, three. Alright. Almost done.

Let's look on the rim. I have one more to go. Here's a blue-orange. We're lucky the blue has already found its center. I'll slap with the left, like that, and now, with the left hand I do the 1-2-3 move. One, two, three, and then I'm going to fix that white with my right hand. First the orange finds its center, and then we fix the white, one, two, three; And now we've completed the middle layer. The middle layer's probably the longest step in the process because you have four cubes to fix. Great. We're halfway through our algorithm and we have two-thirds of the cube completed.

Before we do step five, we need to learn some simple notation. There are six faces on the cube, and according to convention, they are labeled front, and back, right and left, up and down. We abbreviate these with their first letters: F, B, R, L, U, and D. Note that in our algorithm the up face will always be yellow and the down face will always be white. I don't know about the others, but up face will always be yellow. When we use a letter to represent a move, it means to imagine that you're looking at that face then twist that face in the clockwise direction. For example, the U move, if I'm looking at the up face, then a U move would look like this. I'm twisting it clockwise. The R move would be to look at the right face and twist it clockwise. I'll do it slowly, just like that. That's a one move.

To move counter, clockwise we use the prime symbol. For example, the move R' would undo the last R move by turning the right face counterclockwise. So here's the move R', like so. Notice that the R move moves the right face away from you. But the L move moves the left face towards you. That can be a little confusing. Then the L move would look like, I'm going to look here and turn clock-wise. That's an L move, and there's L', or from here, there's L'. From here, here's R and going back is R'. It sounds confusing, but as a practical matter, we mainly perform R, U, and F moves and their reverses. By the way, mathematicians might prefer to say things like R inverse and write it this way, but, but R' is much easier to say and write.

So we're ready for step five, which I call the FURU'R'F' step—see how it's written—where our goal will be to create a yellow cross on the top face. So we don't have a yellow cross. We have a yellow line here; that's kind of nice, but I want a whole yellow cross. And the best time to perform this step is at nine o'clock. Now what do I mean by that? If you're lucky, you'll have on the top face two yellow edge pieces that are touching diagonally, and also touching the center. So you would have three yellows that form nine o'clock. If you have that, you're in good shape. You'll only have to do this next step once. If you don't have it, like here, we're going to have to do this step at least twice.

So now here's the FUR U'R'F' step. So the FUR is performed clockwise, and the U'R'F' step is done counterclockwise. Here we go. FUR, F, U, R, U', R', F'. And notice, we now have nine o'clock. You might have to do that FUR U'R'F' move twice to get nine o'clock, but once you have nine o'clock, you only have to do it one more time. If the position looked like here, and it was three o'clock, then make it nine o'clock. If the position looked like here, like 3:30, make it nine o'clock. These two yellows are away from you. And we do FUR U'R'F' one more time. Alright. Here we go, F, U, R, U', R', F', and we now have a yellow cross. Congratulations. You're done with step five. If you want to practice this move a few more times, go right ahead. You can do FUR U'R'F' all you'd like, and unless you make a mistake, you won't disturb the bottom two layers. If you do make a mistake and create a mess, well, it's a good time to practice steps one to five anyway.

Are you ready for step six? We're going to make the top entirely yellow and best of all, you already know how to do it. We just use the Fun move that I taught you at the end of step three. Remember how it went? Out, twist, in, twist, out, twist, twist, in. Now. before you do the move, you look at the top face here and count the number of yellow corners that are on the very top. How many do I have here? I have two. Too bad. The best number to have is one. If you're lucky, you'll only have one yellow corner. But if you have zero or two yellow corners, then you're going to have to do the Fun move step a few times. By the way, it's impossible to have exactly three yellow corners. That's, actually, a consequence of those even positions that we talked about earlier—but I digress.

So here I have two. Now when you have two on the top, what you do is you rotate your cube until you find a yellow on the face—the front face here—in the upper left corner. So I have a yellow here. Do I have it anywhere else? No. No. No. So the only way I can orient this is with the yellow in the upper, left corner of the front face. Here I am looking at it, and now we do the Fun move at least once, maybe twice. Here we go. I'm going to go out, twist, in, twist, out, twist, twist, in. Lucky me. I now have one yellow corner. If I had two yellow corners I'd orient my cube until I found a yellow over here, but with one yellow corner, it's nicer. You just orient the cube until the one yellow sticker here is in the bottom, left corner. So now I'm looking here on the up face. My yellow corner is here, and I'm going to do this Fun move at least once, maybe twice. I can tell from here I'm going to need to do it twice. So we'll do it once, out, twist, in, twist, out, twist, twist, in; still one yellow corner. Once you only have one, you're in good shape. You're always going to have one, or you'll be done. I orient my cube so that one yellow corner is over here in the bottom, left. I'll do Fun move one more time, and we'll be done with this step, out, twist, in, twist, out, twist, twist, in. It's looking magical isn't it? So now the top face is entirely done.

We are so close to being done. Here we are at step seven. At the end of this step all of the top corners will be perfect. The first thing you do is you look around the top rim and see if any of the sides have matching corner colors. So usually I do, but I think this time I don't. That's okay. Red-orange, green-blue, orange-red, and blue-green. Well, in this situation it doesn't matter how you orient the cube, so let's do the R'F move now. I find that this is probably the hardest step to learn. It's only nine twists, but it's worth memorizing the mantra, so repeat after me: R'F R'B2 RF'R'B2 R2. I'll say it again: R'F R'B2 RF'R'B2 R2, and that's it. The B2 means to twist the back side twice, like that. Doesn't matter whether you twist it clockwise or counterclockwise, it has the same effect. If I do B2 again, I'm back to where I was. And R2 means to do the R move twice, like one, two. I'll do it again, R2, one, two.

Let's do this step very slowly. Of all the steps, this was the one that I found myself messing up the most, and if you mess up, you'll have to start all over again, but think of it as good practice of the earlier steps. Since I don't have any matching corners, it doesn't matter how I orient it as long as the yellow side is on top. Here we go. I'll do it slowly: R'F R'B2 RF'R'B2 R2. Now, when we have finished this step, we now have at least one side that has matching corner colors. Let's see; that's red-orange, green-red, blue-blue, that's good, orange-green. So take the blue-blue, and that should be on your back. I like to match it up with the actual blue side. I just think it looks nicer. So here I have the blue-blue on the back, and now we do R'F one more time, and once we do it, all those corners are going to be perfect. One more time, R'F R'B2 RF'R'B2 R2, and now we'll orient so that our matching colors are matching. And look at that; isn't that pretty? You have red, green, orange, and blue.

Ready for step eight, the final step of solving the Rubik's Cube. At this point, everything should be in its proper position and orientation, except for three or four edge pieces on the top. If you only have three edge pieces out of position, then you'll have one completely pristine side, and just like with step seven, you'll want that to be on the back side. Now let me see; do I have any? No. This is out of position. This is out of position. I have four out of position. So just like with step seven, it doesn't matter how I orient the cube this time, but we're going to have to do this Furl move a couple of times. So here we go. We'll have to do this two, maybe three times. I call this the Furl step with an exaggerated F because of the way the move is spelled out. I'll display it for you now, but I remember it with a simple mnemonic. Here it is. Look at it. And here's my mnemonic. As I think about Furl, I start with FFU. I'll do that for you here. We'll do F, F, U, and then I bring both sides down. That's the R'L, both sides down. Then I dial around. That's FF. Then I bring both sides up. That's RL', and then that's enough, UFF. So I do up, F, F. Now you'll notice we have a pristine side. So if you didn't have a pristine side before, you will now. We're going to do this one more time, maybe twice. We do Furl one more time. I'll say my words this time instead of the notation, so Furl. So I do FFU, then both sides down, dial around, both sides up, and that's enough. And look at that. We have solved the Rubik's Cube. Remember, when you start that last step, that the pristine side has to be on the back, facing away from you.

If you practice this method you can comfortably solve the cube in under five minutes. I can usually do it in under three minutes, and if you use your fingers very efficiently, like my daughter does, you can do it in about one minute. It can take about 180 twists to perform, so to do it in three minutes requires that you spend about one second per twist. You may ask, what's the fewest number of moves needed to solve the cube? It was recently proved, in 2010, that every cube is never more than 20 twists away from being solved. That number can't be lowered since there are some positions that provably require at least 20 moves to complete. In fact, if you're curious, here's a position known as Super Flip that's known to require 20 moves. From the solved position you can create Super Flip using these 20 moves.

Interestingly, you'll notice that all of the corner pieces are in their natural position. I have the yellows where they belong, the reds where they belong, the whites, the blues, everything is great. And ,in fact, even the edge pieces are in their appropriate positions, but they all have exactly the wrong orientation. So this piece here is supposed to be the yellow-red piece, but in fact, it's the yellow-red, but it's flipped. This is supposed to be the yellow-green piece. It is, but it's flipped. That's why they call it Super Flip. This piece is supposed to be red and white. Everything is flipped. So even though this position looks almost solved, it's been proved that it can't be solved in less than 20 twists. Naturally, people who are speed cubers use algorithms that are different from what we learned in this lecture. They move their fingers incredibly fast, and their methods combine several steps at once. The world's fastest solvers can do a randomly scrambled cube in about 10 seconds. I'm happy if I can solve it in under three minutes.

The Rubik's Cube combines mental dexterity with physical agility. Our next lecture on Sudoku is purely an intellectual challenge. There we will develop a toolbox of strategies that will allow you to solve almost any Sudoku you encounter, and I'll see you then. In the meanwhile, I'll have a go at this cube.

Solving Sudoku
Lecture 10

P uzzles like sudoku and KenKen® are fun because they rely entirely on logic. This lecture on sudoku is purely an intellectual challenge. In this lecture, you will develop a toolbox of simple strategies that will allow you to solve almost any sudoku puzzle you encounter. Strategies include tic-tac-toe and crosshatching processes, miniboxes, completed lines, right angles, and some advanced techniques for very challenging sudoku puzzles. In addition, you will be introduced to the rules of KenKen®.

Sudoku Strategies

- Without a doubt, Rubik's Cube has been the most successful physical puzzle ever invented, but in the last 10 years, the world's most popular puzzle, requiring less physical dexterity and more logical reasoning than Rubik's Cube, is sudoku.

- Part of sudoku's enduring popularity is that the challenge can be described in a single sentence: Enter the numbers one through nine in such a way that each number appears once in every row, column, and three-by-three box. Every sudoku puzzle will have a unique solution, and if the puzzle is well crafted, it should be solvable using just pure logic. No guessing should be required.

Sudoku Puzzle

		9			6			
		8			4			
					1	2		3
							4	
	5						7	
	2							
6		4	7					
			8			5		
			9			8		

- Sudoku is a mathematical game, and it's not because the grid is filled with numbers. It would be just as mathematical if each square had to be filled with a letter or color. What makes sudoku mathematical is that in order to solve it, you need to think like a mathematician by looking for patterns and using careful logic.

- A sudoku puzzle is played on a nine-by-nine grid consisting of 81 squares with some number of initial clues. It has nine rows, nine columns, and nine boxes. The numbers that can potentially go in a square are called the candidates for that square.

- The wrong way to start a sudoku puzzle is to enter the candidate numbers for each square in hopes of finding a square with a single candidate. You might want to do this if you get stuck near the end, but you definitely don't want to do this at the beginning of the puzzle. In fact, you want to take the opposite approach. Instead of determining which numbers can go in each square, you want to determine which squares can take each number.

- A sudoku puzzle known as the pi puzzle is an 18-clue puzzle. It appears in the book *Taking Sudoku Seriously* by mathematicians Jason Rosenhouse and Laura Taalman. Not only is the puzzle rotationally symmetric, but the digits of this puzzle also come from the first 18 digits of pi: 3.14159265358979323.

Pi Puzzle

7	2							
	5				9			
				3	8			
			4			5		
		3				9		
		1			3			
			2	5				
			6				3	
							1	9

- Every sudoku has nine rows and nine columns, but if you focus on the thick lines, it sort of looks like a big tic-tac-toe board. You can think of it as having three big rows and three big columns. Look for a number that appears twice in the same big row or big column. In the case of the pi puzzle, the number 3 appears twice in the middle big column (big column 2)—in little columns 5 and 6.

- Look at the other little column, which is little column 4, in big column 2. Where can the third 3 go in that little column? It can't go in the top box or the middle box because both of those already have 3s, so it must go in the bottom box. There's only one place it can go within the bottom box because columns 5 and 6 have 3s, and there is only one open spot in column 4.

Tic-Tac-Toe Process

7	2							
	5				9			
			3	8				
			4			5		
		3				9		
		1			3			
			2	5				
			6				3	
			3				1	9

- The number that was just entered into the puzzle is called a hidden single, which is a number that has only one legal square in a row, column, or box. The best way to find hidden singles is through the tic-tac-toe process.

- In this puzzle, you are able to fill in most of your numbers by judicious use of the tic-tac-toe and crosshatching processes. With tic-tac-toe you need two repeated numbers in the same big row or column. When two numbers are not in the same big row and column, then you can sometimes use crosshatching.

- For example, if you crosshatch the 3s in column 3 and in row 3, you find that no 3 can appear anywhere in the top left box of the puzzle except for one position: column 1, row 2. Then, two more 3s are eliminated as potential candidates, leaving you with two more 3s

Crosshatching Process

7	2					3	9	
3	5				9	3		
				3	8	9		
			4			5		3
		3				9		
		1			3			
3	3		2	5				
			6				3	
			3				1	9

7	2					3	9	
3	5				9	3		
				3	8	9		
			4			5		3
		3				9		
		1			3			
3	3		2	5				
			6				3	
			3				1	9

7	2					3	9	
3	5				9			
				3	8	9		
			4			5		3
		3				9		
		1			3			
3	3		2	5				
			6				3	
			3				1	9

being placed in the puzzle. Now, you've placed every 3 on the grid, and you won't ever have to deal with that number again.

- When a number can only find two possible squares in a box, lightly pencil in that number in both places. If both of those places were in the same row or column, that's called a pointing pair, and that can sometimes eliminate candidates from the other boxes. If you find two numbers that can only go in the same two spots in a box, then they form a hidden pair, and those spots must contain those numbers.

- Look for more places to crosshatch. When you scan the grid, look for certain structures. For example, the top left box has a two-by-two minibox. There is also a completed line inside the box that is located in the middle on the bottom of the puzzle. In addition, there are a few boxes containing right angles. All of these structures tend to be very helpful.

Miniboxes, Completed Lines, and Right Angles

- For example, the right angle located in the bottom right corner of

7	2					3	9	
3	5				9			
				3	8		9	
			4			5		3
		3				9		
		1			3			
	3		2	5				
			6				3	
			3				1	9

the puzzle contains three unfilled squares in a row and three unfilled squares in a column, which is sometimes susceptible to crosshatching, which then sometimes causes a chain reaction of solutions.

- With tic-tac-toe and right angles, you need two numbers to make progress, but with miniboxes, you often need just one number to make progress.

- We started our puzzle by looking for numbers that appear a lot, because they tend to produce the most useful tic-tac-toes, right angles, and miniboxes, and because they tend to produce very useful crosshatches. In addition, there is a structure called a completed line, which consists of three numbers that completely fill a row or column of a box.

- Completed lines let you start a tic-tac-toe with one number instead of two. When starting a sudoku puzzle, the first thing you look for should be completed lines.

- At some point, the tic-tac-toe process stops working, and there may not be any crosshatches that jump out at you. What do you do when you get stuck? Walk away and come back to it later. After taking a break, you'll often see things that you missed before.

- Then, examine the numbers that are almost finished, but if you're still stuck, try the following techniques: Scrutinize your rows, columns, and boxes that are almost finished and look for naked singles, which are squares that can only take on one value. Naked singles become more common as the row, columns, and boxes start

Completed Pi Puzzle

7	2	9	1	4	6	3	5	8
3	5	8	7	2	9	1	4	6
4	1	6	5	3	8	7	9	2
8	9	7	4	1	2	5	6	3
2	4	3	8	6	5	9	7	1
5	6	1	9	7	3	8	2	4
9	3	4	2	5	1	6	8	7
1	8	2	6	9	7	4	3	5
6	7	5	3	8	4	2	1	9

to fill up. Don't forget chain reactions. Anytime you get a new piece of information, see what chain reaction that causes.

Solving Difficult Puzzles: Sudoku and KenKen®

- Using the techniques in this lecture, you can solve most if not all of the puzzles that you'll find in newspapers and magazines, but to solve the most difficult sudoku puzzles—typically labeled as tough, fiendish or diabolical—you might need a few more tools in your toolbox. To use these techniques, you sometimes need more information than you have written in your puzzle.

- The method that you've been learning focuses on numbers that can only go in a small number of squares. When you've reached a position where you're really stuck and you can't make any more progress through tic-tac-toe, crosshatching, hidden pairs, and naked singles, then it's time to reverse that approach and look for squares that can only take a few numbers. In other words, now and only now, it may be time to pencil in the candidates for each square. Be especially on the lookout for squares that can only take two numbers.

- The first thing to look for is a naked pair, which consists of two squares in the same row, column, or box that can only take the same two numbers. There's an extension of the naked pair concept called a naked triple, which consists of three squares in the same row, column, or box that can only take on three values.

- Another neat idea is known as X-wing. Suppose the number 5 only has two places it can go in column A, say in rows C and D, and suppose that in column B, 5 can only go in the same two rows. The X-wing rule says that there can't be any 5s in rows C and D. X-wings can be pretty tricky to spot, but when you find them, they tend to simplify the puzzle quite a bit.

- Another advanced solving technique is called unique rectangle, which is based on the fact that every sudoku puzzle is required to have a unique solution. This way, the newspaper or book with the puzzle can print the one solution to the puzzle instead of showing

X-Wing Rule

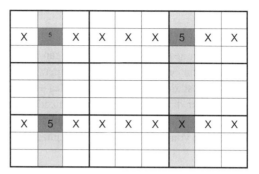

many possibilities. Another reason the solution has to be unique is because otherwise, a solution would require you to do some guessing, and all sudoku puzzles are supposed to be solvable without requiring any guessing. When solving sudoku, you can sometimes exploit uniqueness.

- Strictly speaking, all sudoku puzzles are supposed to be solvable by pure logic, and no guessing is required. On the other hand, if you filled up most of the puzzle and reach a point where you get stuck, then sometimes it is helpful to try a quick guess and see what happens.

- You should choose a square that has two possible values that will cause a big chain reaction. Circle your guess, and put everything else in colored pencil. Typically, one of two things will happen: Either the chain reaction will lead to a solution to the puzzle, or it will lead to some kind of logical contradiction, such as a row that must have two 5s in it, in which case you know that your initial assumption was wrong.

- There are many variations on the sudoku puzzle, and many of the techniques that you learned in this lecture will transfer to other puzzles. The sudoku variation known as KenKen® combines the logic of sudoku with some actual reasoning about numbers as well.

Similar to sudoku, every row and column must contain the numbers one through six, and each cage indicates what the numbers add, subtract, multiply, or divide to. Numbers can be repeated in the same cage, but not in the same row or column.

KenKen®

24x		10+		10+	7+
5−	4		1−		
	2−	2÷			5−
3−			2−		
	9+			11+	
3	6+		3÷		

Suggested Reading

Gordon, *Solving Sudoku.*

Miyamoto, *Brain-Busting KenKen®.*

Riley and Taalman, *No-Frills Sudoku.*

Rosenhouse and Taalman, *Taking Sudoku Seriously.*

Snyder, *The Art of Sudoku.*

Stephens, *Mastering Sudoku Week by Week.*

Stuart, *The Logic of Sudoku.*

1. Solve the sudoku puzzle below. It only has 18 clues, but you can do it!

		9			6			
		8			4			
					1	2		3
							4	
	5						7	
	2							
6		4	7					
			8			5		
			0			8		

(Puzzle appears in the book *No Frills Sudoku,* by Brainfreeze Puzzles, Philip Riley and Laura Taalman, © 2011. Used with permission.)

2. Solve the "silicon sudoku" below.

2	8							
		1	6	7	9			
		5					4	
		6						
		7	2	4	5		3	
					1		9	
					6		5	
		3	8	1	4		2	7
1	4							

(Copyright © 2008 by Thomas Snyder. Used with permission. For more puzzles like this, see GrandmasterPuzzles.com.)

3. Solve the KenKen® puzzle below. Each row and column uses the numbers 1 through 6. The number in each cage (heavily outlined set of squares) indicates what the numbers must add, subtract, multiply, or divide to. Numbers may be repeated in a cage, but not in the same row or column.

24x		10+		10+	7+
5–	4		1–		
	2–	2÷			5–
3–			2–		
	9+			11+	
3	6+		3÷		

(Puzzle provided by the website KenKen.com. © 2012. Used with permission. KenKen® is a registered trademark of Nextoy, LLC. All rights reserved.)

Solving Sudoku
Lecture 10—Transcript

Without a doubt, Rubik's Cube has been the most successful physical puzzle ever invented. But in the last 10, years the world's most popular puzzle, requiring less physical dexterity and more logical reasoning, is Sudoku. Here's a typical Sudoku puzzle. Part of Sudoku's enduring popularity is that the challenge can be described in a single sentence: Enter the numbers one through nine in such a way that each number appears once in every row, column and three-by-three box. That's it. Every Sudoku puzzle will have a unique solution, and if the puzzle is well crafted, should be solvable using just pure logic. No guessing should be required.

Is Sudoku a mathematical game? Absolutely, and it's not because the grid is filled with numbers. It would be just as mathematical if each square had to be filled with a letter, or a color, or one of nine vegetables. What makes Sudoku mathematical is that in order to solve it, you need to think like a mathematician by looking for patterns and using careful logic. I think Sudoku is great mathematical training for kids, and for adults it's a fun way to keep your mind active and sharp. I'm definitely a big fan of this puzzle.

Before I teach you a good strategy for solving Sudoku, let me say a few words about some of the mathematical questions that pertain to this puzzle. With the Rubik's Cube, we asked, how many positions are possible, and what's the fewest number of moves needed to solve them? Let's look at some related questions here starting with how many different Sudoku puzzles are there? As a warm-up question let's first count the number of baby Sudoku puzzles, sometimes referred to as Shidoku. In Shidoku, you must fill out a four-by-four grid with the numbers one through four in such a way that every number appears in each row, column, and two by two box. For example, here's a typical Shidoku puzzle. These problems tend to be very easy to solve. For instance, here, once you notice that a two has to go here and a three has to go here, then the puzzle pretty much solves itself at that point, resulting in this completed grid.

The math question is, how many possible completed grids exist? For starters, look at the box in the top, left corner. We know that the number of ways to arrange the numbers one through four is $4 \times 3 \times 2 \times 1$, $4! = 24$. Once you've chosen the order of these four numbers, say, like so, there are two ways to finish the first row and two ways to finish the first column, say like so. And it can be shown that no matter how you've chosen all these numbers, there are exactly three ways to fill out the rest of the box. I'll leave it as an exercise for you to show that if you put a one in this spot, then there's just one way to finish, but if you put a two in that spot, then there are two ways to finish. Hence, there are exactly three ways, $1 + 2$ ways, to finish this puzzle. So, altogether, the number of possible 4×4 Shidoku grids is $24 \times 2 \times 2 \times 3$, 288 ways to finish the puzzle.

So how about nine-by-nine Sudoku grids? Using similar symmetry arguments and lots of brute force computing, it was shown in 2006 that there are over 6.67 sextillion possible nine-by-nine completed Sudoku grids. That's nearly seven billion trillion possibilities, and it's more than 100 times as large as the number of achievable Rubik's Cube positions, and that's just the number of final answers. The number of initial grids that can lead to these answers is even larger, so there should be no shortage of puzzles any time soon.

Here's a related question. Every Sudoku puzzle is required to have a unique solution. Is it possible to be given 50 numbers and not have a unique solution? How about 60 or 70 numbers? Believe it or not, it's possible to be given 77 of the 81 numbers and still not have a unique solution. Now how is that possible? Suppose I showed you this much of the puzzle, 77 of the squares have been filled. We know the missing numbers are two and three, yet we don't know if they go like this, 2, 3, 3, 2 or like that, 3, 2, 2, 3. Either way, we have a valid, completed grid.

Here's a much trickier question that was only resolved recently. What is the smallest number of clues needed to make a Sudoku puzzle uniquely solvable? For example, with no clues there are more than six sextillion ways to complete the Sudoku. It's easy to see that seven clues isn't enough either. Why? With seven clues there has to be at least two missing numbers. With two missing numbers you can't possibly have a unique solution. Right? Say two and three were missing, both of them were missing, then for any valid solution we could interchange all the twos with the threes and get another valid solution. That's why some hard Sudoku puzzles might have one missing number, but it will never be missing two. So the natural question becomes, what is the smallest number of clues that you can be given and still have a unique solution?

There are many examples of puzzles with 17 clues that have a unique solution. Here's one of them. This puzzle has 17 clues, count them, but it only has one unique solution. In 2012 it was finally shown using clever search strategies and lots of computer time that there is no 16-clue puzzle that leads to a unique solution. But other questions still remain open. For example, did you ever notice that practically every crossword puzzle is rotationally symmetric? That means that if you rotate the puzzle 180°, then the black squares are still in the same positions. The same is true with Sudoku. In most Sudoku puzzles found in books and magazines, it's customary for the starting clues to be placed in a rotationally symmetric way. For example, here's a Sudoku with 18 clues, placed in a rotationally symmetric way. If you rotated this board 180°, you'd have numbers in the same spots. The 17-clue puzzle that we saw earlier is not rotationally symmetric, and so far nobody's been able to find one, so it's still an open question if 18 clues is the minimum.

Here's an interesting 18-clue puzzle. It appears in the book *Taking Sudoku Seriously*, by mathematicians Jason Rosenhouse and Laura Taalman. Not only is the puzzle rotationally symmetric, but in the spirit of rotational symmetry, the digits of this puzzle come from the first 18 digits of Pi. You gotta love it. There's a 31415926. It's great, and it's rather pretty to look at. But enough talking about Sudoku. Let's now learn the strategies that will allow us to solve most Sudoku puzzles quickly and easily.

I should tell you, by the way, that I used to be pretty terrible at Sudoku until I sought advice from an expert. As luck would have it, one of my very own students, a math major at Harvey Mudd College named Palmer Mebane, was an expert at puzzles. Actually, that's an understatement. Palmer was the 2011 United States puzzle champion and later that year was winner of the World Puzzle Championships. He learned his Sudoku techniques from Thomas Snyder, also known as Doctor Sudoku, who is, himself, a past U.S. Puzzle Champion and three-time World Sudoku Champion. I'm very grateful to Palmer and Tom for allowing me to share some of their techniques with you.

After learning these techniques you should be able to do just about any Sudoku puzzle that you come across. Dare I say, you'll find them as easy as Pi.

To prove my point, let's look at that Pi puzzle from earlier. Here it is; just 18 digits. How do we get started? Before I go any further, let's make sure that we define all of our terms properly. A Sudoku puzzle is played on a nine-by-nine grid consisting of 81 squares with some number of initial clues. It has nine rows, nine columns, and nine boxes. The numbers that can potentially go in a square are called the candidates for that square. For example, in our Pi puzzle, this square over here it can't be a 1, 2, 4, 5, 6 or 9, so the candidates for that square are three, seven and eight, although soon enough we'll see why that square has to be a three.

I used to go about Sudoku all wrong. I would enter the candidate numbers for each square in hopes of finding a square with a single candidate, and some books and websites actually take that approach. But I'm here to tell you that this is the wrong way to start the puzzle. You might want to do this if you get stuck near the end, but you definitely don't want to do this at the beginning of the puzzle. In fact, you want to take the opposite approach. Instead of asking for each square which numbers can go in this square, you want to ask for each number which squares can take this number.

Let me illustrate. Let's start by looking at the number that appears most in this grid that would be the number three, which appears four times in this grid. Next we'll be able to place some new threes using a process that I call tic-tac-toe. Now every Sudoku has nine rows and nine columns, but if you focus on the thick lines, it sort of looks like a big tic-tac-toe board right? You can think of it as having three big rows, big row one, big row two, big row three and three big columns, one, two and three. Now look for a number that appears twice in the same big row or big column. Here, the number three appears twice in the second big column, that's in little column five and little column six. Now let's look at the other little column that would be column four, and I ask you where can the third three go in that little column? Now it can't go in the top box because of this three; it can't go in the middle box because of that three; so it must go in the bottom box over in one of these spaces, but there's only place it can go in that box, so the three must go there. So I call this tic-tac-toe.

By the way, we call the number that we just entered into the puzzle a Hidden Single. That's a number that has only one legal square in a row, column, or box. So the only legal place that a three could go in that column was there, so that's what made it a hidden single. The best way to find hidden singles is through the tic-tac-toe process. So let's do it again. This time notice that the big middle row has two threes in it, right here and there, so if we focus on the other row, we do tic-tac-toe. Now hold on a second; the third three must be in one of these two open spots, but it can't be here because of the three below it, so it must go here. Now the third big column has two threes in it, so we can do tic-tac-toe again. Alright, so let's see. Tic-tac-toe, we have to have a three in one of, here, one of these three spots. But correction; it can't be here because of the other three, so there are only two possible locations for the three.

Now listen to this because it's important. If a number has only two possible locations inside a box, then I will write that number real small inside of its two possible squares. Let me say that again for emphasis. For most of the puzzle, the only time to write a little number in the puzzle is if that number has only two places to go inside a box. Not three, not four, two places to go. I usually write them in pencil so they can be erased later, as needed. Alright, let's do another example of this. The third big row has two threes in it, here and there, so tic-tac-toe gives us tic-tac-toe, but it can't go there. So it has to be one of these two spots, so we pencil them in. Now there's one more tic-tac-toe on the board, but it doesn't use threes. Do you see it? In the last big column, we have two nines. So doing tic-tac-toe with them gives us two places where the nines can go up here. Tic-tac-toe can't be here, so it has to be one of those two places, and we mark them like so.

By the way, let me say something about pencil marks. You'll notice that I put all the threes in their upper right corner of the square, and I put all my nines in the lower right corner of the square. And if you think of a square as having nine places for numbers—1, 2, 3, 4, 5, 6, 7, 8, 9—I'll always put my pencil-mark numbers in the same place, just to be consistent. Now there are no more places to perform tic-tac-toe, so it's time to learn a new technique.

With tic-tac-toe you needed two repeated numbers in the same big row or column. When two numbers are not in the same big row and column, then we can sometimes use crosshatching. So what's that? For example, if you crosshatch the threes, the three in this column and the three in this row, we get that no three can appear anywhere in this box except for here. And notice how this three eliminates this three as a potential candidate leaving us with this three here. It also eliminates this three here, so the only place for a three in this box would be here. We've now placed every three on the grid, and we won't ever have to deal with that number again. If I were doing this on paper, I might put a check mark above that three to indicate that I don't have to worry about threes anymore.

Let's look for more places to crosshatch. When I scan the grid with my eyes, I look for certain structures. I see the top, left box has a two-by-two mini box; I see a completed line inside this box; and I see lots of boxes containing right angles, here's one, there's one, there's one. All of these structures tend to be very helpful. Let's start with this angle. This box will contain three unfilled squares in a row, and three unfilled squares in a column, which is sometimes susceptible to crosshatching. Notice that this row has a five, and this column has a five, so when we crosshatch, there's only one place the five can go, namely here, in this square, creating another mini box. As soon as you fill in a new number, you should see what kind of chain reaction it causes. For instance, if we do tic-tac-toe with the fives, we get that a five must be—let's see, tic-tac-toe—has to be in one of these two squares. And also, because of that five we have, tic-tac-toe has to be in one of these two squares. That's actually good news, and I'll say more about that later.

Okay. Let's go for another right angle. Here we can plow through the blank spaces of this box crosshatching with ones. Right? I have a one up here and a one over there, so that means a one has to go here. Once we have a one, this creates a chain reaction, another tic-tac-toe, tic, tac, and one of these two has to be one. Wait a minute; let's not forget that it could also cause a chain reaction here. Tic-tac-toe, one of these must two must be one as well.

Let's do one more angle. Looking up here, now, if I look at that six it plows through this column fine, but nowhere else. So there are three places the six can go in that box, so we don't write anything down with that. On the other hand, the number two will crosshatch very nicely. See the two plows here. The two plows there, with one place for the two right there. Next, once we get a number, we should do tic-tac-toe—tic, tac, toe. One of these two has to be a two. Good. And then, tic-tac-toe, well this seems to leave three places for the two. Now, as it turns out, the two can't go over there, but I haven't explained why yet so, I won't pencil anything in here.

I'm done with angles. Now let's explore some mini boxes starting with this nice little mini box over here. With tic-tac-toe and angles, we needed two numbers to make progress. But with mini boxes, you often need just one number to make progress. Now when plow this white space with this eight, that means we're going to have to have an eight in one of these two squares, so I'll pencil some eights in over there. And when I plow this white space with the one—right, you see the one going all the way here—well, that's going to force me to have a one in one of these two squares, so I'll pencil them in there. Aha! Look what happens. Notice that one of these squares has to be a one. Thus, no other ones can appear anywhere in that row, right? Because one of these is going to be a one. We call this situation a pointing pair. You can think of these ones as like pointing a ray gun across its row, eliminating all other candidate ones. In particular, this one is no longer a candidate, so now there's only one one left in this box, namely this one. So we can write it in.

Let's look at another mini box. Here I have a nice mini box that's waiting for something to happen. When we check out this column, we find a missing four and six, right? Four and six are not in this box, so that means that I can't have fours or sixes anywhere here. That means that a four and six must go in here in some order. I don't know which of these is the four and which of these is the six, but I do know that these two squares can only contain a four or six since they can't go anywhere else. So let's write them in. We call this a hidden pair. So these two numbers have to be four and six in some order. No other number would be allowed in there.

We saw another hidden pair earlier over here. You see the 5-9 and the 5-9? Since five can only go in these two places and nine can only go in these two places, then they must contain these numbers five and nine in some order.

Let's pause. Catch our breath here, and let me ask you, what six numbers must occupy these six squares? I want you to give me the answer in increasing order. What are the six numbers in these squares? 2, 3, 4, 6, 8, 9. What numbers are missing from here? Say the answer in increasing order. The missing numbers are one, five, seven. That means that the numbers in these three squares must be one, five, and seven in some order. Now the one can't go here because of that one, and the one can't go here—why can't the one go here? Because of that pointing pair of ones. It's firing its ray gun at it. So the only legal place for the one in this box is here. The other numbers must be five and seven in some order, but because of the five here, we're going to have to have the five and seven here and there. And this five, by the way, forces us to have a five and a nine. We weren't sure what their order was before, but we know now that these must be nine and five to fit over there. Now, let's see, what else do I know?

Let's look at the fourth column here, this column here. We have seven of our nine numbers. It's only missing which two numbers? I have 1, 2, 3, 4, 5, 6, 7, so we're missing eight and nine, and because there's a nine there, those eight and nine are going to have to go like that.

This opens up the puzzle considerably, and the next few steps of the puzzle are pretty easy. Let's see. Now that we got the eight and the nine, let's do some tic-tac-toe. We have 8-9 here, 8-9 here. I'm going to have to have 8-9 here, exactly, and because of the nine, they have to be eight and nine like that. That leaves for us in this box the remaining three numbers. We have 2, 3, 5, 6, 8, 9 in this box, so the missing three numbers are one, four, and seven. Now because of this one, one of the ones has to go here. We don't know which one, and then the four and seven are somewhere else. But check this out. We call this situation a pointing triple. One, four and seven, because they're here in some order, they can't be anywhere else in this column. This eliminates all other ones, fours, and sevens as candidates for this column. So if I eliminate ones, fours, and sevens from here I see that this can't be a one, so a one must go there, and this can't be a four, so the four must be there. We call that, by the way, a 4-gone conclusion. Sorry about that.

That forces the last square up here to be a six, and what's left? Looking at this middle column, the only two numbers left in this column have to be six and seven in some order. I'll just pencil in the six and seven in both places. Now let's examine the remaining two squares over here. The must contain two and five in some order. But because of this five, this square here can't be a five, so it can only be a two, just like that. So a square that can only take on one value, like a two here, is called a naked single, and they become more common as our rows, columns, and boxes start to fill up. Naturally, the other missing number here must be five. That five sets off another chain reaction. We must have a five here. Tic, tac, toe puts a five over here, eliminating the five below, so forcing us to have a five. I might put a check mark above my fives because now the fives are finished.

Let's look for another naked single. In the top row we're missing the digits eight and nine, but this square can't be a nine because of that nine down there, so it must be an eight, forcing the nine to go here. And because now we're left with one place for the eight, the eight would have to go there. That forces the other numbers in this row to be four and six in some order, and that leads to another hidden pair. This is 2-7 and 2-7 in some order. Now what? There are still parts of our puzzle we haven't explained yet. Let's look at this mini box down over here. When I look at this mini box, this two clears out that row, and that gives us a nice pointing pair of twos down below. Now, with this pointing pair of twos, it fires its ray gun forcing—notice it's going to eliminate that two—forcing us to have a seven here and a two there.

What next? Well, let's see. We have a bunch of nines on the board. In fact, we have seven nines on the board. Maybe we can finish them off. So with our nines we do tic, tac, toe. Can't be there, so it must be there, and one to go. Once you have eight numbers, the ninth is forced. Tic-tac-toe has to be there.

Although we've completed more than half the puzzle, some challenges still remain. That's part of what makes Sudoku so addictive, by the way. As you figure out more and more numbers, you feel as if the puzzle should get easier, but that's not always the case. It may be that you've only reached the low-hanging fruit, and the remaining numbers might require a ladder. Now at some point, tic-tac-toe stops working, and there may not be any crosshatches that jump out at you. The question is, what do you do when you get stuck? Here are my suggestions.

Suggestion number one: Walk away and come back to it later. After taking a break, you'll often see things that you missed before. Examine the numbers that are almost finished, but if you're still stuck, let's try these techniques. Scrutinize your rows, columns, and boxes that are almost finished, and look for naked singles. Don't forget chain reactions. Any time you get a new piece of information, see what chain reaction that causes. Finally, you could use the advanced tools that we'll talk about about later in this lecture.

In this puzzle, we finished off numbers three, five, and nine. What's the next best candidate? Well, let's see. We've actually solved six of the ones here, and when I look at the penciled-in ones, we see that two of the boxes have hidden pairs. There's a hidden pair of ones here and a hidden pair of ones there. There's only one box where we haven't said anything about ones, so let's take a look at that box. Now when I crosshatch my ones in that box, I go here and there. That leaves a pair of ones possibly over here, but that's a pointing pair. Right? Those two ones are going to eliminate the one from this box, forcing a one to go over there. And once I have a one over here, then the remaining two boxes here are four and seven in some order. Anything left with the ones? I have a pair of ones here, a pair of ones there. They form a little rectangle. There's nothing I can do with those right now, so I'm going to leave them alone.

Let's try another number. Let's say, two. So let's take a look. We have two, two, two. Let's take a look at this box. Now when I crosshatch my twos, two and two. Oh, that's nice. There's only one place for the two over here. And this sets off a nice chain reaction. We' have tic, tac, toe—tic, tac, oh, toe. We cross out this two. We're left with one over here, and now the twos are history. We've now dealt with our ones, twos, and threes. Let's look at the fours.

I think there's not much that happens with the fours. All I can say is in this box, then because of that four, I know I have to have a pair of fours in here, so I can pencil that in. How about the sixes? There's nothing obvious that happens with the sixes so let's move on to the sevens. So seven, seven, seven. Wait a second. I see something interesting here. This seven in this column, focusing on this box, gives me a pointing pair of sevens after I go through here and I crosshatch the seven there. That leads to a pointing pair of sevens down there, and now I can do tic-tac-toe. Right? With tic, tac, because this gives us the column, toe gives me a seven right over there. Great. Okay, and, let's see, does that give me anything else? That seven, what reaction does that cause? Crosshatching there. I have to have a seven in one of these two boxes, so I'll pencil those in.

Finally, let's see what eights give us. In this box here, there are two places the eights can go, here or there, so we'll pencil that in. And in this box, let's see, there are two places for eights to go there, so I'll pencil those in. That's nice. And now let's look at this box. Let's see, eights over here and here. Oh, this is good. I have a pair of eights that can go here. Now let's pause for a moment. A one can only go in these two places. An eight can only go in these two places. Even though a seven would like to be considered for that place, there's no room for the seven here. These ones and eights are claiming those two, so that means the seven can't go here, and it must go there. This tells us, by the way, looking over here, that the 4-7 has to be four and seven, in that order. And the number missing from this row—because I know this is one and eight in some order, and I have 2, 6, 9, 7, 3 and 5—this has to be a four. And now the rest is easy. You might say that the puzzle practically solves itself. And there we have it. We're done. We just finished a puzzle that had only 18 clues, using rather simple techniques.

Let's recap. In this puzzle, we were able to fill in most of our numbers by judicious use of tic-tac-toe and crosshatching. These would often lead to hidden singles, numbers that could only find one place to go in a row, column, or box. When a number could only find two possible squares in a box, we would lightly pencil in that number in both places. If both of those places were in the same row or column, that's called a pointing pair, and that can sometimes eliminate candidates from the other boxes. And if you find two numbers that can only go in the same two spots in a box, then they form a hidden pair, and those spots must contain those numbers.

We started our puzzle by looking for numbers that appear a lot, since they tend to produce most useful tic-tac-toes, right angles, and mini boxes, and since they tend to produce very useful crosshatches. There was one other structure that I mentioned, but we never got to exploit it. It's called a completed line.

A completed line consists of three numbers that completely fill a row or column of a box, like in this example. Completed lines let you start a tic-tac-toe with one number instead of two. Look outside the box—think outside the box—and look for numbers that are in the other two columns. Now look for any numbers that are not in the box below. So for instance, here, I see eights and nines in the other two columns that aren't in the box that contains the completed line. The number eight forces us to have one of these two squares below as an eight, giving us a pointing pair of eights in the bottom box. And this forces a pair of eights in one of the middle box squares. The nine helps us even more. This nine in the top box forces this nine in the bottom box, giving us this nine in the middle box—giving us our nines and subsequently our eights.

When starting a Sudoku puzzle, the first thing I look for are completed lines. Here's a puzzle created by Thomas Snyder. I like Tom's puzzles because they tend to have an artistic quality about them or some hidden joke beneath the surface. He created this puzzle for the Silicon Valley puzzle fest. If you look closely, you'll see that most of the clues combine to create Si, the chemical abbreviation for the element silicon. Even the extraneous clues have some meaning, since silicon is the 14th element of the Periodic Table and has atomic weight 28. I'll let you have the fun of solving this puzzle yourself, but the key to solving it is to exploit the three completed lines here.

Using the techniques that we know, you can solve most, but not all, of the puzzles that you'll find in newspapers and magazines, but to solve the most difficult Sudoku puzzles, typically labeled as tough, fiendish or diabolical, we might need a few more tools in our toolbox.

I'll now share with you some of my favorite techniques, but to use them, we sometimes need more information than we've written in our puzzle. The method I've been teaching you focuses on numbers that can only go in a small number of squares. When you've reached a position where you're really stuck and you can't make any more progress through tic-tac-toe, crosshatching, hidden pairs, and naked singles, then it's time to reverse that approach and look for squares that can only take a few numbers. In other words, now, and only now, it may be time to pencil in the candidates for each square. Be especially on the lookout for squares that can only take two numbers.

The first thing to look for are what's called naked pairs. A naked pair consists of two squares in the same row, column, or box that can only take the same two numbers. Let's start with an abstract example, then a real one. Here, the squares indicated in this grid cannot be 1, 2, 4, 5, 6, or 8. They can only be seven or nine. So since we have two squares that can only accept seven or nine, those squares must be seven or nine in some order. That now gives us a pointing pair, which can be used to figure out other squares. For instance, the seven in this column has to go there.

Here's a real-life example. We've solved most of the puzzle, but now we're stuck. Try as we may, we can't make any more progress using our current techniques. Really, you just have two options here: either fill in the rest of the pencil marks, or take a wild guess. I'll say more about the guessing strategy later, but let's fill in the pencil marks now.

Notice, by the way, that there are only 13 squares that need new pencil marks. That's way less than going through every square at the start. Look at the squares that can only take two values. Most of them are pointing pairs that we've looked at before, but some have not yet been exploited. Do you see the naked pair? It'll use one of these squares. Hint: it's in this row.

Here they are. These two squares can only be six or nine. As a result, no other sixes or nines can appear in that row, so we can remove them as candidates. So we erase this six, and this six, and this nine, leaving us with a naked single. Now that we know that this square must be seven, this causes a pretty big chain reaction that solves the rest of the puzzle.

There's an extension of the naked-pair concept called naked triples. A naked triple consists of three squares in the same row, column, or box that can only take on three values. For example, if these three squares can only take on the values one, two, or three, then nothing else in that row can have one, two, or three. In fact, we can reach the same conclusion even if the situation were like this. It's still the case that these three squares can only take the values one, two, and three. In fact, even this situation is a naked triple, where we have three squares that can take on the values 1-2, 1-3, or 2-3. It's still the case that no other ones, twos, or threes can go in that row.

Here's another neat idea known as X-wing. It goes like this. Suppose the number five only has two places it can go in column A, say here and there. And suppose that in column B, five can only go in the same two rows, like here. The X-wing rule says that there can't be any fives in any of these locations. That's pretty cool and powerful. Why is that? The reason is that if the five in column A goes here, then it can't go here. So the only place left in column B is here. In other words, if this is a five then so is this. On the other hand, by the same reasoning, if the five in column A goes here, then the five in column B must go there. You see where the name X-wing comes from? Looking at this big X, we're guaranteed to have a pair of fives on the corners of this rectangle, so fives can't go anywhere else in these rows. X-wings can be pretty tricky to spot, but when you find them, they tend to simplify the puzzle quite a bit.

Now let me show you my favorite advanced solving technique. It's called unique rectangle. It's based on the fact that every Sudoku is required to have a unique solution. This way the newspaper or book with the Sudoku can print the one solution to the puzzle instead of showing many possibilities. Another reason the solution has to be unique is because, otherwise, a solution would require you to do some guessing, and all Sudokus are supposed to be solvable without requiring any guessing. When solving the Sudoku, you can sometimes exploit uniqueness.

Let's me start by showing you an illegal Sudoku situation. Here we have a situation where there are four squares that form our rectangle in the same big column that can only take on the same two values. Here, seven and eight. We call this a forbidden rectangle. Now what makes this illegal? Similar to the X-wing situation, there are exactly two possibilities. If this number is seven, then that forces our rectangle to look like this. Whereas if this number were eight, our rectangle would look like this. The trouble is that these two scenarios are perfectly interchangeable. If there's a legal way to finish this Sudoku, then there'd have to be a legal solution using that rectangle. Either way, every row, column, and box will have a seven and eight, and nothing else will be disturbed. Do you see that? For instance, if this were a legal solution, then if we interchanged the two sevens and the two eights, then this would also be a legal solution. So how do we exploit this situation? Suppose when solving a Sudoku, the candidates for these four squares looked like this. And again, I have to emphasize, those four squares we're looking at are all in the same big column. Three of the four squares have candidates seven and eight, while the fourth square of the rectangle can be seven, eight, or nine. I claim that the fourth square has to be nine. Why? If the fourth square is not nine, then all four squares would have candidates seven and eight, giving us a forbidden rectangle. And this would prevent us from having a unique solution.

Strictly speaking, all Sudoku puzzles are supposed to be solvable by pure logic and no guessing is required. On the other hand if you filled up most of the puzzle and you reach a point where you get stuck, then I sometimes find it easier to try a quick guess and see what happens. I'll typically choose a square that has two possible values, and that will cause a big chain reaction. When I do this, I'll circle my guess and put everything else maybe in colored pencil. Typically, one of two things will happen. Either the chain reaction will lead to a solution to the puzzle, in which case you're happy, or, it will lead to some kind of logical contradiction like a row that must have two fives in it, in which case you know that your initial assumption was wrong. Mathematicians, by the way, call this proof by contradiction. Either way you're happy. You've either solved the puzzle or at least you've made progress.

Here's another puzzle from *No-Frills Sudoku*. It's one of the last puzzles in the book, and it's given a four-star rating for difficulty. Starting with these 18 clues and using the techniques we've learned, I reached this situation before getting stuck. Even after adding pencil marks, I didn't see any way, any naked pairs or triples that help us, nor do I see any X-wings or unique rectangles. So now might be a good time to try a guess. Just about any square with two values should cause a pretty big chain reaction here. Let's look at this square in the middle of the puzzle. It can be a five, or it can be an eight. And it's not innately obvious which number it should be. As you can verify for yourself, if you guess the number eight, then you reach a contradiction. Consequently, the number in this box has to be five, and if you put five in that square, that leads to a pretty quick solution of the rest of the puzzle.

By the way, there are many variations on the Sudoku puzzle and many of the techniques that we've learned in this lecture will transfer over. My favorite Sudoku variation is KenKen®, which combines the logic of Sudoku with some actual reasoning about numbers as well. Similar to Sudoku, every row and column must contain the numbers one through six, and each cage indicates what the numbers add, subtract, multiply, or divide to. Numbers can be repeated in the same cage, but not in the same row or column. Puzzles like Sudoku and KenKen® are fun because they rely entirely on logic.

In our final lectures, we turn our attention back to games that involve only pure logic and strategy, beginning with, perhaps, the most famous game of all time.

Mathematics and Chess
Lecture 11

In this lecture, you will learn about one of the world's oldest games: chess. When playing a game of chess, you don't perform many mathematical calculations, like you do in backgammon or poker, but the game is still very mathematical. When playing chess, you're constantly looking for patterns, experimenting with different strategies, and building a sophisticated toolbox from a simple set of rules. This lecture will draw connections between mathematics and chess and give you tips that are sure to improve your game.

The Game of Chess
- The game of chess is played on an eight-by-eight checkerboard. There are two players, white and black. Each player has 16 chessmen, consisting of eight pieces and eight pawns. Among the eight pieces, each player has a king, a queen, two rooks, two bishops, and two knights. The player with the white pieces always makes the first move.

Chessboard

R	N	B	Q	K	B	N	R
P	P	P	P	P	P	P	P
P	P	P	P	P	P	P	P
R	N	B	Q	K	B	N	R

- The squares of the checkerboard alternate as light and dark colors. Also, the bottom right-hand corner square is required to be light colored. Be sure to place the white queen on the light square and the black queen on the dark square. A way to remember this is to think that the queen's dress has to match her shoes.

- The king can move one space in any direction—forward, backward, right, left, or diagonally. The rook, the piece that's shaped like a castle, can move forward, backward, left, or right. It cannot move diagonally, and unlike the king, which can only move one square at a time, a rook can go as many squares as you'd like.

- While a rook can only move horizontally or vertically, a bishop can only move diagonally. A bishop in the center of the board attacks 13 other squares, but a bishop on the corner only attacks 7 other squares. That's one reason why a bishop is less valuable than a rook. On an empty board, a rook can attack 14 squares no matter where it's located. Also, a rook can get from anywhere to anywhere in just two moves, but a bishop is forever restricted to the color that it started on.

- The queen combines the powers of the rook and the bishop. A queen is like the king on steroids: It can move as many squares as it wants—vertically, horizontally, or diagonally. Thus, on an empty board, a queen located in the center can attack 27 other squares. Even a queen in the corner can attack 21 squares. The queen is the most powerful piece.

- All pieces can be blocked by their own pieces. On the other hand, if a piece encounters a piece of the opposite color, then it can capture that piece, and the captured piece is permanently removed from the board. When the pieces described so far—the king, queen, rook, and bishop—are in their initial positions, they are incapable of moving because they're all locked in by their own pieces.

- The only piece that's allowed to jump over other pieces is the knight, whose piece is usually represented by a horse. The knight makes an interesting L-shaped move. In the opening position, a knight has just two legal places it can go.

- Both players start with eight pawns. Pawns are only allowed to move forward; they can never go backward. From its original position, a pawn can move forward either one or two spaces. After its initial move, it can only move forward one space at a time. Although pawns move forward, they capture diagonally, so if an opponent's piece is directly in front of it, the pawn can't move forward, but if an opponent's piece is diagonally in front of it, the pawn can capture it.

- There's a capturing rule for pawns that doesn't occur very often. If your pawn is on the fifth row—or, as chess players call it, the fifth rank—and your opponent moves his or her pawn two spaces so that it's next to your pawn, then you can, for the next turn only, capture that pawn as if it only moved up one square. This is called capturing en passant.

- If a pawn reaches the last row of the board, the eighth rank, then that pawn is promoted to a queen. Technically, you could turn it into a rook, bishop, or knight, but it's extremely rare that you'd want to. It can even become a queen if you still have another queen on the board. When you promote your pawn to a queen, it's usually a decisive advantage because you've turned the weakest piece into the strongest piece.

- When a player's king is under attack, that's called check. When you're in check, your next move must take you out of check, and you can do this one of three ways: move the king to a safe spot, block the attack by placing a piece in between the attacker and the king, or capture the piece that is attacking the king. The king is never allowed to move into check, nor can you move a piece that would leave the king in check.

- Every move in chess uses just one piece—with one exception, called castling, which involves the king and the rook. If a king and rook have not yet moved during the game and there are no pieces in between, then the king can move two spaces toward the rook, and the rook goes on the other side of the king. This is either called castling on the king's side or castling on the queen's side, depending on which side you choose to perform this move. You are not allowed to castle if your king is in check, and the king can't land on or pass through a square that's under attack.

- The goal of chess is to put your opponent in check in such a way that he or she can't move out of check—that's called checkmate, and the game is over.

Chess Strategy and Tactics

- You can basically divide the game of chess into three parts: the opening, middle game, and endgame. In the opening, your goal is to move your pieces off of your back rank and onto more productive locations. That's called developing your pieces.

- A piece that's closer to the center of the board can attack more squares than a piece that's close to the boundary. The three key principles of the opening are to develop your pieces, control the center, and watch out for king's safety.

- In the opening, it's good to try to castle your king for two reasons: It allows one of your rooks to get into the action conveniently, and in the initial position, the king is somewhat vulnerable to attack.

- It is important to remember the following rule: Don't bring out your queen too early in the game because it allows your opponent to attack you while developing their pieces.

- Once both sides have developed most of their pieces, you move into the middle game phase of chess, during which you are trying to find and exploit weaknesses in your opponent's position while trying not to be exploited by our opponent. The secret to winning in the middle game is to be on the lookout for tactical opportunities.

- If each pawn is worth one point, then a knight or a bishop tends to be worth three points. The rook is worth five points, and the queen is worth nine points. The king, although not as powerful as the other pieces, has infinite value because if you lose your king, you lose the game. You can use these numbers to determine if it's worth making certain exchanges.

- What most chess tactics have in common is that they tend to do two things at once, such as attacking two pieces at the same time. When a single piece attacks two pieces at once, that's called a fork. When you put your opponent in check, he or she is required to defend the king in some way, so if you can attack your opponent's king and another piece, you may be able to capture the other piece. Queens and knights are especially well suited to this kind of attack.

- A tactic called pinning can happen when two valuable pieces are somehow in line with each other. For example, if the black knight is on the same file as the black king, then if the white rook attacks the black knight, then the knight is pinned because it can't move off the file without exposing the king to check. The player with the black pieces can try to defend the knight with his or her bishop, but then the white pawn attacks, and the black knight is lost. (See figures.)

- A great way to accomplish two things at once is through the use of discovered attack, especially a discovered check. This happens when moving one piece out of the way enables an attack from a different piece.

- Once you have a material advantage—for example, once you're up a piece or maybe a pawn or two—you should simplify by trading pieces of equal value for two reasons: By reducing the number of pieces on the board, you limit your opponent's ability to wage a counterattack, and as the amount of material decreases, your relative advantage increases. For example, if you have one more piece than your opponent, then instead of being up four pieces to three, it would be more decisive to be up three pieces to two or two pieces to one.

R		B		K	B		R
	P	P			P	P	P
P		P					
				N			
					N		
P	P	P	P		P	P	P
R	N	B			R	K	

R		B		K	B		R
	P	P			P	P	P
P		P					
				N			
					N		
P	P	P	P		P	P	P
R	N	B		R		K	

- Be careful not to trade too many pawns away because you'll probably need them to win. For example, suppose you were able to capture all of your opponent's pieces, and you were left with just your king and one other chess piece. It would definitely be better for that other piece to be a pawn than a bishop because it turns out that it's impossible to checkmate your opponent's king with just a king and bishop or, for that matter, just a king and knight. Even if

Pinning

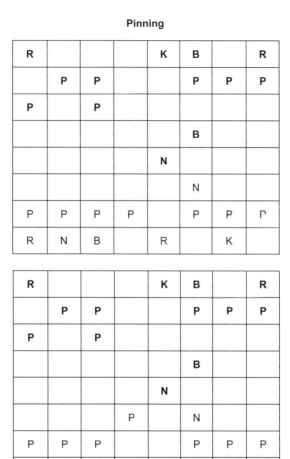

R				K	B		R
	P	P			P	P	P
P		P					
					B		
				N			
					N		
P	P	P	P		P	P	P
R	N	B		R		K	

R				K	B		R
	P	P			P	P	P
P		P					
					B		
				N			
			P		N		
P	P	P			P	P	P
R	N	B		R		K	

your opponent is trying to get checkmated, you can't do it. Such games must end in a draw.

- Likewise, it's impossible to force your opponent into checkmate with two knights against a king, and it's extremely difficult to do with one knight and one bishop against a king, assuming that there are no other pawns on the board. However, with a king and pawn, you have the potential to turn that pawn into a queen, and with a king and queen, it's easy to checkmate your opponent.

- At the end of the game, let's say that it's just you, your queen (perhaps a pawn that was turned into a queen), and the opposing king. Computer scientists have shown that if you have the queen, it's your move, and there are no other pieces on the board, then you can always force checkmate within 10 moves. The basic idea is that you have to drive your opponent's king to one of the edges of the board because it's impossible to checkmate him or her in the interior. After that, you walk your king to help the queen deliver the final blow.

- In recent years, our knowledge of the endgame has changed profoundly through the use of computers. Using a dynamic programming process called retrograde analysis, computers have worked backward from every possible checkmate position with up to six pieces on the board to determine the guaranteed best move from every chess position with six or fewer pieces. For each of these positions, the computer can tell you, if the position is not a draw, how many moves until the winning player can checkmate the other.

- Outside the endgame, computers don't yet play perfect chess. On the other hand, it's fair to say that computers have mastered the game. It was 1996 when a computer first beat the world's best player in a game of chess, and computers are now dominant in chess. No human has beaten the top computer chess program since 2005.

Suggested Reading

Emms, *Concise Chess.*

Fischer, *Bobby Fischer Teaches Chess.*

Nunn, *Learn Chess.*

Seirawan and Silman, *Play Winning Chess.*

Watkins, *Across the Board.*

Problems

1. What tends to be more valuable: a knight and a bishop or a rook and two pawns?

2. Find a winning move for White in the position below. (Note: The bold letters are black pieces; the non-bold letters are white pieces.)

	K				**R**		
P							**P**
	P		**R**		**P**		
		P		**P**			
	N						
	P				R	P	
P	B		Π		P		P
	K						R

3. What's the right move for White in this position?

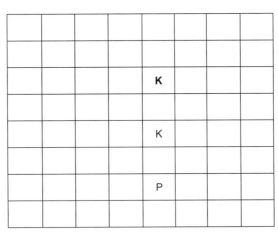

Mathematics and Chess
Lecture 11—Transcript

In this lecture, I plan to talk about one of the world's oldest games, namely the game of chess. Now when playing a game of chess, you don't perform many mathematical calculations like you do in backgammon or poker, but the game is still very mathematical. After all, mathematics is the science of patterns, and in the game of chess you're constantly looking for patterns, experimenting with different strategies, and building up a sophisticated toolbox from a simple set of rules. I hope that by the end of this lecture you'll see that playing chess is more like doing real mathematics than just about any other game.

Not surprisingly, many of the world's best players have come from strong mathematical backgrounds. Two of the best chess players who ever lived, Emanuel Lasker and Max Euwe, had PhDs in mathematics, and both were world champions. Lasker was the undisputed world champion for 27 years. Euwe proved in his dissertation that with the rules of the time, an infinitely long game of chess was theoretically possible. I should warn you that I'm not a chess expert, but I used to play the game very seriously in high school. I was a rated player and captain of my chess team and have the dorky yearbook pictures to prove it. At least my ability to play chess was better than my sense of fashion.

In this lecture, I'll draw more connections between mathematics and chess, show you a classic mathematical chess puzzle along the way, and give you many tips that are sure to improve your game. By the way, chess puzzles have attracted some of the best minds in mathematics from Leonhard Euler to Carl Friedrich Gauss, to Noam Elkies, who, at age 26, became the youngest tenured full professor at Harvard. So let's quickly review the rules of chess.

The game of chess is played on an eight-by-eight checkerboard. There are two players, white and black. Each player has 16 chessmen consisting of eight pieces and eight pawns. Among the eight pieces, each player has a king, a queen, two rooks, two bishops and two knights. Initially, the board is set up in this way, and white always makes the first move. Notice that the squares of the checkerboard alternate as light colored and dark colored. Also, the bottom, right-hand corner square is required to be light colored. I have found that in advertisements that use chess sets, they tend to get that wrong about 50% of the time. Just remember the dieter's creed: light is right. Also, be sure to place the white queen on the light square and the black queen on the dark square. In other words the queen goes on her color, or another way of saying it is, the queen's dress matches her shoes.

Let's quickly describe how the pieces move, beginning with the all-important king. The king can move one space in any direction, forwards, backwards, right, left, or diagonally. For example, a king here could move to any of these squares.

Now let's look at the rook, the piece that's shaped like a castle. A rook can move forwards or backwards, left or right. It cannot move diagonally, and unlike the king, which can only move one square at a time, a rook can go as many squares as you'd like. For example, on this empty board, a rook on this square can reach any of these squares. While a rook can only move horizontally or vertically, a bishop can only move diagonally. For example, on this empty board, a bishop on this square can reach any of these squares. Notice that a bishop in the center attacks 13 other squares, but a bishop on the corner only attacks seven other squares. That's one reason why a bishop is less valuable than a rook. On an empty board, a rook can attack 14 squares no matter where it's located. Also, a rook can get from anywhere to anywhere in just two moves, but a bishop is forever restricted to the color that it started on.

The next piece we look at is the queen. The queen combines the power of the rook and the bishop. A queen is like the king on steroids. Well, that sounds pretty funny, but whatever. It can move as many squares as it wants, vertically, horizontally, or diagonally. Thus on an empty board, a queen located in the center can attack 27 other squares. Even a queen in the corner can attack 21 squares. Without a doubt the queen is the most powerful piece.

Thus far, I've illustrated how the pieces move on an empty board, but all pieces can be blocked by their own pieces. For example, a white rook on this square with some other pieces around it could only move to these eight squares. On the other hand, if it encounters a piece of the opposite color, then it can capture that piece, and the captured piece is permanently removed from the board. Notice, by the way, that when the pieces are in their initial positions, all the pieces we've described so far, the king, the queen, the rook, and the bishop, are incapable of moving. They're locked in by their own pieces. The only piece that's allowed to jump over other pieces is the knight, whose piece is usually represented by a horse.

The knight makes an interesting L-shaped move. For example, a knight in the middle of the board can move to any of these eight squares whereas a knight in the corner could only move to one of these two squares. In the opening position, a knight has just two legal places it can go. For instance, the knight here can move here or there.

Before describing the other rules of chess, I'd like to digress on what is, perhaps, the most famous problem of all time, known as the Knight's Tour. The puzzle was often given to beginning chess players to determine if they had any real special aptitude for the game. The challenge of the Knight's Tour is this: Given a specified starting point, can you move the knight around the chessboard in such a way that it lands on every square without ever repeating a square. Now, I've seen many solutions to this problem, and they usually involve memorizing long sequences of numbers, or visualizing large geometrical patterns, but let me show you a solution, called the Four Diamonds Methods, that's so easy you can do it almost immediately after learning its secret. It also illustrates a useful, general strategy of breaking up a large puzzle into smaller more manageable puzzles.

Now a chessboard has 64 squares, eight rows and eight columns, and it can be viewed as consisting of four quadrants of 16 squares apiece, as shown. We label these quadrants one, two, three, and four. Each of these quadrants can be broken up into four diamonds. The first diamond looks like this. I call it the up diamond because it looks like a line that's sloping up. Notice that a knight could start on any square of this diamond, and in three steps land on all three of the other squares. For instance, if the knight starts here, we can go to here, then to here, then to there. Similarly, we have the down diamond that covers the other corners and the other middle squares. The other two diamonds look like tilted squares. Let's call this one the right wheel since the top of the square is near the upper right corner. And finally we have the left wheel that looks like this. Notice, again, that a right or left wheel can be toured by a knight. To summarize, every square in a quadrant belongs to an up diamond, down diamond, left wheel, or right wheel. Go it? You now know everything you need to know to do the knight's Tour.

Here, let's choose a random starting point. This knight is in quadrant one and it's on one of the up diamond squares. We'll mark that with a U. Next, the knight jumps to the other up diamond squares in quadrant one, like so— from here to there and there. Notice that when you started, you had a choice of which direction to go. Be sure to choose a direction that doesn't paint yourself in a corner. For instance, you should tour the up diamond this way, ending near the center, instead of touring it this way, since you'd end up painting yourself into a corner with no escape. Ending in the center, we can jump to an up-diamond spot in quadrant two and repeat the process.

Next we do the same for quadrants three and four, ending in this square. We've covered 16 squares of our board. Next we move to a new square in quadrant one. Now let's see. It's on a right wheel, so we now cover the right-wheel squares of quadrants one, two, three, and four, just like we did before. So there's quadrant one, then quadrant two, then quadrant three and ending in quadrant four over here.

Next, we jump to a down diamond, let's say, in quadrant three, and we jump to the rest of the diamond squares, like so, ending here. And finally, we jump to one of the left wheels that are left over. And it's easy to see that we can cover the rest of the squares from here. Ta-da! And we're done. You now know how to do a Knight's Tour.

Like with some of the puzzles we solved in this course, the solution involves a macro. That is, our solution is composed of efficient combinations of moves. Here we saw that within each quadrant, there were four move macros that where combined to form useful 16-square macros which could be stitched together to provide a solution. We've now described each of the pieces in chess. Now let's look at the pawns.

Both players start with eight pawns. Pawns are only allowed to move forwards; they can never go backwards. From their original position, a pawn could move forward one or two spaces. After its initial move, it can only move forward one space at a time. Although pawns move forwards, they capture diagonally. So if an opponent's piece is directly in front of it, the pawn can't move forward, but if an opponent's piece is diagonally in front of it, the pawn can capture it. For example, a game of chess might begin this way: White moves the pawn in front of his king two spaces, and black does the same. Now, if white moves the pawn in front of his queen two spaces, like this, then black could capture that pawn like so. Although white could recapture the pawn with his queen.

There's one other capturing rule for pawns that doesn't occur very often. If your pawn is on the fifth row, or as chess players call it, the fifth rank, and your opponent moves his pawn two spaces—so let's say moves his pawn two spaces so it's next to yours, like so—then you can, for the next turn only, capture that pawn as if it only moved up one square, like so. This is called capturing en passant, but it doesn't arise in practice too often. But the next pawn property is extremely important. If a pawn reaches the last row of the board, the eighth rank, then that pawn is promoted to a queen. Technically, you could turn it into a rook, bishop or knight, but it's extremely rare that you'd want to. It could even become a queen if you still have another queen on the board. When you promote your pawn to a queen, it's usually a decisive advantage, since you've turned the weakest piece into the strongest piece.

Here, in this position, there's nothing black can do to prevent white from promoting his pawn to a queen, after which, black's king is under attack, and it's forced to move here. By the way, when a player's king is under attack that's called check. For example, in this position, if white moves his rook here, then black is in check. When you're in check, your next move must take you out of check, and you can do this one of three ways. One, you could move the king to a safe spot, like so. Or two, you can block the attack by placing a piece in between the attacker and the king, like so. Or three, you can capture the piece that's attacking the king, like so. Naturally, since white doesn't want to lose his rook, putting black in check would be a blunder here. Note that the king is never allowed to move into check or move a piece that would leave the king in check.

Just one more rule. Every move in chess uses just one piece with one exception. It's called castling, and it involves the king and the rook. If a king and rook have not yet moved during the game, and there are no pieces in between, then the king can move two spaces towards the rook and the rook goes on the other side of the king, like so. This is called castling on the king's side. Or, you can castle on the queen's side, like so. Note that you are not allowed to castle if your king is in check, nor can the king land on or pass through a square that's under attack.

The goal of chess is to put your opponent in check in such a way that they can't move out of check. That's called checkmate, and the game is over. For example, in our last problem it's white's move, and he can move here for checkmate. The king is attacked and has no safe moves. Here is the shortest game of chess possible. It's called Fool's Mate. Here's how it goes. White plays here, then black plays there. Then white plays here, and then black moves his queen all the way over here for check. Now the king can't move out of check—has no place to go. The queen here can't be captured, and no piece can come between the queen and the king, so it's checkmate.

Now let's start learning some chess strategy and tactics. You can basically divide the game of chess into three parts: the opening, the middle game, and the endgame. We'll talk about each of these parts of the game with an emphasis on what you might call the most mathematical aspects of chess. In the opening, your goal is to move your pieces off of your bank rank and onto more productive locations. That's called developing your pieces. As we've noticed, a piece that's closer to the center of the board can attack more squares than a piece that's close to the boundary. So for example, if we ignored our opponent's pieces for now, we would try to make moves like this. Bring your middle pawns to the center. Bring both of your knights here. Develop your bishops. Castle and centralize your rooks to reach a position like this.

Of course, you don't expect your opponents to let you get away with all this since they have similar goals, but the three key principles of the opening are one, develop your pieces; two, control the center; and three: watch out for king's safety. Let me say a few words about the third point.

In the opening, it's good to try to castle your king for two reasons. One, is it allows one of your rooks to get into the action conveniently. The second is that in the initial position the king is somewhat vulnerable to attack. If you're playing an inexperienced player, you can often win in four moves with something called Scholar's Mate, and it goes like this: White moves the pawn in front of the king, up two spaces. And let's say black does the same. Then white moves the queen over here, attacking black's pawn—threatening black's pawn. So black protects it with the knight. Then white brings his bishop here. Notice how white has two pieces, the bishop and the queen, attacking this vulnerable pawn, which is only defended by black's king.

Now if black doesn't see this, then black will lose. For example, suppose black brings out her other knight here developing a piece and attacking white's queen. That seems okay on the surface, but then white simply captures black's pawn with his queen and the game is over, checkmate. You see why? The king can't move, has no safe place to go, can't capture the queen because it's protected by the bishop and the queen can't be captured.

This strategy works well and quickly against a novice, but if you use it against an experienced player, you can easily find the tables turned. Here let me show you what can happen if you try Scholar's Mate against an experienced player. We start off as before. White attacks with the queen. Black defends with the knight. White brings out the bishop, attacking the pawn. But now, when white attacks with the bishop, black attacks the queen with this pawn. Let's say white moves the queen here, so he's still attacking the vulnerable pawn. Now black plays her knight here, which does several things at once. It develops her knight. It protects her vulnerable pawn from that queen, and it attacks white's pawn over here, which could come in handy later.

If white is in single-minded pursuit to get a quick checkmate, he might move this pawn two spaces. The reason he might do that is his goal is to move that pawn one more space next turn, attacking the knight, hoping the knight will run away, then white can checkmate black. But, now black responds by moving his other knight over here, which is attacking white's queen, as well as this unprotected pawn. Now black is on the attack. The only safe place for the queen that protects this pawn as well as that pawn from the knight is over here. Now black moves this pawn up two spaces, seizing control of the center, and attacking white's bishop. So let's say white takes the pawn. But now, black can actually take this pawn with her bishop, which is attacking white's poorly placed queen. The queen can't take the bishop because it's defended by the knight. So the queen here has no safe place to go. White has to block this attack with the knight or the pawn, and white is on the ropes no matter what. In his worst scenario, white plays the knight here and says, okay, I'll just block the queen with the knight. But then, black moves his knight here for check. The king is in check. That knight can't be captured, so the king has to move over here. But then black moves his bishop over there for checkmate. The king can't move safely here, here, or there, and it can't be blocked. The black bishop can't be captured, so it's checkmate. The moral of this story is don't bring out your queen too early in the game. It allows your opponent to attack you while developing their pieces.

Once both sides have developed most of their pieces, we move to the middle game phase of chess. Here we're trying to find and exploit weaknesses in our opponent's position and try not to be exploited by our opponent. This is my favorite part of the game. The secret to winning in the middle game is to be on the lookout for tactical opportunities. But before I go into specific tactics it's useful to know the relative value of pieces, and here's where a little math comes in. If we think of each pawn as being worth one point, then a knight or a bishop tends to be worth three points. The rook is worth five points, and the queen is worth nine points. And the king, although not as powerful as the other pieces, has infinite value, since if you lose your king, you're lost.

Where do these numbers come from? Mostly through experienced chess players, but they make sense. For instance, earlier we saw that on an empty board, a rook always attacks 14 other squares, and the bishop attacks from seven to 13 squares. Thus a bishop is worth less than a rook, but two bishops will attack anywhere from 14 to 26 squares, so it makes sense that two bishops would be worth a little bit more than a rook, as is the case, because 3 + 3 is greater than five. Likewise, a queen combines the power of a rook and a bishop, so it makes sense that its value of nine would be close to the rook and bishop total, which is eight. The queen is a little more valuable, since the bishop is restricted to a single color.

You can use these numbers to determine if it's worth making certain exchanges. For example, what's more valuable, a rook or a bishop and a pawn? Since a rook is worth five points, and a bishop and pawn is worth four points, you should be willing to trade a bishop and pawn for a rook if given the opportunity. Or you wouldn't sacrifice your rook to capture a bishop and a pawn. That would be a bad exchange. You'll see that what most chess tactics have in common is that they tend to do two things at once, like attacking two pieces at the same time.

When a single piece attacks two pieces at once, that's called a fork. For example, in this position here, if white moves his pawn, like so, then it's attacking black's knight and bishop. After black moves one of those pieces, the pawn can take the other. When you put your opponent in check, they are required to defend the king in some way, thus, if you can attack your opponent's king and another piece, you may be able to capture the other piece. Queens and knights are especially well suited to this kind of attack, and we'll see some examples of this later.

The next tactic worth learning is pinning. A pin can happen when two valuable pieces are somehow in line with each other. For example, in this position, black's knight is on the same file as the king, so if white attacks the knight with his rook, like so, then the knight is pinned, since it can't move off the file without exposing the king to check. Black can try to defend the knight with her bishop, but then white attacks with his pawn, and black's knight is lost.

The next position combines forks and pins. It's white's turn to move. What should he do? White may be tempted to take black's unprotected pawn with his queen, but that would be a mistake since black can move his knight here, putting white in check while forking white's king and rook. White cannot capture the knight with his pawn since that pawn is pinned by black's queen. After the king moves, black would take the rook. So, what should white do instead? White would like to move his knight here to cause check, which would fork black's king and queen, but that square is guarded by black's bishop. On the other hand, that same bishop is also guarding black's knight. We say that black's bishop is overworked since it can't perform both duties, protecting the forking square and the knight. White takes advantage of this by taking black's knight with his rook. If black recaptures with the bishop, then white can fork the king and the queen with the knight. Black is in check and will lose her queen next move.

Another great way to accomplish two things at once is through the use of discovered attack, especially a discovered check. This happens when moving one piece out of the way enables an attack from a different piece. It's white's turn to move, and he cleverly moves his pawn forward forking black's knight and bishop. Now that might look like a mistake since the pawn is attacked twice—by the bishop and the queen and defended just once. But if the bishop takes the pawn, then white takes black's knight, and by doing, so unleashes a discovered check. Black's king is being attacked by white's rook, and no matter what black does, let's say, moving the king over, then white will capture black's queen. Even if black captures the original pawn with the queen instead, she still loses a piece, since after white takes black's queen and black recaptures with the bishop, black still loses her knight because of discovered check.

Probably black's best response to the pawn move is to take the knight like so, but after white recaptures with his rook, black's bishop is still pinned and will be captured by the pawn next turn.

Here's my favorite double-attack problem. It comes from the 1975 Yugoslav Championship. The game is close. White is up by a pawn, but white has a clever move that instantly wins him a piece. Take a moment to look for it, but it's pretty subtle. I've left out one detail. White has not yet moved his king or rooks, so he's allowed to castle on either side. And if he castles on the queen's side, then look what happens. Talk about accomplishing two things at once. Not only does white move his king and his rook, white's rook is now putting black in check while white's king is now attacking black's rook. No matter what black does he, will lose the rook.

By the way, once you have a material advantage, say you're up a piece or maybe a pawn or two, what should you do then? The answer is simple, simplify. Once you have an advantage, you want to trade pieces, of equal value, of course, for two reasons. One, by reducing the number of pieces on the board, you limit your opponent's ability to wage a counter attack.

As the amount of material decreases, your relative advantage increases. For example, if you have one more piece than your opponent, say, an extra bishop, then instead of being up four pieces to three, it would be more decisive to be up three pieces to two or two pieces to one. For example, in one of our recent positions, white just captured black's bishop. After black recaptures the pawn, white should simplify the position by trading queens, like so. White should then use his material advantage to capture a few more pawns and try to force black to trade rooks. If white does this, he should be able to win.

But be careful not to trade too many pawns away since you'll probably need them to win. For example, suppose you were able to capture all of your opponent's pieces, and you were left with just your king and one other chess piece. Would it be better for that other piece to be a bishop or a pawn? You would definitely be better off with a pawn because it turns out it's impossible to checkmate your opponent's king with just a king and bishop, or, for that matter, just a king and a knight. Even if your opponent's trying to get checkmated you can't do it. Such games must end in a draw. Likewise, it's impossible to force your opponent into checkmate with two knights against a king, and it's extremely difficult to do with one knight and one bishop against a king, assuming there are no other pawns on the board. But, with a king and pawn you have the potential to turn that pawn into a queen, and with a king and a queen it's easy to checkmate your opponent.

So with that said let's look at some problems that arise in the endgame of chess, namely how to promote your pawn to a queen and how to force checkmate once you've done so. We'll just focus on the simplest situation where you have a king and a pawn versus your opponent's king starting with what you might call a simple race, like in this situation. It's black's turn to move. White wants to promote his pawn to a queen by reaching the eighth rank. Can black get there on time? What do you think, just looking here? What do you think? Visually, the pawn looks a bit closer to the goal than the king, and yet, looks can be deceiving.

To answer questions like these mathematically, we create a square with one side going from the pawn to the end. It's black's move, and if he can get inside the square, then he can capture the runaway pawn. Since black can move his king into that square, he can get there just in time, like so. So even though the pawn gets promoted to a queen, the black king is there to capture it, so the game ends in a draw.

Now in the last problem, white could not move his king to support his pawn. If the king can be of help, then the pawn has even more chances to succeed. Let's look at some common endings with two kings and a pawn. Let's start with the situation where the white pawn is on the leftmost or rightmost file. Here, white's strategy is simple. He wants to get his king to one of these squares. If he can do so without losing the pawn along the way, then that pawn will make it to the eighth rank. Black, on the other hand, wants to have her king in one of these squares; by doing so, she can prevent white from winning. To illustrate my point, suppose black's king is here. Try to put white's king anywhere that will give him a winning position. Move the pawn anywhere on that file too. White can't force a win from here.

Here, look at this position. If it's black's turn to move, then she has no legal moves. And since she's not in check, this is called stalemate, which is an automatic draw. On the other hand, if it's white's turn to move, then he either has to leave the pawn unprotected like this, losing the pawn, or, white must protect the pawn moving here, which is stalemate again since black can't move.

When the pawn is on another file, white generally has more winning chances. For example, can white force a win from this position, or can black force a draw? The answer is that white can force a win regardless of whose turn it is. White's strategy is to get his king in front of a pawn like a parent leading their child safely across the street. White wants to bring his king to one of these key squares. For instance, after two moves the position might look like this. Now in the endgame, when two kings are facing each other with just one square between them, the person who does not have to move is said to have the opposition, and that's generally a good thing because it forces the other player to move out of the way. So if it's black's turn to move here, then white has the opposition. White's goal is to wind up with his king on one side, black's king on the opposite side, and then march his pawn up the middle.

250

Let's say black moves here. Then white maintains the opposition by moving here. Now black is forced off the file, and there's nothing black can do to stop white's pawn from becoming a queen, like so, and white will win from here.

Be careful when playing to try to keep your king ahead of your pawn. Otherwise, you just might push your child into the street, and bad things can happen. For instance, if in this position white had played like so, black now has the opposition. So if white plays check, like so, then white can't regain the opposition because the pawn is in the way. If white plays here, then black plays there. Black has the opposition, and white cannot force a win from here, since if white plays check, then black plays here, and now, white must either lose the pawn or play here for a draw due to stalemate.

If we go back to this position, we see that if white had to move, he can't win, and if black has to move, he loses like so. In most chess positions it's better for it to be your move than your opponent's. But in this position, neither side wants to be on move. When it's your turn to move, but any move you make will worsen your situation, you're in zugzwang, a German word that means "forced to move." We'll encounter more zugzwang situations in other games of strategy that we'll explore next lecture.

But let's wrap things up by quickly demonstrating what to do after you've turned your pawn into a queen and it's just you, your queen, and the opposing king.

Computer scientists have shown that if you have the queen, and it's your move, and there are no other pieces on the board, then you can always force checkmate within 10 moves. The basic idea is that you have to drive your opponent's king to one of the edges of the board, since it's impossible to checkmate him in the interior. After that, you walk your king to help the queen deliver the final blow.

Here, let's take this random position and see if we can checkmate in less than 10 moves. Notice that it's usually not productive to put the king in check too much. Why? Well, since the king is forced to move anyway, there's no real need to attack the square that the king is currently on because it has to move off that square anyway. You basically just want to continuously restrict the squares available to the king until it's forced onto one of the edges. For example, from here, I'd start by moving the queen to there, restricting the black king to one of these places. Let's say the king moves over here. Now, the king is going to try to stay as close to the center as possible, so let's move the queen a little bit closer, further limiting the king's options. And let's say the king goes here. Then I'm going to move the queen closer, not putting it in check, just forcing the king to move to the second rank or file.

Let's say the king goes there. Next we'll move the queen to third file, so now the king has to stay on the first or second file, like so, and let's say the king goes over here, alright, and so on. I'll move the queen to here, and maybe the king goes there, and I'll move the queen here, so now it's forced to stay on this edge. The king goes here. Now I'll start bringing in the king in for the kill, like that, and like that, and like that. So here's the position. If the king moves here, then you can checkmate the king either this way—checkmate— or, you could checkmate the king that way. And I mention that because this is what you would do if you had had a rook instead of a king. So even if I only had the power of a rook, this would be the checkmating move. On the other hand, if the king had, instead of moving here, if the king had moved there, then, you can checkmate the king this way. But just be careful not to play over here because if you did, well, that would be stalemate and the game would be a draw.

In recent years, our knowledge of the endgame has changed profoundly through the use of computers. Using a dynamic programming process called retrograde analysis, computers have worked backwards from every possible checkmate position with up to six pieces on the board to determine the guaranteed best move from every chess position with six or fewer pieces. For each of these positions the computer can tell us if the position is not a draw, how many moves until the winning player can checkmate the other. For example, it's been shown that if white plays this position just right, white can checkmate black in 262 moves. It's been said that even a grand master would not have a clue how to play such a position perfectly. One chess expert called the moves "scary because you know they are the truth, God's Algorithm—it's like being revealed the Meaning of Life, but you don't understand one word."

By the way, when I see this position involving a king and two knights, it reminds me of something I just learned about chess that completely surprised me. Remember when I said earlier that a king and two knights cannot force checkmate against another king by itself? However, a king and two knights can sometimes force checkmate against a king with a pawn. The reason is that the only way two knights can checkmate the king is if the king is in the corner of the board, but the knights can't force the king there without causing stalemate along the way. But if the king has a pawn that can occasionally move without being promoted to a queen, then the king and two knights can checkmate the king without causing stalemate along the way.

Outside the endgame, computers don't yet play perfect chess. On the other hand, it's fair to say that computers have mastered the game. It was 1996 when a computer first beat the world's best player in a game of chess. The program, Deep Blue, developed by IBM, beat the reigning world champion, Garry Kasparov. Deep Blue was able to example 200 million positions per second. Kasparov won the six-game series with a score of four to two, but, a year later in a rematch, Deep Blue beat Kasparov 3.5 to 2.5. Draws count as half a game for both players. Computers are now dominant in chess. Since 2005, no human has beaten the top computer chess program.

As I said at the beginning, chess is a wonderful game where you get a chance to think logically and creatively, just like doing mathematics. Chess is also a wonderful gateway to many other games of strategy, which we'll explore next lecture. But until then, have a good day, mate!

Winning Ways—It's Your Move!
Lecture 12

opefully, this course has given you a better appreciation of mathematics and games. Aside from being a lot of fun, games are also good for you and society as well. In this course, you've learned some of the calculations you do when playing games, but similar ones can be done in many aspects of your life. In this lecture, you will learn about impartial games, including NIM and chomp. You will also learn how computers and humans match up when it comes to games and puzzles.

NIM

- Very broadly speaking, most games seem to fall into one of three categories. The first one is games where whoever is the last player to move wins. This includes games like chess and checkers, but also games you may not have played before, such as NIM. Second, there are games where the goal is to be the first player to create some sort of structure, like in tic-tac-toe. Third, there are games where the winner is determined by whomever accumulates the most stuff—whether it is the most points, like in Scrabble, or the most territory, like in Go.

- NIM is a two-player game played with several piles of coins. The players take turns removing as many coins as they'd like from any pile. You can only take coins from one pile, and you must take at least one coin. Whoever takes the last coin is the winner. Once you know the math behind this game, you'll almost certainly be able to win against anyone who does not know the secret.

- The optimal strategy was given by the mathematician Charles Bouton in 1901. It was one of the first games ever to be given a complete mathematical strategy. Suppose the game reduces to a single pile of coins, then the optimal strategy is obvious: If it's your turn, just take all the coins and you win.

- Suppose the game has just two piles of coins: One pile has nine coins, and the other has five coins. If you take four coins away from the larger pile, then both piles now have five coins. Because both piles have the same number of coins, you can now win, by using a symmetry strategy. Thus, you are guaranteed to take the last coin.

- With two-pile NIM, the good positions, the ones that you want to create, are those that have two piles with an equal number of coins. The bad positions, which you don't want to create, are those that have two piles with a different number of coins. If you give your opponent two equal piles, then your opponent must make them unequal. Any move that they make, because they're only allowed to take from one pile, is going to cause those piles to be unequal.

- Conversely, when your opponent gives you two unequal piles, you can always make them equal again just by taking from the larger pile until the sizes are the same. That's a general feature of games like this. From a good position, all of your opponent's moves go to bad positions, and when your opponent moves to a bad position, there will always be at least one move that will take you to a good position.

- Suppose that you have a NIM position with three or more piles to choose from. In this case, the situation becomes much more interesting. In fact, you can still win this game by exploiting symmetry, but in a not-so-obvious way. It's based on the fact that all numbers can be uniquely expressed using powers of two.

- For example, the numbers one through seven can each be represented using the numbers one, two, and four, as follows.

$$1$$

$$2$$

$$3 = 2 + 1$$

$$4$$

$$5 = 4 + 1$$

$$6 = 4 + 2$$

$$7 = 4 + 2 + 1$$

- By inserting the number eight, we can get the numbers eight through 15, and so on.

$$8$$

$$9 = 8 + 1$$

$$10 = 8 + 2$$

$$11 = 8 + 2 + 1$$

$$12 = 8 + 4$$

$$13 = 8 + 4 + 1$$

$$14 = 8 + 4 + 2$$

$$15 = 8 + 4 + 2 + 1$$

- Suppose you were playing three-pile NIM, and the piles had sizes 13, 10, and 6. What should you do? If we write each number in terms of powers of 2, we get the following: 13 can be expressed as $8 + 4 + 1$, 10 as $8 + 2$, and 6 as $4 + 2$.

$$13 = 8 + 4 + \quad + 1$$

$$10 = 8 + \quad \quad 2$$

$$6 = \quad \quad 4 + 2$$

- To reach a good position, you want to get an even number of 8s, 4s, 2s, and 1s. In this situation, you already have an even number of 8s, an even number of 4s, and an even number of 2s, but you have an odd number of 1s. By eliminating the 1 from the first number—that is, by turning 13 into 12—you arrive at a good position. This is a good position because any move that your opponent makes is guaranteed to cause an 8, 4, 2, or 1 to appear an odd number of times.

- For example, suppose your opponent takes three coins from the 10 pile, turning 10 into 7. Writing 7 in terms of powers of 2, you get that 7 is 4 + 2 + 1. You now have one 8, three 4s, two 2s, and one 1. You now have an odd number of 8s, an odd number of 4s, and an odd number of 1s.

$$12 = 8 + 4$$

$$7 = \quad 4 + 2 + 1$$

$$6 = \quad 4 + 2$$

- In order to get an even number of 8s, you're going to have to go from one 8 to no 8s. That can only happen if you take coins from the pile of 12. You also need to lose a 4 because you have three 4s, which is an odd number of 4s, and you need to gain a 1 because you have one 1 and need to get two of them (an even number of them). Hence, the 12 pile has to transform into the following.

$$1 = \qquad + 1$$

$$7 = \quad 4 + 2 + 1$$

$$6 = \quad 4 + 2$$

- Therefore, the winning move—in fact, the only winning move—is to reduce 12 coins down to one coin. You have two 4s, two 2s, and two 1s, so you have reached a good position, and if it's your opponent's turn to move, any move he or she makes is going to disrupt the parity of the 1s, 2s, and 4s. At least one of those parities has to change, giving your opponent a bad position. Then, you can restore that to a good position.

- Almost all impartial games can be viewed as special cases of the game NIM. The major tools used in the analysis are two of the major problem-solving themes of this course: reducing to smaller problems and taking advantage of parity.

Chomp

- Chomp is an interesting impartial game that is not equivalent to NIM because the player who makes the last move is the loser, not the winner, in chomp. The game of chomp starts with a rectangle—for example, an eight-by-four checkerboard. Players take turns chomping off squares from the board. When a square is chomped off, it is removed, along with all squares above it and to the right of it.

- Players take turns chomping off squares, and the goal is to not take the last square, which is located in the bottom left corner of the board and is known as the poison square. This rule is needed to keep the game interesting. Otherwise, the game would end on the first move because the first player would just chomp the square in the bottom left corner, and everything would be chomped off.

- Once an optimal strategy is found, a mathematical proof has shown that it has to be a win for the first player. This argument works for a rectangular board of any size with more than one square in it.

- Suppose that you are the first player. What should your first move be? Consider the position when you chomp off only the upper right corner. That creates either a good position or a bad position.

							chomp

- If it's a good position, then, assuming you play perfectly, your opponent can't prevent you from winning from that position. If it's a bad position, then that means that your opponent can somehow force a win by making a chomping move from that position that will give him or her a good position that you can't beat.

- Suppose that your opponent's winning response to your move is to chomp off the square in the following position.

- Then, that would make the following a winning position that you could not defeat.

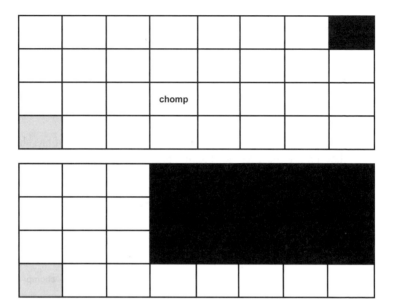

- However, if that's a theoretically unbeatable position, then you could have made that move yourself on the first move, resulting in that same position, and then you would have a forced win from that position. In other words, playing the top corner is either a winning move or it's not. If it's a winning move, then you make it. If it's not a winning move, then you can legally play the response to that move and win from there. Mathematicians call this sort of argument an existence proof. You know who the winner is; you just don't know how the winner wins.

Games and Puzzles: Computers versus Humans

- The easiest games for computers are those where they can play perfectly from any position, including tic-tac-toe and NIM. Next in difficulty are games that computers know how to play perfectly from the beginning of the game, but not necessarily if thrown into a random middle position that it would never reach if it played well from the beginning. These include games like checkers.

- What's more interesting are the games where humans and computers are still pretty close in terms of ability. For example, it seems that computers are among the world's best players in chess, backgammon, Scrabble, Yahtzee, and the television game show *Jeopardy!*, but there are still some games that humans, at least for the top-performing people, still have an edge over computers—at least for now. Although there has been a lot of progress in the last decade, computers are not yet considered to be the top players of bridge, poker, or go.

- Mathematics, games, and puzzles all begin with a set of objects that have various rules defined for them. For instance, with chess or Rubik's Cube, you have pieces that move in certain ways. In mathematics, you have numbers that combine in different ways, and the better you are at combining these rules, the more often you'll be successful at defeating your opponent, solving the puzzle, or proving the theorem. Games, puzzles, and mathematics all provide great intellectual satisfaction, and they're all a lot of fun once you get the hang of them.

Suggested Reading

Albert, Nowakowski, and Wolfe, *Lessons in Play.*

Beasley, *The Mathematics of Games.*

Berlekamp, Conway, and Guy, *Winning Ways for Your Mathematical Plays.*

Epstein, *The Theory of Gambling and Statistical Logic.*

Guy, *Fair Game.*

Juhnke, *Beginning Arimaa.*

Nowakowski, *Games of No Chance.*

Stewart, *How to Cut a Cake and Other Mathematical Conundrums.*

Wells, *Book of Curious and Interesting Puzzles.*

1. Suppose a rook starts at the bottom left corner of a chessboard, and two players take turns moving the rook. On a player's turn, the rook can either be moved horizontally in the eastward direction or vertically in the northward direction. The player who brings the rook to the northeast corner is the winner.

   a. On an eight-by-eight board, what are the winning positions, and who has the advantage in this game?

   b. On a four-by-eight board, what are the winning positions, and who has the advantage in this game?

2. The following questions apply to the game of NIM.

   a. Find the only winning move when the piles have sizes 24, 14, and 19.

   b. If, for this turn only, you can add coins to a pile, then find two other winning moves.

3. On an eight-by-eight checkerboard, show that chomping the point (2,2) (diagonally next to the *poison* square (1,1)) is a winning move for the first player.

Winning Ways—It's Your Move!
Lecture 12—Transcript

In our previous lecture, we focused on the game of chess, but of course, there are many other games of strategy that lead to interesting mathematical questions, and armed with the proper insights, these games and questions can be conquered by the mathematically inclined player. Very broadly speaking, most games seem to fall into one of three categories. One, games where whoever is the last player to move wins. This includes games like chess and checkers, but also games you may not have played before like NIM, Cram, and Domineering. Two, there are games where the goal is to be the first player to create some sort of structure like in tic-tac-toe, Hex, or Connect Four. And thirdly, there are games where the winner is determined by whoever accumulates the most stuff, whether it be the most points like in Scrabble, or the most territory in games like Go. I'll say a little bit about all three of these types of games in this lecture.

In Lecture 1, we were introduced to the game of Cram where two players take turns placing dominoes on a checkerboard. Whoever places the last domino is the winner. We saw that the second player could force a win by imitating the first player's moves in a symmetric way, but, suppose we were shown a random, nonsymmetric position, like this one. Played on a four-by-eight board, here, if it's your turn to move, can you find a winning move? I'll answer that question later.

Here's another game that can be played on a checkerboard, sometimes called Northcott's Game. White and black have eight checkers that they're allowed to move along the columns of the checkerboard. They're only allowed to move forwards, not backwards, and they're not allowed to go past the opposing checker. For example, if you move here, then I can't move this checker anywhere past here. As in the game of Cram, whoever makes the last move is the winner.

If both players start in this position, then do you see a winning strategy? Here, the second player can force a win by adopting a symmetric strategy. Let's say the first player moves this checker forwards five spaces. Let's say you went one, two, three, four, five. Then, the second player can move this checker five spaces, one, two, three, four, five. If you move this checker up two, then I'll move this checker up two, and so on. By playing in this way, the second player is guaranteed to make the last move. It's not a very interesting game I agree, but now suppose you saw some other unsymmetrical, random position like this. Now, what's the winning strategy? Again, not so clear.

In this lecture, I'll teach you how to play this game perfectly, but first we need to learn about an important mathematical game. The game is known as NIM, which may come from the word for "take". Notice that if you turn the word NIM upside down, you get WIN, and indeed, once you know the math behind it, you'll almost certainly be able to win against anyone who does not know the secret.

NIM is a two-player game played with several piles of coins. The players take turns removing as many coins as they'd like from any pile. You can only take coins from one pile, and you must take at least one coin. Whoever takes the last coin is the winner. For example, suppose there are three piles of coins with seven here, five here, and four there, and then you take four coins from here; then I take two coins from here. Then you take one coin from here and so on. Whoever takes the last coin is the winner. So, how should you play this game?

Now the optimal strategy was given by the mathematician Charles Bouton in 1901. It was one of the first games ever to be given a complete mathematical strategy. Suppose the game reduces to a single pile of coins, then the optimal strategy is obvious. If it's your turn, just take all the coins, and you win. Not a very interesting game. Now suppose the game has just two piles of coins. Let's say one pile has nine coins and the other has five coins. Then what would you do? If you take four coins away from the larger pile, then both piles now have five coins. Since both piles have the same number of coins, you can now win, by using a symmetry strategy. Do you see it?

If I take two coins from this pile, then you take two from that pile. If I take one from here, then you take one from there, and so on. Thus, you are guaranteed to take the last coin. To summarize, with two-pile NIM the good positions, the ones that you want to create, are those that have two piles with an equal number of coins. The bad positions, which you don't want to create, are those that have two piles with a different number of coins. Notice that if you give your opponent two equal piles, then your opponent must make them unequal. Any move that they make, since they're only allowed to take from one pile, is going to cause those pile to be unequal. And conversely, when your opponent gives you two unequal piles, you can always make them equal again, just by taking from the larger pile until the sizes are the same. That's a general feature of games like this. From a good position, all of your opponent's moves go to bad positions, and when your opponent moves to a bad position, there will always be at least one move that will take you to a good position.

Now suppose that you have a NIM position with three or more piles to choose from. Here the situation becomes much more interesting, yet, believe it or not, you can still win this game by exploiting symmetry, but in a not-so-obvious way. It's based on the fact that all numbers can be uniquely expressed using powers of two. For example, the numbers one through seven can each be represented using the numbers one, two and four, like so. By inserting the number eight, we can get the numbers eight through 15, and so on. Now suppose you were playing three-pile NIM, and the piles had sizes 13, 10, and 6. What should you do? If we write each number in terms of powers of two, we get 13 can be expressed as $8 + 4 + 1$; 10 is $8 + 2$, and 6 is $4 + 2$. To reach a good position, you want to get an even number of eights, fours, twos, and ones.

Now look at our situation, we already have an even number of eights, and an even number of fours, and an even number of twos, but we have an odd number of ones. So what do you do? By eliminating the one from the first number, that is by turning 13 into 12, we arrive at a good position. Why is this a good position? What makes it good? Notice that any move that your opponent makes is guaranteed to cause an eight, four, two, or one to appear an odd number of times. For example, suppose your opponent takes three coins from the 10 pile, turning 10 into seven. If we write seven in terms of powers of two, we get that seven is $4 + 2 + 1$. We now have one eight, three fours, two twos and one one. So, what do we have now? Now we have an odd number of eights, an odd number of fours, and an odd number of ones. So how can you get even with your opponent?

In order to get an even number of eights, we're going to have to go from one eight to no eights. So that can only happen if we take coins from the pile of 12. Now what else do we need to do? We need to lose a four because right now we have three fours; that's an odd number. And we need to gain a one because right now we have one one, and we need to get two of them. We need to get an even number of them. So, hence the 12 pile has to go from this to that. So the winning move, and in fact, the only winning move is to reduce 12 coins down to one coin. Now you'll notice we have two fours, two twos, and two ones, so we have reached a good position, and if it's your opponent's turn to move, any move they make is going to disrupt the parity of the ones, twos and fours. At least one of those parities has to change, giving them a bad position, and then we can restore that to a good position just like we did.

Now you may ask what would happen if the game started in this position and you had to go first. What should you do? The answer is to make a small move that doesn't make it obvious for your opponent. For instance, in this position don't remove the coin from pile one because now you'd have a two-pile position, and that would simplify the game too much. I might just take one or two coins from the seven pile or maybe from the six pile. Suppose you took one coin from the six pile, giving us this position. So counting the fours, twos, and ones, we have even, odd, odd, so the winning move must change the parity of the twos and the ones because they are both odd. There's only one way to do it. Do you see it?

Well in order to have an even number of twos I'm going to have to deal with the seven pile. So, in that second pile you must lose a two and a one going from here to there, turning seven into four. As I said before, once you know the secret to winning at NIM you can pretty much beat anyone who doesn't know it.

By the way, once you know the secret winning strategy for NIM, you can even give your opponent some extra options and you'll still be able to win. For example, you can let them keep the coins that they remove and allow them to add those coins to a pile if they wish. This is sometimes called poker NIM. Now this only delays the inevitable because you can immediately reverse or undo their move. For example, if you move to the winning position, one, two, three—you see that's a winning position—and your opponent adds seven coins to the first pile creating eight, two, three, then you can reverse that move simply by taking those seven coins away and bringing it back to one, two, three.

We've spent a lot of time talking about NIM because many games are really just NIM in disguise. For example, remember Northcott's Game at the beginning of the lecture? Here, white and black took turns moving checkers towards each other along the columns of the checkerboard. That game was really just a dressed-up version of NIM, since you could think of each column as representing a pile where the number of coins is the number of spaces between them. So for example, in this position, this represents the number one, this represents one, this represents two, three, four, five, six, and five, so that would be the NIM position, and if your opponent moved, let's say, this up, right now there are five spaces between them. If you move this up two, now there are three spaces between you. That would be like going from a pile of five chips down to a pile of three chips. I'll leave it as an exercise for you to show that one of the winning moves from this position would be going from a pile of four down to a pile of one, so here I see a pile of four. How do I make it a pile of one? I put one space in between, and now, I, if I'm playing this position, am in a winning position.

Now, again, notice that I can win even if I let you move backwards. That's just like adding coins to a pile, which I can undo by moving checkers forward the same amount. So for instance, if you say I'm going to move this back three, well, then I'll move my checker forward three, and I've maintained the same distance that I had before.

Even a game like Cram, where players take turns placing dominoes on our checkerboard, that's actually a giant version of NIM. This, believe it or not, is NIM in disguise, but it's not so obvious why. Now here are some features that Cram and NIM have in common. First of all, the players take turns making moves. They're placing dominoes on the board. Whoever makes the last move wins. The games are finite meaning they can't go on forever. At some point, we run out of space or we run out of chips. And, very importantly, the game is impartial. What that means is that for any position, both players have the same move options available, right? I'm allowed to put pieces down horizontally or vertically. The same rules apply to you.

For example, in Cram, either player can put their dominoes anywhere on the board, but in the game of Domineering, white can only place dominoes horizontally, and black can only place dominoes vertically. That would not be impartial. Such games are called partisan. Typically, a partisan game has pieces of two different colors, like in the games of chess, checkers, and go. Those are partisan games. Now what makes NIM such a fundamentally important game is the following theorem proved independently by mathematicians R.P. Sprague and P.M. Grundy in the 1930s. It essentially says this: Every finite, impartial game where whoever makes the last move wins, can be transformed into a game of NIM. That's why NIM is such an essential game to master.

For example, consider the Cram position that we saw earlier. Notice that, really, you can break this down into five regions, five connected regions. In a very real sense, this region acts like one coin, since if we move here, there's nothing left. It's like removing the one coin. Likewise, this region is like a single coin, and this region actually behaves like two piles of one coin each, since if you place a domino wherever, like, say, here, your opponent can mimic it. If you place a domino here, your opponent can mimic it. It's like having two separate coins. If you take one, then I'll take the other. So in a very real sense, this region acts like two piles of one coin, which, for all practical purposes, is like a single pile with zero coins.

This region here acts like a pile of two coins. Why is that? There are three possible moves. Making a move like this or that leaves us a position with value one, and moving like this, gives us two single squares, which have a value of zero. So since we can legally move to a position of value zero or a position of value one, that's just like having two coins where we can move to either a pile with one chip or zero chips. So we assign it a value of two. By the way, these values are sometimes referred to as Nimbers.

Finally, it can be shown that this position here has nimber three, since depending on how you move, you either create a position of value two, or value one, or value zero. This acts like a zero position. And, for that matter, this acts like a one position, and this acts like a two position. Since we can reach the Nimbers zero, one, or two, this is just like a pile of three coins, so we give this region a value of three. Altogether our position here is equivalent to a NIM position with coin sizes zero, one, one, two and three. If it's your turn to move, what should you do? Well, you can win by turning a one into a zero, giving us a good position, zero, one, two, three. You can see that zero, one, two, three is a winning position, so that's the move you should make. Or, you could turn the three into a two, and that would give you a good position, a more obviously good position, zero, one, one, two, two. You have a very symmetric position that you can mimic your opponent's strategy by using symmetry.

There are a few other minor details, but the take home message is this: Almost all impartial games can be viewed as special cases of the game NIM. And the major tools used in the analysis are two of the major problem-solving themes of this course: reducing to smaller problems and taking advantage of parity.

Here's an interesting impartial game that's not equivalent to NIM called Chomp. The game of Chomp starts with a rectangle. Let's say this eight-by-four checkerboard. Players take turns chomping off squares from the board. When a square is chomped off, it is removed along with all squares above it and to the right of it. For example, if the first player chomps here, then all of these squares are removed from the board. If the next player chomps here, then all of these squares are removed. Players take turns chomping off squares, but now the goal is to not take the last square, which we can think of as poison. You don't want to take the last square. This rule is needed to keep the game interesting; otherwise the game would end on the first move. The first player would just take that square, and everything would be chomped off.

Because the player who makes the last move is the loser, not the winner, this game is not equivalent to NIM. In fact, I don't know the optimal strategy for Chomp, but there is a beautiful proof that once an optimal strategy is found, it will have to be a win for the first player. The argument works for any-sized rectangular board with more than one square in it, and here's how it goes. Suppose I go first. I'm the first player. I want to prove that I have a winning strategy. What should my first move be? Consider the position when I chomp off only the upper, right corner. Now that's either a good position or a bad position. If I chomp off the upper right corner, what is it? Is it good or bad? I don't know.

If it's a good position, then assuming I play perfectly, then my opponent can't prevent me from winning from here. If it's a bad position, then that means that my opponent can somehow force a win. That means that my opponent can make a chomping move from here that will give him a good position that I can't beat. Let's suppose his winning response to my move is to chomp off this square. Then that would make this a winning position that I could not defeat. But wait a second. If that's a theoretically unbeatable position, then I could've made that move myself on the first move, resulting in that same position, and then I would have a forced win from here. In other words, playing the top corner is either a winning move or it's not. If it's a winning move, then I make it. If it's not a winning move, then I can legally play the response to that move and win from there. Q.E.D.

Mathematicians call this sort of argument, an existence proof. You know who the winner is; you just don't know how. This is reminiscent of something we saw in the very first lecture with the game of Hex. In Hex, the red player is trying to build a bridge from the red sides before blue builds a bridge from the blue sides. For example, here's a game that was just won by red. In Lecture 1 we proved that Hex can never end in a draw, and as a consequence of that, if we ever discover how to play the game perfectly, it's a guarantee that it will be a win for the player who goes first. As you might suspect on this 11-x-11 board, the strongest first move would be in the dead center of the board, like so. But this move is so strong that in most Hex matches online and in tournaments, they give the second player an interesting option. Let's say that red goes first. On blue's turn, blue can either place her piece anywhere, or she can decide that she likes red's position even more and decide to play the game as red instead of blue; then the rest of the game continues in the normal way. The result of this option is that red's first move won't be too strong, since that move could be used against him. Theoretically, this makes the game a win for the second player, since if the first player's move is bad, then the second player accepts it and wins from there. But if the first player's move is good, then the second player just adopts it and wins from there. Either way, the second player wins.

By adopting this rule, the game tends to get off to a very balanced start since the opening move can't be too weak or too strong, or at least it's not in the first player's interests to begin with a very strong move or a very weak move.

In the gaming community, this type of rule is known as the pie rule, since it's reminiscent of dividing a pie or a cake.

This leads to an interesting mathematical tangent. Suppose two people wish to share a cake. How can it be done so that both people are satisfied that they each have at least half of the cake? Let me bring out a cake for you.

The simplest solution is to let one person cut the cake into two pieces and let the other one choose which half they want. This gives the first person every incentive to divide the cake as evenly as possible, because if it's too asymmetric, they're going to come out the loser.

What if there are three or more people? How can everyone be assured of getting the right proportion of cake? Here's a way that three people can split the cake so that everyone thinks they got at least a third of it. One person moves the knife from one side of the cake to the other. So here's player one, they go, moving it to my right here, right, right, right, until one person says stop. Maybe it's the person with the knife, maybe it's one of the other two. At that point, whoever shouts first, stop, must be convinced that they have at least $1/3$ of the cake because otherwise they wouldn't have said stop. So whoever called stop must be satisfied with their situation. The other two people feel as if at least $2/3$ of the cake remains because otherwise one of them would have said stop. So now, what's remaining is cut in half by the previous method, so somebody who doesn't have this piece of cake takes the knife, and then they're asked to cut while the other person chooses.

So now it's cut in half by the previous method, so now each of them will feel that they have at least $1/3$ of the cake so everyone is satisfied. This method can be easily extended to four or more people too. Of course, the problem can get trickier when you have indivisible quantities like cars, and houses, or even pizzas that are half pepperoni and half anchovies when the people have different tastes. There's been an enormous amount of work in what are called fair division problems by mathematicians and economists, so you might say that what I've shown you is just the icing on the cake.

Let's get back to games. My favorite game of strategy for children is the game Connect Four, also known as Four in a Line, or the Captain's Mistress.

You can think of it as a more complex version of tic-tac-toe. There are two players, white and black, and we'll say that white will always go first. The players take turns dropping checkers into a grid that has six rows and seven columns, so let's say in the middle of the game here, black plays here, and white plays here, and black plays here, and so on. The object of the game is to be the first player to get four of their checkers in a line, either four in a row, four in a column, or four diagonally. For example, in this position if it's white's turn to move, then white can win by playing right over here, or even right up here on top. But that's a winning move because he has four on the diagonal.

The reason I like this game so much for kids is that at each turn there are, at most, seven possible choices, not dozens of choices, like in chess, but enough to keep it interesting. Unlike the other games we've played in this lecture, this game can result in a tie, but if white plays perfectly, she can always force a win. But if white deviates from the perfect strategy, then black can often win, or at least force a draw. When I play this game with children, I let them play white and use two checkers on the first move. Although the game's been around for many decades, it was only solved in 1988 when white's optimal strategy was discovered. Can you guess what is white's best opening move?

The best first opening move is for white to play in the center column, like so. That makes intuitive sense since there are seven lines that use that center point. You could get four in a row, either this four in a row, this four in a row, this four in a row, this four in a row. You can get four in a row vertically. You can get four in a row from this diagonal. You can get four in a row from that diagonal, so there are seven lines that use this point. By contrast, the other checker locations can appear on either three, four, or five lines. As I've said, when white starts in the middle, she can force a win by playing properly. If she starts one column to the left or right of center, then she can't force a win. And black can force at least a draw. And surprisingly, if white starts in one of these other four locations, then black can actually force a win if he plays properly.

In case you're wondering, here are black's best opening moves. If white starts anywhere but the center, then black should play right next to that checker on the side closest to the center. So for instance, if white plays here, then black should go right next to it here. Whereas if white played in that spot, if white plays here, then black should play in the center there. And by the way, if white plays in the center, what should black do? Well, although in theory white can force a win from here so black can't force a win or draw, black's best response is right on top of that white checker, like so.

This game is fundamentally different from tic-tac-toe in a few ways. First of all, although the first player has an advantage, the second player has lots of winning chances. For example, it was shown that if the first three moves of the game were played completely at random, white randomly drops a checker, then black randomly drops a checker, then white randomly drops a checker, and both players play perfectly after that, then more often than not, it's black that wins the game.

Here are four tips for winning Connect Four. Many of these tips apply to other games as well. Tip number one: Appreciate the center column. Notice that every four in a row horizontally, I should say, and every four on a diagonal must intersect the center column. See how fundamental that center column is? In fact, the only way to win without using the center column is with four consecutive checkers in a single column, so the more checkers you have in the middle column, the better your chances are. It's obvious once it's pointed out to you, but prior to that, I didn't know that. We saw this idea in chess as well. Pieces that are near the center of the board tend to have more mobility and influence than pieces kept near the boundary.

Tip number two: Create and guard against double threats. Just like in chess, it's often good to try to do two things at once. For example, if you can get an open-ended three in a row, then you're guaranteed four in a row on your next turn. Tip number three: Make forcing moves that threaten four in a row, directly or indirectly. Try to set up two ways to win so that in order for your opponent to not lose the first way, they have to lose the second way. For example, in this position here, it's black's turn to play, and black would like to force white to play here so black can win here. Black can do that by playing here, threatening to make this diagonal. When white plays here to stop it, black will win there. And tip number four: Be patient and ponder parity. If you wait long enough and parity is on your side, your opponent will be forced to play into your hands. We've seen how parity plays an important role in many games and puzzles, including NIM, peg solitaire, and chess. In fact, the experts in this game, use the same term, zugzwang, for moving when you don't want to.

Let's see how it applies to Connect Four. In this position, black has $^3/_4$ of a diagonal, and if white plays here, then black will win. It would be a mistake for black to play there now since white would simply block the threat here. But black can just wait patiently and play in the other six columns. Since there are 23 unoccupied places in the other columns, then the 24th move will be made by white in the fifth column, allowing black to win on the next turn. By the way, you'll notice that black's winning move occurs in the second row. Because each column has six spaces, black will usually win in row two, four or six, while white will typically win in row one, three or five. The general rules and the optimal strategy were discovered through a combination of careful, logical thinking and a smart use of computers to find a set of rules for playing the game that made the program unbeatable.

One of the first programs to play perfectly was called Victor, named because it never lost, and from the first name of its programmer, Victor Allis, who solved the problem as part of his Master's thesis on artificial intelligence. Computers have solved many other games as well. For example, in 2007, the game of checkers was officially proved to be a draw if both players don't make any mistakes. The proof was brute force to the extreme. It began with a complete solution to all games with fewer than 10 checkers on the board. That's about 39 trillion positions. Then it took another 18 years, at one point using more than 200 computers working on the problem full time. Even still, the game was only solved in the weak sense, in that they proved that neither player can force a win. To solve the game completely, they would need to be able to determine the best move from every conceivable position. Such is the case with games like Connect Four and NIM, but not games like checkers.

Nonetheless, the program that was finished in 2007, called Chinook, cannot be beaten, but it took many years to reach that stage. Along the way, the program had to compete with some pretty smart humans, most notably a mathematician named Dr. Marion Tinsley. Tinsley was, without a doubt, the strongest checker player that ever lived. In his 45 years of playing tournament checkers, having played thousands of games, Marion Tinsley had only lost seven games, two of which were against the computer Chinook. On the other hand, he had four wins against Chinook before it knew how to play perfectly. In one championship match, the computer made a mistake on the 10th move. Tinsley said, "You're going to regret that," and won the game 26 moves later. Apparently, he found the only winning line of attack because Tinsley was able to look more moves ahead. A few years later the computer would be able to look even farther, but Tinsley passed away before they could ever finish a rematch.

The computer went on to beat the second best player in the world, and it is now, certainly, unbeatable—certifiably unbeatable. In the 1990s Chinook was the first computer program to ever win the world-champion title in a competition against humans. Shortly after that, great progress was made in computer chess, mostly due to faster processing speed and the ability to look deeper at every position.

Some people say that computers take the fun out of a game, but I think they often lead humans to better understand the games and puzzles that we enjoy. For instance, computers have led us to some enormous breakthroughs, recently with Rubik's Cube and Sudoku. Prior to 2010, we did not have proof that every cube could be solved within 20 moves or that every Sudoku puzzle requires at least 17 clues. Computers can also teach us how to become much better at games and puzzles ourselves. For example, in the game of backgammon, thanks to computers using neural net technology, experts play backgammon very differently than they did 10 to 20 years ago. The best computer programs now are considered to be as strong or stronger than the best players in the world.

I'm pretty sure that if you played one of these programs for an hour a day, taking note of all the mistakes that you made, then by the end of the year you would be a very strong player. In fact, if you then invented a time machine and went back in time 30 or more years, you'd be one of the strongest players in the world.

Something similar occurred with the game of Scrabble. The best Scrabble programs play as strong as the top human players and serve as a serious learning tool for any aspiring players.

Computers can improve our ability with puzzles, too. For example, there are lots of apps for improving your Sudoku. My favorite one is by Jason Linhart called *Enjoy Sudoku*, which works on most electronic devices. You can take a picture of a Sudoku, and it will load it into your phone or tablet, or you can enter a puzzle manually, or you can ask it for a puzzle of any desired difficulty. Best of all, when you get stuck it'll provide you with the simplest hint that will allow you to make progress on the puzzle, and if the hint doesn't make sense to you, like look for a hidden pair, it offers tutorials.

So what are the most difficult games for humans and computers to play? The easiest games, at least for computers, are those where they can play perfectly from any position, including tic-tac-toe, Connect Four, NIM, and Ghost. Next in difficulty are games that computers know how to play perfectly from the beginning of the game, but not necessarily if thrown into a random middle position that it would never reach if it played well from the beginning. These include games like checkers and Othello. What's more interesting are the games where humans and computers are still pretty close. For example, it seems that computers are among the world's best players in chess, backgammon, Scrabble, Othello, Yahtzee, and the TV game show *Jeopardy!* But there are still some games that humans, at least for the top performing people, still have an edge over computers, at least for now.

Although there's been a lot of progress in the last decade, computers are not yet considered to be the top players of bridge or poker. Even farther down the line is the ancient Chinese game of Go. The game of Go is played on a 19-x-19 board.—that's 361 possible spaces—and stones are allowed to placed anywhere on the board, thus for most of the game, a player has around 200 possible moves per turn, compared with chess where there are on average just a few dozen possible moves per turn. This makes the game much harder for computers to analyze, and the best computers have yet to beat any professional players. In fact, from 1985 to 2000, there was a $1 million prize offered for the first computer program that could beat a professional Go player. That prize money was never collected.

The game of Go has been analyzed for much smaller board sizes, but the strategy for mini-Go is much different from the traditional game. Although progress in game-playing software has been made in the last few years, you could say that there's still a long way to go.

What is it about games and puzzles that attracts mathematicians? Mathematics, games and puzzles all begin with a set of objects that have various rules defined for them. For instance, with chess or Rubik's Cube you have pieces that move in certain ways. In mathematics, you have numbers that combine in different ways. And the better you are at combining these rules, the more often you'll be successful at defeating your opponent, solving the puzzle, or proving the theorem.

Games, puzzles and mathematics all provide great intellectual satisfaction, and they're all a lot of fun once you get the hang of it. We've seen that how assigning numerical quantities to our game often leads to better play. For instance, in blackjack, we keep track of a running pip count. In chess and bridge we assign the pieces and cards numerical values, and in most impartial games, we can assign numbers called Nimbers that tell us almost everything we need to know about a position.

Well, we've come to the end of this course. I hope it's given you a better appreciation of mathematics and games. Aside from being a lot of fun, games are also good for you and society as well. Games train you to be a decisive decision-maker. We take calculated risks every day of our lives. In this course, we've learned some of the calculations you do when playing games, but similar ones can be done in many aspects of your life. When faced with different possible choices of action, try to look at the downside and the upside, the risk and reward. Playing games and solving puzzles can be a lot of fun and the better you understand these games, the more you will win, which adds to your enjoyment. But even your losses can be valuable learning experiences. By studying why you lost, it makes you a better player, and ultimately, a better decision-maker.

Games and puzzles are great for kids. For example, some schools are now teaching Rubik's Cube in the classroom. Now why do they do this? Not because it will help them understand quantum physics, although the movement of the corner cubes is similar to the behavior of quarks, I'm told. But rather, it's because it teaches the value of practice and reinforces the idea that sometimes, to reach your long-term goal, you need to achieve many intermediate goals along the way. I've seen many college students who were able to use their prowess at various games to get interviews and jobs with companies.

A former research student of mine told me that he got a job with Yahoo as a programmer despite having very few programming courses because he was an expert at playing a new game called Arimaa. Yahoo figured that anyone who reached such a level of expertise would have to be a creative, smart, and competitive person, so they took a calculated risk and hired him. He wound up writing software for them, which they patented, that saved the company a ton of money.

Games are a great family activity that can be appreciated on multiple levels by children and adults. They're also a fun way to learn some interesting mathematics, and of course, games and puzzles are a great way to keep your mind active and sharp. Games have benefits for society, too. Scientists have turned some of their mysteries into puzzles and games and have brought them to the gaming community. As people worked to improve their score, scientists have been able to obtain a better understanding about things like how proteins fold and multiply, and that's led to the design of new life-saving drugs.

But of course, the main reason we play games and solve puzzles is to have fun and experience the intellectual satisfaction of rising to a challenge. I've had a great deal of fun preparing this course for you and have a better understanding of many more games and puzzles because of it, and I hope you have as well. Thank you for joining me.

Solutions

LECTURE 1

1. Moving backward with multiples of 7, you see that $51 - (7 \times 7) = 2$. So, the first player can force a win by starting with 2 and then, on successive turns, jumping to the totals 9, 16, 23, 30, 37, 44, and finally 51.

2. Play in the upper left corner, forcing your opponent to play in the middle top. Then, play in the central square, and you will win on the following turn.

3. The largest piece can go on three pegs. Then, the next largest piece has three choices. Then, the next largest piece has three choices, and so on. Hence, a position can be created in $3 \times 3 \times \ldots \times 3 = 3n$ ways. By placing the pegs down from largest to smallest, you are assured of creating a legal position.

LECTURE 2

1.

    a.   There are $6 \times 6 \times 6 = 216$ equally likely ways to roll three different-colored dice. Because six of these are three of a kind (namely, (1,1,1), (2,2,2), ... (6,6,6)), then the probability of three of a kind is $6/216 = 1/36$. Another way to do this problem is that regardless of what the first die is, the second die has a 1/6 chance of matching it, and the third die also has a 1/6 chance of matching it. Hence, the probability is $1/6 \times 1/6 = 1/36$.

    b.   Consider any roll (x, y, z) where the sum $x + y + z \leq 10$. By "flipping the dice over," you create the roll $(7 - x, 7 - y, 7 - z)$ with a sum of $21 - (x + y + z)$, which will necessarily be greater than or equal to 11 (because $x + y + z$ is at most 10). Hence, every small roll "holds hands" with a large roll. So, by symmetry, half the dice rolls (108 of them) will be small, and half will be large.

c. There are 108 small rolls, but you lose if the three dice are (1,1,1), (2,2,2), or (3,3,3). Hence, your chance of winning a small bet is 105/216 = 35/72 (and your chance of losing is, therefore, 37/72).

d. Your expected value on a "small" $1 bet is 35/72(1) + 37/72(–1) = –2/72 = –1/36 = –0.027777... . Hence, you expect to lose about 2.8 cents per dollar bet.

2. The number of ways to roll 2, 3, 4, 9, 10, 11, or 12 is (1 + 2 + 3 + 4 + 3 + 2 + 1)/36 = 16/36. Its expected value is 2(2/36) + 1(14/36) – 1(20/36) = –2/36 ≈ –0.0555. So, you lose, on average, about 5.55 cents per dollar bet.

3.

a. Treating $5 as a single betting unit, this is the same problem as when you start with 3 units and your goal is to reach 12 units before going broke. For a fair game, the probability of success is 3/12 = 1/4 = 0.25.

b. The chance of winning two bets in a row is (0.5)(0.5) = 0.25.

c. Apply the gambler's ruin formula with p = 0.6 and q = 0.4, so q/p = 2/3. Thus, if you start with 3 units and bet 1 unit at a time, the probability of reaching 12 units is (1 – (2/3)^3)/(1 – (2/3)^{12}) = (0.7037...)/(0.9923...) ≈ 0.7092. This is much better than placing two big bets in a row, where the chance of success is just (0.6)(0.6) = 0.36.

LECTURE 3

1. hit

2. stand

3. split

4. double down

5. stand

6. hit

7. double down

8. hit

9. stand

10. hit

11. stand

12. hit

13. double down

14. stand

15. hit

16. double down

17. double down

18. hit

19. split

20. double down

21. You would need at least 1/3 of the 26 cards to be 10, J, Q, or K, so at least 9 of the 26 must be 10, J, Q, or K.

LECTURE 4

1. Suppose that Rose plays row 1 with probability x and row 2 with probability $1 - x$. Then, when Colin plays column 1, her expected payoff is $2x - 5(1 - x) = 7x - 5$. When Colin plays column 2, her expected payoff is $-3x + 8(1 - x) = 8 - 11x$. These lines intersect when $7x - 5 = 8 - 11x$, which happens when $18x = 13$, or $x = 13/18$. Hence, Rose should play row 1 with probability $x = 13/18$ and play row 2 with probability $1 - x = 5/18$. Doing so, she achieves a value of $7x - 5 = 91/18 - 5 = 1/18$, regardless of the strategy that Colin uses. Likewise, Colin can ensure that Rose has no more than her expected payoff of 1/18 by choosing column 1 with probability y, where $2y - 3(1 - y) = 1/18$, so that $5y = 3 + 1/18 = 55/18$. Therefore, Colin chooses column 1 with probability $y = 11/18$ and column 2 with probability 7/18. (Verifying, $-5y + 8(1 - y) = -5(11/18) + 8(7/18) = 1/18$). The value of the game is 1/18, so the row player wins, on average, 1/18 of a unit per game under the equilibrium strategy.

2.

    a.   When Rose adopts the proposed strategy, then when Colin plays column 1, Rose's expected payoff is $A(D - C)/E + C(A - B)/E = (AD - BC)/E$. When Colin plays column 2, Rose's expected payoff is $B(D - C)/E + D(A - B)/E = (AD - BC)/E$ again. Either way, and even if Colin mixes strategies 1 and 2, Rose's expected payoff is $(AD - BC)/E$.

        A similar calculation shows that when Colin adopts the proposed strategy, Rose has an expected value of $(AD - BC)/E$, regardless of which row she chooses, because $A(D - B)/E +$

$B(A - C)/E = (AD - BC)/E$ and $C(D - B)/E + D(A - C)/E = (AD - BC)/E$.

b. Here, $A = 2$, $B = -3$, $C = -5$, and $D = 8$, so $E = A + D - B - C = 18$, and $V = (AD - BC)/E = (16 - 15)/18 = 1/18$, as desired.

3.

a. The payoff matrix for this game, where the rows and columns represent rock, paper, and scissors (in that order) is as follows.

0	−3	10
3	0	−1
−10	1	0

b. When Rose adopts the (1/14, 10/14, 3/14) strategy, then it's easy to verify that when Colin plays any column, Rose's expected payoff is zero. (For instance, against column 1, her expected payoff is $0(1/14) + 3(10/14) - 10(3/14) = 0$.) Likewise, if Colin adopts this strategy, Rose achieves an expected payoff of zero, regardless of which rows she plays. The value of this game is, of course, zero.

c. Here, the payoff matrix would look like the following.

0	−b	a
b	0	−c
−a	c	0

Naturally, because this is a symmetric game, the expected payoff should be zero. If Rose chooses her rows with proportions $c{:}a{:}b$ (that is, with probabilities $c/(a + b + c)$, $a/(a + b + c)$, $b/(a + b + c)$), then she achieves an expected payoff of zero against any column strategy. The same result applies to Colin as well.

LECTURE 5

1.

    a.   The probability that the first card is low (2 through 9) is 8/13 ≈ 0.6

    b.   So, a reasonable estimate that all three cards are low would be about $(0.6)^3 = 0.216$.

    c.   The exact probability that all three cards are low is (32/52) (31/51)(30/50) ≈ 0.224.

    d.   Appropriate fair odds would be about 78 to 22, or roughly 3.5 to 1.

2.

    a.   Because you have the 6, 7, 8, and 9 of diamonds, your hand will improve with any diamond, any 5, or any 10. There are nine remaining diamonds, three 5s, and three 10s (because you are careful not to double count the 5 of diamonds or 10 of diamonds). Thus, your hand has 15 outs.

    b.   By the rule of 4, your chance of improving your hand is about 60%. But because you have more than 9 outs, the more accurate "3x + 9 rule" puts the probability closer to 54%.

    c.   With one more card remaining, the rule of 2 says that your chance of winning is about 30%. The more accurate rule of 2.2 says that your chance of winning is about 33%.

    d.   You are being asked to risk $10 to gain $40, so the pot is offering you four-to-one odds, which is very favorable because your chances are 33%. (It would have been a borderline decision if the pot were offering two-to-one odds.)

3.

    a.   Keep the pair of jacks.

Solutions

284

    b.   Keep the honors with matching suits: QH and JH.

    c.   Keep the pair of 3s.

    d.   Keep the hearts. Discard the ace.

LECTURE 6

1.

    a.   There are 14 hitting numbers: All 11 direct 3s, plus the roll 21 (which is the same as the roll 12) and the roll 11. So, the probability of hitting is 14/36.

    b.   There are 15 hitting numbers: All 11 direct 5s, plus 41 and 32. So, the answer is 15/36.

    c.   A checker 12 away can only be hit by 66, 44, and 33, so the probability of hitting is 3/36.

    d.   There are 20 numbers that contain 3 or 5 directly, plus combination shots 11, 21, 41 (careful not to double count 32), and 44, and 66 for a total of 27/36. So, the probability of hitting is 27/36 = 3/4.

2.

    a.   (4/6)(4/6) = 16/36 = 4/9.

    b.   (2/6)(2/6) = 4/36 = 1/9.

    c.   Subtracting the two above answers from one: 1 – 4/9 – 1/9 = 4/9.

3.

    a.   You have 10 bad rolls (any roll that contains a 1, except for double ones). So, your chance of getting both checkers off this turn is 26/36 = 13/18 ≈ 0.72.

b. Your opponent has 7 bad rolls (32, 31, 21, 11) and, thus, 29 good rolls. In order for her to win, you must get a bad roll and she must get a good roll. Thus, her chance of winning is (5/18) (29/36) = 145/648 ≈ 0.22.

c. Even though her chance of winning is under 25%, she should actually take this double. The reason is that if you roll a bad number, which happens about 28% of the time, then she can win automatically, by redoubling you. Because your chance of winning from that position is only 7/36, you will have to drop the redouble.

d. Even though your opponent has a take, it is still correct to double. You currently own the cube at 2. If you don't double, then you win 2 points 78% of the time and lose 2 points 22% of the time for an expected value of 2(0.78) − 2(0.22) = 1.12. If you double, your winning chances go down to 72% (because your opponent will double you out if you fail to get two checkers off this turn), but your expected value is 4(0.72) − 4(0.28) = 1.76, which is much higher than 1.12 when you don't double.

LECTURE 7

1.

a. Because there are three choices for the row 1 number and three choices for the row 2 number, there are nine equally likely outcomes, five of which win for your opponent: namely, (4,5), (4,7), (2, 3), (2, 5), and (2,7). Hence, your opponent wins 5/9 of the time.

b. Row 2 loses to row 3 5/9 of the time—via (3,8), (3,6), (5,8), (5,6), (7,8)—yet row 3 loses to row 1 5/9 of the time—via (8,9), (1,4), (1,9), (1,2), (6,9).

2.

    a. $P(A > B) = 1/6 + (5/6)(1/2) = 7/12$. (Explanation: A wins if A rolls a 6, or A wins if A rolls a 3 and B rolls a 2.)

    b. $P(B > C) = 1/2 + (1/2)(1/6) = 7/12$.

    c. $P(C > A) = (5/6)(5/6) = 25/36$.

    d.   Choose C because it has a better than 50% chance of winning against A.

3.   Your opponent is an enormous favorite. (Why else would she offer you the bet?) Your score will be much higher than hers until your team has a game with zero runs. Then, your product will be zero for the rest of the season. It's almost never happened that a baseball team has gone the entire season scoring at least one run each game.

4.   Your friend has a quarter and a nickel. *One* of the coins was not a nickel, and indeed the quarter is not a nickel.

LECTURE 8

1.   The rectangles surrounding buttons 2 and 4 are even; the rectangles surrounding buttons 6 and 8 are odd, so you press buttons 6 and 8. After that, you'll press any lit corners and, if necessary, the center. After pressing buttons 6 and 8, corners 1 and 3 will be on (and corners 5 and 7 will be off). So, corners 1 and 3 should also be pressed. Light 5 will still be on, so it should be pressed as well.

2.

    a.   The following numbers are oddballs: 9, 2, 6, 13, 8, 4, 10.

    b.   Because there are seven oddballs, the puzzle cannot be solved.

3. Mark the holes of the puzzle with symbols x, y, and z, as follows.

$$x$$
$$y \quad z$$
$$z \quad x \quad y$$
$$x \quad y \quad z \quad x$$
$$y \quad z \quad x \quad y \quad z$$

The symbols x, y, and z have the same meaning as before. Notice that every three consecutive squares contains an x, y, and z. If you add up all the occupied holes, you get a grand total of $y + z = x$. Thus, a single peg can only end up on a square labeled with x. Because the holes on the second row have labels y and z, you can't end up with a single peg there.

LECTURE 9

1. Answers may vary.

2. Perform this move six times, and you'll be back to where you started.

3.

    a.   This will create a checkerboard pattern.

    b.   This will create six "spots."

    c.   This will create a striped pattern.

Solutions

288

1.

5	3	9	2	7	6	4	8	1
2	1	8	3	9	4	7	5	6
7	4	6	5	8	1	2	9	3
8	6	3	1	2	7	9	4	5
9	5	1	4	3	8	6	7	2
4	2	7	6	5	9	1	3	8
6	8	4	7	1	5	3	2	9
1	9	2	8	4	3	5	6	7
3	7	5	9	6	2	8	1	4

2.

2	8	9	4	5	3	7	1	6
4	3	1	6	7	9	2	8	5
7	6	5	1	8	2	3	4	9
5	1	6	9	3	8	4	7	2
8	9	7	2	4	5	6	3	1
3	2	4	7	6	1	5	9	8
9	7	8	3	2	6	1	5	4
6	5	3	8	1	4	9	2	7
1	4	2	5	9	7	8	6	3

3.

24x		10+		10+	7+
4	**6**	**3**	**1**	**2**	**5**
5–	4		1–		
1	**4**	**6**	**5**	**3**	**2**
	2–	2÷			5–
6	**3**	**2**	**4**	**5**	**1**
3–			2–		
2	**5**	**4**	**3**	**1**	**6**
	9+			11+	
5	**2**	**1**	**6**	**4**	**3**
3	6+		3÷		
3	**1**	**5**	**2**	**6**	**4**

LECTURE 11

1. A knight and bishop tend to be worth about six points. A rook and two pawns tend to be worth seven points, so the rook and two pawns are generally better.

2. White's bishop should capture the pawn, pinning the black rook, which it can take next turn. If Black captures the bishop with its pawn, then the white rook can take the black rook.

3. White should move the pawn forward. This gives White the opposition, which will force the black king to move off of the file. (If the black king moves backward, then the white king moves forward, maintaining the opposition.) When the black king moves off of the file, White moves to the other file and eventually marches his or her pawn up the middle.

LECTURE 12

1.

   a. The winning positions are when the rook is on the main diagonal (going from the bottom left corner to the upper right corner). This is a win for the second player because the first player is forced to move off the diagonal, from which the second player will be able to move back on the diagonal. Ultimately, the second player will reach the upper right hand corner, which is on the diagonal.

   b. If the game were played on a four-by-eight board, then the first player can force a win by moving the rook to the right four squares (to the square $(5,1)$). The winning squares are $(5,1)$, $(6,2)$, $(7,3)$, and $(8,4)$.

2.

   a. Writing the numbers in terms of powers of two, you have as follows.

$$24 = 16 + 8$$

$$14 = 8 + 4 + 2$$

$$19 = 16 + 2 + 1$$

There are an even number of 16s, 8s, and 2s and an odd number of 4s and 1s. The only winning play must remove a 4 from the second number and gain a 1. In other words, you must remove 3 coins from the second pile, leaving 11 coins. In doing so, all of the 16s, 8s, 4s, 2s, and 1s appear an even number of times.

    b.   You can add 4 and 1 to the first pile, creating 29 coins, or you can add 4 and lose 1 from the third pile, creating 22 coins.

3.   After the first player chomps the (2,2) square, the only squares remaining are in the first row and first column, which is a symmetrical position. From here, the first player can simply "mimic" the moves of the second player. For instance, if the second player chomps the fifth square in the first column, then the first player can respond by chomping the fifth square in the first row. Eventually, the second player will be forced to take the poison square.

Credits

KenKen® is a registered trademark of Nextoy LLC. Puzzle content ©2013 www.kenken.com. All rights reserved.

Bibliography

Albert, Michael H., Richard J. Nowakowski, and David Wolfe. *Lessons in Play: An Introduction to Combinatorial Game Theory.* Wellesley, MA: A K Peters, 2007. This is the best introduction to the subject of combinatorial game theory, including impartial and non-impartial games. Very readable.

Ball, W. W. Rouse, and H. S. M. Coxeter. *Mathematical Recreations and Essays.* New York: Dover Publications, 1892. Reprinted in 2010. This is one of the original books pertaining to the mathematics of games, puzzles, and entertaining mathematical problems, including material on the Tower of Hanoi, the Fifteen Puzzle, and the knight's tour.

Beasley, John D. *The Ins and Outs of Peg Solitaire.* Oxford: Oxford University Press, 1989. Everything you ever wanted to know about peg-jumping games.

———. *The Mathematics of Games.* New York: Dover Publications, 1989. Reprinted in 2006. This is probably the book that you should buy for this course. It's inexpensive, well written, and covers most of the major topics: games of chance, zero-sum games, parity, puzzles, and games of pure strategy.

Berlekamp, Elwyn R., John H. Conway, and Richard K. Guy. *Winning Ways for Your Mathematical Plays.* 4 volumes, 2nd ed. Wellesley, MA: A K Peters, 2001–2004. These volumes provide the complete theory of combinatorial games, where two players take turns moving until one player can no longer move.

Binmore, Ken. *Fun and Games: A Text on Game Theory.* Lexington, MA: D. C. Heath, 1992. This textbook would be suitable for undergraduate math majors wishing to learn the basics of game theory.

Browne, Cameron. *Connection Games: Variations on a Theme.* Wellesley, MA: A K Peters, 2005. This book provides descriptions, strategies, and common plays in games like Hex, where the object of the game is to connect your pieces in some way. The book is comprehensive, but somewhat hard to read.

————. *Hex Strategy: Making the Right Connections.* Wellesley, MA: A K Peters, 2000. A comprehensive book on the game of Hex, including its history, mathematical theory, and especially strategies for playing the game.

Chen, Bill, and Jerrod Ankenman. *The Mathematics of Poker.* Pittsburgh, PA: ConJelCo LLC, 2006. This book goes beyond the basics and lays down a mathematical framework, including game theory, to explain the proper frequency of bluffing and how often it should be done.

Clay, Robin. *Backgammon in a Week.* London: Hodder & Stoughton, 1992. A quick introduction to the game that offers solid strategic advice.

Diaconis, Persi, and Ronald Graham. *Magical Mathematics: The Mathematical Ideas That Animate Great Magic Tricks.* Princeton, NJ: Princeton University Press, 2012. This book contains many new ideas that connect mathematics and magic. Written by world-famous mathematicians who are also experts in the performing arts.

Duke, Annie, and John Vorhaus. *Decide to Play Great Poker: A Strategy Guide to No-Limit Texas Hold'em.* Las Vegas, NV: Huntington Press, 2011. A very readable book offering good general strategic advice.

Emms, John. *Concise Chess: The Compact Guide for Beginners.* London: Everyman Chess Series, 2003. Short but effective introduction to chess and tactics.

Epstein, Richard A. *The Theory of Gambling and Statistical Logic.* 2nd ed. San Diego: Academic Press, 2009. A classic book on gambling and its mathematical analysis—from casino games to the stock market. Specific games include craps, blackjack, and bridge. Mathematics is at the undergraduate math major level.

Fischer, Robert. *Bobby Fischer Teaches Chess.* New York: Bantam, 1972. This is included as a sentimental favorite, because it was the book that Professor Benjamin read in middle school that turned him on to chess.

Frey, Alexander H., and David Singmaster. *Handbook of Cubik Math.* Cambridge, UK: Lutterworth Press, 1982. Singmaster is a recognized authority on the cube. The authors walk the reader through the concepts and notation for understanding Rubik's Cube so that they can both solve and understand the solution.

Gardner, Martin. *Aha! Gotcha* and *Aha! Insight.* 2-volume collection. Washington, DC: Mathematical Association of America, 2006. A collection of puzzles and paradoxes designed to develop critical-thinking skills. The *Gotcha* portion has more philosophy, and the *Insight* portion has more puzzles.

————. *The Colossal Book of Short Puzzles and Problems.* Edited by Dana Richards. New York: W. W. Norton, 2006. This book contains 340 puzzles that appeared in Martin Gardner's "Mathematical Games" column for *Scientific American.*

————. *Perplexing Puzzles* and *Tantalizing Teasers.* 2-volume collection. New York: Dover Publications, 1988. A fun collection of puzzles that should appeal to audiences of all ages.

Gillis, Harvey. *Backgammon: Decision Analysis for Success.* Appears in Vol. 2, Issue 2 of *PrimeTime Backgammon*, the official magazine of the U.S. Backgammon Federation, March/April 2011, located at www.usbgf.org.

Gordon, Peter. *Solving Sudoku: Hundreds of Puzzles Plus Techniques to Help You Crack Them All.* New York: Sterling Publishing, 2006. A solid introduction to sudoku-solving techniques.

Griffin, Peter A. *The Theory of Blackjack: The Compleat Card Counter's Guide to the Casino Game of 21.* 5th ed. Las Vegas: Huntington Press, 1996. This is the standard reference for the mathematical underpinnings of blackjack, from the derivation of basic strategy to the effectiveness of card-counting systems.

Guerrera, Tony. *Killer Poker by the Numbers: The Mathematical Edge for Winning Play.* New York: Kensington Publishing Corp, 2007. This book gives a reasonable explanation of expectation and pot odds and then applies it to many commonly occurring situations in no-limit hold'em poker.

Guy, Richard K. *Fair Game: How to Play Impartial Combinatorial Games.* Arlington, MA: COMAP Mathematical Exploration Series, 1989. A complete and lighthearted treatment of impartial combinatorial games, written by one of the pioneers of the field.

Haigh, John. *Taking Chances: Winning with Probability.* Oxford: Oxford University Press, 2003. Written for a general audience but with lots of surprises, even for the mathematically experienced. Highly recommended.

Harrington, Dan, and Bill Robertie. *Harrington on Cash Games: How to Win at No-Limit Hold'em Money Games.* Henderson, NV: Two Plus Two Publishing, 2008. One of the most popular books on hold'em strategy in cash games.

―――. *Harrington on Hold'em: Expert Strategy for No-Limit Tournaments, Volume 1: Strategic Play.* Henderson, NV: Two Plus Two Publishing, 2004. One of the most popular books on tournament hold'em strategy. The first author has one of the best records in tournament poker. The second author is one of the best expositors on the game of backgammon, and his writing is equally clear with poker.

Harris, Dan. *Speedsolving the Cube: Easy-to-Follow, Step-by-Step Instructions for Many Popular 3-D Puzzles.* New York: Sterling Publishing, 2008. Learn to solve Rubik's Cube the way an expert does it. If you want to bring your time below 30 seconds, then this is the book for you.

Hess, Dick. *Mental Gymnastics: Recreational Mathematics Puzzles.* New York: Dover Publications, 2011. For the reader looking for new puzzles, with a strong mathematical flavor.

Hinebaugh, Jeffrey P. *A Board Game Education: Building Skills for Academic Success.* Lanham, MD: Rowman & Littlefield Education, 2009. This book promotes the idea that board games can provide a valuable educational experience for children of all ages.

Hoffman, Louis. *Puzzles Old and New.* London: Martin Breese, Ltd, 1893. Reprinted in 1988. One of the first books to describe mechanical puzzles, including the Fifteen Puzzle, with a vast assortment of arithmetical and word puzzles as well.

Joyner, David. *Adventures in Group Theory: Rubik's Cube, Merlin's Machine, and Other Mathematical Toys.* Baltimore, MD: Johns Hopkins University Press, 2002. This book provides an interesting introduction to the advanced mathematical subject of group theory, using Rubik's Cube and its variations as motivation.

Juhnke, Fritz. *Beginning Arimaa: Chess Reborn beyond Computer Comprehension.* Flying Camel Publications, 2009. A strategy guide for this relatively new game where humans will likely outperform computers for a long time. The author is a two-time Arimaa world champion and did mathematics research with Professor Benjamin as an undergraduate.

MacKinnon, Robert F. *Bridge, Probability, and Information.* Toronto: Master Point Press, 2010. Mathematical concepts for experienced bridge players.

Magriel, Paul. *Backgammon.* 2nd ed. Clock & Rose Press, 2004. Updated from 1976 version. Widely considered to be the bible of backgammon, due to its clarity of exposition. This is probably the first book you should read on the subject.

Mao, Tyson. *You Can Solve the Cube.* John George Productions, 2008. This instructional DVD can teach anyone how to solve Rubik's Cube, using the method explained in this course. Strategies for speed cubing and blindfold cubing are also provided.

Miyamoto, Tetsuya. *Will Shortz Presents Brain-Busting KenKen®: 100 Challenging Logic Puzzles That Make You Smarter.* New York: Saint Martin's Griffin, 2011. The title says it all.

Moshman, Colin, and Douglas Zare. *The Math of Hold'em.* Suwanee, GA: Dimat Enterprises, 2011. Serious math for serious poker players.

Niederman, Derrick. *The Puzzler's Dilemma: From the Lighthouse of Alexandria to Monty Hall, a Fresh Look at Classic Conundrums of Logic, Mathematics, and Life.* London: Duckworth Overlook, 2012. Fresh insights on the design and analysis of puzzles, especially classical ones, and how they arise in real life. The author is a mathematician and an expert designer of word puzzles, logic puzzles, and crosswords.

Nowakowski, Richard J., ed. *Games of No Chance.* Cambridge, UK. Cambridge University Press, 1996. A collection of articles on games that involve no randomness. Includes a great article on how the game of checkers was solved and a biography of Marion Tinsley, a mathematician who played practically perfect checkers. Also contains articles on chess endgames, go, dots and boxes, and Nine Men's Morris.

Nunn, John. *Learn Chess.* London: Gambit Publications, 2010. This is Professor Benjamin's recommended introductory book. It covers all the basic tactics, and the writing is exceptionally clear. The author also happens to be a trained mathematician.

Packel, Edward. *The Mathematics of Games and Gambling.* 2nd ed. Washington, DC: Mathematical Association of America, 2006. A terrific textbook that covers gambling and betting strategies and the mathematics behind it. Only requires a high school mathematics background.

Paymar, Dan. *Video Poker: Optimum Play.* Pittsburgh: ConJelCo, 1998. This book covers strategies for playing various video poker games with the goal of making the right decisions to maximize your win rate.

Poundstone, William. *Fortune's Formula: The Untold Story of the Scientific Betting System That Beat the Casinos and Wall Street.* New York: Hill and Wang, 2005. A history of the Kelly criterion used for gambling and investing.

Riley, Philip, and Laura Taalman. *No-Frills Sudoku.* New York: Puzzlewright Press, 2011. All of these puzzles have just 18 clues to start, which is conjectured to be the bare minimum needed for a rotationally symmetric sudoku. Puzzles range from easy to very challenging.

Rosenhouse, Jason. *The Monty Hall Problem: The Remarkable Story of the World's Most Contentious Brain Teaser.* Oxford: Oxford University Press, 2009. Everything you ever wanted to know about this paradoxical problem, offering multiple explanations and variations.

Rosenhouse, Jason, and Laura Taalman. *Taking Sudoku Seriously: The Math behind the World's Most Popular Puzzle.* Oxford: Oxford University Press, 2011. In a clear and entertaining style, the authors show how mathematics can improve your understanding of sudoku. But more importantly, they demonstrate how sudoku can also improve your understanding of mathematics.

Ross, Ken. *A Mathematician at the Ballpark: Odds and Probabilities for Baseball Fans.* New York: Pearson Education, 2004. The game of baseball is full of numbers. This book, written by a past president of the Mathematical Association of America, will help you understand the game better.

Rubens, Jeff. *Expert Bridge Simplified: Arithmetic Shortcuts for Declarer.* New York: Bridge World Books, 2009. The author is a professor of mathematics, a bridge expert, and an editor. The book explains how to calculate the odds of making various plays in bridge. The book assumes a bit of bridge experience on the part of the reader.

Schlesinger, Don. *Blackjack Attack: Playing the Pros' Way.* 2nd ed. Oakland, CA: RGE Publishing, 2000. A valuable collection of articles for the practical card counter.

Seirawan, Yasser, and Jeremy Silman. *Play Winning Chess*. London: Everyman Chess Series, 2003. This book will take you from beginner to intermediate level with an emphasis on understanding the concepts of force, time, space, and pawn structure.

Sklansky, David. *The Theory of Poker*. 4th ed. Las Vegas: Two Plus Two Publishing, 2001. One of the first, and still one of the best, books for describing the mathematics that underlies many versions of poker, including Texas Hold'em. The author is considered one of the game's premiere authorities on the theory of poker.

Slocum, Jerry, and Dic Sonneveld. *The 15 Puzzle: How It Drove the World Crazy*. Beverly Hills, CA: Slocum Puzzle Foundation, 2006. Everything you ever wanted to know about the history and mathematics of this popular puzzle. Beautifully illustrated.

Slocum, Jerry, David Singmaster, Wei-Hwa Huang, Dieter Gebhardt, and Geert Hellings. *The Cube: The Ultimate Guide to the World's Bestselling Puzzle*. New York: Black Dog & Leventhal, 2009. Learn to solve and understand the standard Rubik's Cube and many of its variations. Very modern, with colorful illustrations.

Snyder, Arnold. *Blackbelt in Blackjack: Playing 21 as a Martial Art*. Oakland, CA: RGE Publishing, 1998. The editor of the respected journal *Blackjack Forum* gives the ins and outs of card counting (the hi-lo count and variations) along with shuffle tracking and team play.

Snyder, Thomas. *The Art of Sudoku*. San Francisco: Grandmaster Puzzles, 2012. Sudoku puzzles with an elegant artistic quality to them with increasing levels of difficulty. Created by a three-time world sudoku champion.

Stephens, Paul. *Mastering Sudoku Week by Week: 52 Steps to Becoming a Sudoku Wizard*. London: Duncan Baird Publishers, 2007. This is Professor Benjamin's recommended book for learning sudoku strategy, focusing on the thought process involved in solving challenging puzzles and practical tactics.

Stewart, Ian. *How to Cut a Cake and Other Mathematical Conundrums.* Oxford: Oxford University Press, 2006. A fun collection of recreational mathematics articles, including some on the topic of fair division. The author has a reputation for clear mathematical writing with considerable wit.

Stuart, Andrew C. *The Logic of Sudoku.* Somerset, UK: Michael Mepham, 2007. This book provides a rather comprehensive description of sudoku strategies, from beginner to very advanced. It is interesting from a mathematical perspective, but maybe not as practical as some of the other books for improving your puzzle-solving time.

Thorp, Edward O. *Beat the Dealer: A Winning Strategy for the Game of Twenty-One.* New York: Vintage Books, 1966. This classic book brought card counting to the masses and made Las Vegas change the rules.

Trice, Walter. *Backgammon Boot Camp.* San Francisco: The Fortuitous Press, 2004. After reading Magriel's book, this should be next on your list. Written by one of the most mathematically talented players of the game.

Vancura, Olaf. *Advantage Yahtzee.* Las Vegas, NV: Huntington Press, 2001. If you ever want to learn the optimal strategy for playing this dice game, then this short book is all you need. The results are based on dynamic programming.

Vancura, Olaf, and Ken Fuchs. *Knock-Out Blackjack: The Easiest Card-Counting System Ever Devised.* Las Vegas, NV: Huntington Press, 1998. This is an "unbalanced count" that tells the player exactly when it is right to take insurance. It's a very practical strategy and is highly recommended.

Von Neumann, John, and Oskar Morgenstern. *Theory of Games and Economic Behavior.* Princeton, NJ: Princeton University Press, 1944. This is the classic book from which modern game theory is derived.

Watkins, John J. *Across the Board: The Mathematics of Chessboard Problems.* Princeton, NJ: Princeton University Press, 2004. A beautifully written book with mathematical problems that come from the chessboard and its pieces. It's not about improving your game of chess, but it may increase your enjoyment of mathematics.

Wells, David. *Book of Curious and Interesting Puzzles*. New York: Dover Publications, 1992. Reprinted in 2006. A collection of classic puzzles from ancient times to the 20th century.

Winkler, Peter. *Bridge at the Enigma Club*. Toronto: Master Point Press, 2010. The author is a distinguished mathematician, computer scientist, cryptographer, and puzzle enthusiast who describes a "zero-knowledge" bidding system that communicates information to your partner without revealing any information to the opposition.

Winston, Wayne L. *Mathletics: How Gamblers, Managers, and Sports Enthusiasts Use Mathematics in Baseball, Basketball, and Football*. Princeton, NJ: Princeton University Press, 2009. The author describes methods that coaches and managers use (or should use) to evaluate players and improve performance. The articles on sports betting are interesting as well.

Woolsey, Kit. *How to Play Tournament Backgammon*. Arlington, MA: Gammon Press, 1993. A short but comprehensive treatment of how the score of your match affects how you play your checkers and use the doubling cube. The author is one of the top players of backgammon and bridge.

Woolsey, Kit, and Patti Beadles. *52 Great Backgammon Tips*. London: Batsford, 2007. A great book for improving your game, written by one of the best players in the world and one of his students.

Notes

Notes